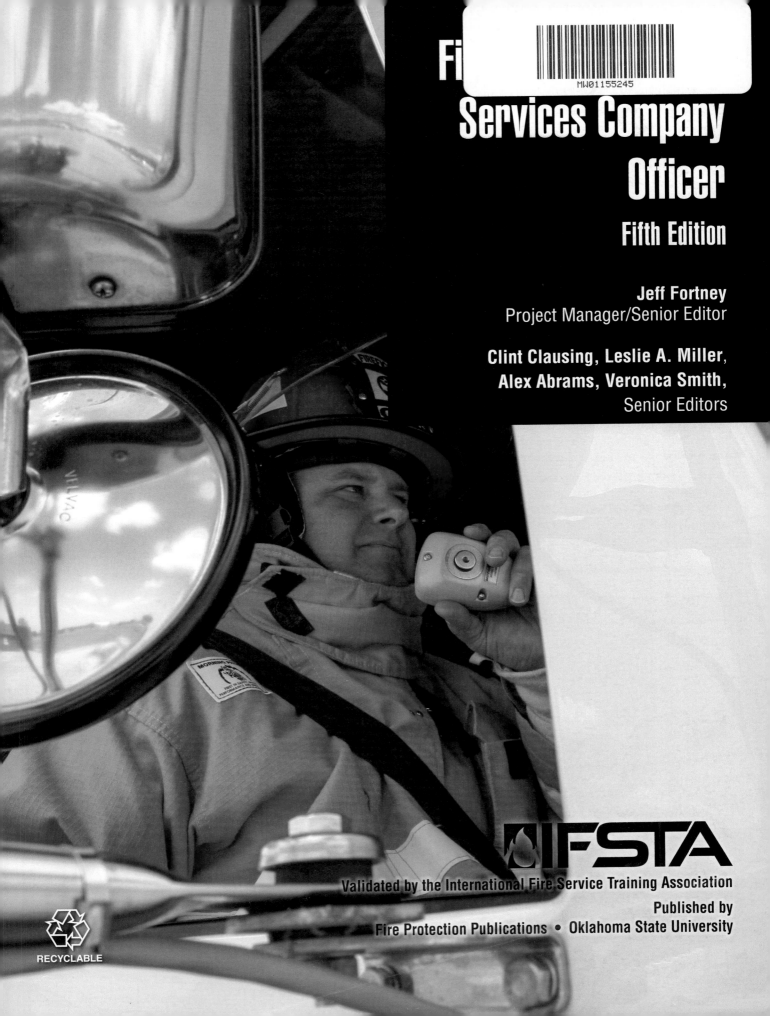

Fire Services Company Officer

Fifth Edition

Jeff Fortney
Project Manager/Senior Editor

Clint Clausing, Leslie A. Miller,
Alex Abrams, Veronica Smith,
Senior Editors

IFSTA

Validated by the International Fire Service Training Association

Published by
Fire Protection Publications • Oklahoma State University

RECYCLABLE

INTERNATIONAL FIRE SERVICE TRAINING ASSOCIATION

The International Fire Service Training Association (IFSTA) was established in 1934 as a *nonprofit educational association of fire fighting personnel who are dedicated to upgrading fire fighting techniques and safety through training*. To carry out the mission of IFSTA, Fire Protection Publications was established as an entity of Oklahoma State University. Fire Protection Publications' primary function is to publish and distribute training materials as proposed, developed, and validated by IFSTA. As a secondary function, Fire Protection Publications researches, acquires, produces, and markets high-quality learning and teaching aids consistent with IFSTA's mission.

IFSTA holds two meetings each year: the Winter Meeting in January and the Annual Validation Conference in July. During these meetings, committees of technical experts review draft materials and ensure that the professional qualifications of the National Fire Protection Association® standards are met. These conferences bring together individuals from several related and allied fields, such as:

- Key fire department executives, training officers, and personnel
- Educators from colleges and universities
- Representatives from governmental agencies
- Delegates of firefighter associations and industrial organizations

Committee members are not paid nor are they reimbursed for their expenses by IFSTA or Fire Protection Publications. They participate because of a commitment to the fire service and its future through training. Being on a committee is prestigious in the fire service community, and committee members are acknowledged leaders in their fields. This unique feature provides a close relationship between IFSTA and the fire service community.

IFSTA manuals have been adopted as the official teaching texts of many states and provinces of North America as well as numerous U.S. and Canadian government agencies. Besides the NFPA® requirements, IFSTA manuals are also written to meet the Fire and Emergency Services Higher Education (FESHE) course requirements. A number of the manuals have been translated into other languages to provide training for fire and emergency service personnel in Canada, Mexico, and outside of North America.

ISBN 978-0-87939-564-3   Library of Congress Control Number: 2014938949

Fifth Edition, First Printing, June 2014   *Printed in the United States of America*

10   9   8   7   6   5   4   3   2   1

If you need additional information concerning the International Fire Service Training Association (IFSTA) or Fire Protection Publications, contact:

Customer Service, Fire Protection Publications, Oklahoma State University
930 North Willis, Stillwater, OK 74078-8045
800-654-4055   Fax: 405-744-8204

For assistance with training materials, to recommend material for inclusion in an IFSTA manual, or to ask questions or comment on manual content, contact:

Editorial Department, Fire Protection Publications, Oklahoma State University
930 North Willis, Stillwater, OK 74078-8045
405-744-4111   Fax: 405-744-4112   E-mail: editors@osufpp.org

Chapter Summary

Table of Contents

List of Tables

Acknowledgements

The fifth edition of the IFSTA **Fire and Emergency Services Company Officer** manual is written to assist fire and emergency services personnel in meeting the job performance requirements of the standard National Fire Protection Association® (NFPA®) 1021, *Standard for Fire Officer Professional Qualifications* (2014). This manual provides the basic level of knowledge that is required for Level I and Level II fire officers and officer candidates.

It should be understood that this manual serves as a training and educational foundation for certification at Levels I and II and as professional development for personnel currently in those positions. Additional reading and course work are highly recommended for all fire officers regardless of their assigned functions or positions within the fire and emergency services organization.

Acknowledgement and special thanks are extended to the members of the IFSTA validation committee. The following members contributed their time, wisdom, and knowledge to the development of this manual:

IFSTA Fire and Emergency Services Company Officer
Fifth Edition IFSTA Validation Committee

Chair
Gary Wilson
Overland Park Fire Department
Overland Park, KS

Vice Chair
Randal E. Novak
Iowa Fire Service Training Bureau
Ames, IA

Secretary
David Lewis
Maryand Fire and Rescue Institute
College Park, MD

Committee Members

Robert Bocanegra, Jr.
Hutto Fire/Rescue
Hutto, TX

David M. Britton
Hilton Head Fire/Rescue
Bluffton, SC

Mike Bucy
Stevens County Fire Protection District #1
Clayton, WA

Michael Byrd
Georgia Public Safety Training Center —
Fire Academy Division
Forsyth, GA

James M. Craft, Jr.
Tarrant County Community College Fire Service
Training Center
Fort Worth, TX

Duane M. Dodwell
Fairfax County Fire/Rescue
Waldorf, MD

Bruce Evans
Upper Pine Fire Protection District
Bayfield, CO

Manuel Fonseca
Nashville Fire Department
Nashville, TN

IFSTA Fire and Emergency Services Company Officer
Fifth Edition IFSTA Validation Committee
continued

Sandee Goulding-Harnum
Safety and Emergency Response Training Centre
Stephenville, NL

Joseph A. Gorman
Texas City Fire Department
Texas City, TX

Donald E. R. Hansen, PhD
Virginia Department of Fire Programs
Glen Allen, VA

Rick Karasaki
Honolulu Fire Department
Honolulu, HI

Merlin Klassen
City of Wetaskiwin
Wetaskiwin, AB

Ryan Lenz
Edmond Fire Department
Guthrie, OK

Rex A. Mott
Oklahoma Fire Service Training
Stillwater, OK

Bill Neville
Penn Valley Fire Protection District
Penn Valley, CA

Donald B. Reyes
Los Angeles Fire Department
Los Angeles, CA

The following individuals and organizations contributed information, photographs, photography assistance, and other assistance that made the completion of this manual possible:

Steve Baker
Ted Boothroyd
Bob Esposito
Ron Jeffers
Rich Mahaney

Edmond Fire Department, Edmond, Oklahoma
    Jake Rhoades, Fire Chief
    Jon Neely, Chief Training Officer /Assistant Fire Chief
    Joe Elam, Training Officer
    Doug Hall, Battalion Chief
    Jerry Harwell, Captain
    Jason Hazzard, Lieutenant
    Benjamin A. Young, Lieutenant
    John D. Block
    Dustin Bowman
    Jeff Fountain
    Lindall Wood

International Association of Fire Chiefs (IAFC)
    Ann Davison

McKinney Fire Department, McKinney, Texas
    Ron Moore

National Fire Protection Association® (NFPA®)
National Institute of Standards and Technology
New Orleans Fire Department, New Orleans, Louisiana
    Chris Mickal, District Chief

Owasso Fire Department, Owasso, Oklahoma
    Chris Garrett, Fire Chief
    Mark Stuckey, Assistant Fire Chief
    Bruce Kelly, Emergency Medical Services Manager
    Matthew Morton, Captain/Acting Battalion Chief
    Mickey Lewis, Captain
    Danise Stanley, Administrative Assistant

Joshua Berk
Patrick Bladen
Scott Graybill
David Huist
Kip A. Jennings
Daniel Johnson
Kevin Lawson
Jarrod Linthiccim
Matt Trout
Steph Wagner
Eric York

Precision Aerospace, Tulsa, Oklahoma State
    Jamie Hutchison
    Barbara Griffith

Stillwater Fire Department, Stillwater, Oklahoma
    Tom Bradley, Fire Chief
    Rick Hauf, Assistant Fire Chief
    Robert Black, Training Officer
    Mike Eytcheson, Captain
    Mike Wilda, Lieutenant
    Dustan Portman
    Greg Scheihing
    Josh Spence

Yates & Associates
    Donny Howard

Fire and Emergency Services Company Officer Project Team

Project Manager/Writer
Jeff Fortney, Senior Editor

Senior Editors
Clint Clausing, Senior Editor
Leslie Miller, Senior Editor
Alex Abrams, Senior Editor
Veronica Smith, Senior Editor

Technical Reviewers
Jerry Holt
    Fire Chief
    Urbandale Fire Department
    Urbandale, Iowa

Michael Arnhart
    Fire Chief
    High Ridge Fire Department
    High Ridge, Missouri

Proofreaders
Veronica Smith, Senior Editor

Curriculum Development
Lori Raborg, Curriculum Coordinator
Lynn Hughes, Lead Instructional Developer
David Schaap, Lead Instructional Developer

FPP Photographers
Jeff Fortney, Senior Editor
Mike Sturzenbecker, Senior Editor
Fred Stowell, Senior Editor
Veronica Smith, Senior Editor

Production Manager
Ann Moffat

Illustrators and Layout Designers
Errick Bragg, Senior Graphic Designer
Ben Brock, Senior Graphic Designer
Missy Hannan, Senior Graphics Designer
Clint Parker, Senior Graphic Designer

IFSTA Projects Coordinator
Clint Clausing

Library Researchers
Susan F. Walker, Librarian
Darcy Rankin, Senior Library Technical Assistant

Research Technician
Jake Zlomie

Editorial Assistant
Tara Gladden

The IFSTA Executive Board at the time of validation of the **Fire and Emergency Services Company Officer**, **5th Edition**, was as follows:

IFSTA Executive Board

Executive Board Chair
Steve Ashbrock
Fire Chief
Madeira & Indian Hill Fire Department
Cincinnati, OH

Vice Chair
Bradd Clark
Fire Chief
Ocala Fire Department
Ocala, FL

IFSTA Executive Director
Mike Wieder
Associate Director
Fire Protection Publications at OSU
Stillwater, OK

Board Members

Steve Austin
Past President
Cumberland Valley Volunteer FF Association
Newark, DE

Claude Beauchamp
Director
Institute of Emergency and Judicial Services
Ottawa, Canada

Roxanne Bercik
Deputy Chief of Training and Support Bureau
Los Angeles Fire Department
Los Angeles, CA

Mary Cameli
Assistant Chief
City of Mesa Fire Department
Mesa, AZ

Chief Dennis Compton
Chairman
National Fallen Firefighters Foundation
Mesa, AZ

John Cunningham
Executive Director
Nova Scotia Firefighter's School
Waverly, NS, Canada

John Hoglund
Director Emeritus
Maryland Fire & Rescue Institute
New Carrollton, MD

Wes Kitchel
Assistant Chief
Sonoma County Fire & Emergency Services
Cloverdale, CA

Brett Lacey
Fire Marshal
Colorado Springs Fire Department
Colorado Springs, CO

Lori Moore-Merrell
Assistant to the General President
International Association of Fire Fighters
Washington, DC

Jeff Morrissette
State Fire Administrator
State of Connecticut Commission on Fire
Prevention and Control
Windsor Locks, CT

Josh Stefancic
Assistant Chief
City of Largo Fire Department
Largo, FL

Paul Valentine
Senior Engineer
Nexus Engineering
Oakbrook, IL

Steven Westermann
Fire Chief
Central Jackson County Fire Protection District
Blue Springs, MO

Introduction

Introduction Contents

Introduction

Introduction

The fire and emergency services professions have a long-established heritage in culture and society. Many deeply rooted traditions continue to influence the organization, structure, operations, and titles used in the services. For instance, the fire and emergency services organization is based on a scalar structure that assigns rank in a hierarchy of authority that is pyramid-shaped. The base of the pyramid rests on the firefighter or emergency medical technician (EMT), while at the top or peak of the pyramid is the fire chief, fire commissioner, or public safety director. Between these extremes are the specialists, such as fire apparatus driver/operators, supervisors, and mid-level managers.

Purpose and Scope

The purpose of **Fire and Emergency Services Company Officer, 5th Edition**, is to provide emergency services personnel with basic information necessary to meet the job performance requirements (JPRs) of National Fire Protection Association® (NFPA®) 1021 (2014) for Level I and Level II Fire Officers. The chapters contain information that is specific to the duties generally assigned to first-line supervisors and mid-level managers.

The scope of the manual is to provide Level I and Level II Fire Officer candidates and current fire and emergency services company officers with basic supervisory and managerial knowledge. This knowledge is necessary to develop skills for ensuring safe, efficient, and effective leadership during emergency operations and nonemergency activities, as well as the daily administration within the organization.

The knowledge of fire behavior, essential fire-fighting skills, and basic emergency medical skills is assumed to have been acquired before moving to the fire officer level. Company officers must be knowledgeable in the following areas:

- Concepts of management, leadership, ethics, and human relations
- Basic administrative duties
- Community risk, awareness, and demographics
- Emergency response duties
- Teaching of skills and knowledge to company personnel

Rank Designations

The first-level supervisor in this hierarchy is the company officer, who is responsible for the operation of a single unit and the personnel assigned. This unit may be an apparatus and a crew that perform rescue, fire suppression, ventilation, or medical services. Or it may be a small workgroup that performs a staff or support function, such as training or administration. NFPA® 1021, *Standard for Fire Officer Professional Qualifications* (2014), uses the designation Fire Officer I to describe the first-level supervisor. Titles assigned to this level generally include lieutenant, engineer, captain, or a similar term.

In large fire and emergency services organizations, a second-level or mid-management supervisor may also exist. This person is also a company officer, but has greater responsibility and authority than the first-level supervisor and is often referred to as captain or senior captain. NFPA® 1021 uses the term Fire Officer II to describe this supervisor/manager.

The authority having jurisdiction (AHJ) determines and assigns the duties, responsibilities, authority, accountability, and rank designations for all fire and emergency services personnel. In some instances, the employer and the labor/employee representative discuss and/or negotiate job duties for various ranks. An AHJ may be one of the following:

- Governing board
- Municipal, state/provincial, or federal political authority
- Military command structure
- Private for-profit company
- Private nonprofit governing board

International Fire Service Ranks

Designations of rank vary widely within the fire and emergency services worldwide. In some organizations, the rank titles are similar to those used in the United States and are based on military rank structures. This situation is particularly true in nations that place the fire and emergency services under the jurisdiction of the military.

Other organizations may use terms that are more closely aligned with the function or duty of the position. For instance, the London (England) Fire Brigade uses the titles station manager, watch manager A, and watch manager B, depending on the number of personnel, units, or facilities for which the officer is responsible.

The AHJ creates the organization, establishes the job performance criteria for each position, develops promotional systems, and hires and trains personnel to staff the organization. Many jurisdictions use standards that have been developed by the (NFPA®) as criteria for organizational responsibilities and JPRs.

NFPA® 1021 places fire officers in four categories or levels based on their assigned duties as follows:

- Level I — First-line supervisor (supervisor)

- Level II — Mid-level supervisor (supervisory/managerial)
- Level III — First-line manager (managerial/administrative)
- Level IV — Department manager or chief (administrative)

IAFC Professional Development Model Designations

The International Association of Fire Chiefs (IAFC) also divides fire officer ranks into four levels in their Professional Development Model. These definitions vary slightly from the NFPA® model shown previously. These variations in designations include:

- Level I — Supervising fire officer (all company officers)
- Level II — Managing fire officer (battalion, district, and assistant chiefs)
- Level III — Administrative fire officer (administrative chiefs in charge of divisions or bureaus within the department)
- Level IV — Executive fire officer (department chief)

While Level I and Level II personnel are considered company officers, Level III personnel are generally regarded as battalion/district chiefs, assistant chiefs, or deputy chiefs. Level III chief officers may be in charge of geographic areas within a response area, a specific number of companies or stations, or administrative functions, such as training, public fire and life safety education, or administration within the organization.

The Level IV designation is reserved for the officer who is in charge of the organization or department chief. Fire Officer Level III and IV requirements are addressed in the Chief Officer manual by the International Fire Service Training Association (IFSTA).

Company officers are the largest single officer group within the fire and emergency services. Level I and Level II officers provide the first level of supervision for line functions, including:

- Fire suppression
- Search and rescue
- Emergency medical services (EMS)
- Fire prevention
- Public fire and life safety education
- Fire cause determination and arson investigation

These officers also supervise and manage staff functions, such as operations, planning, training, logistics, administration, and finance. They have direct contact with the majority of the organization's members and represent the administration to the membership. They are also in contact with external customers and citizens that the organization was created to protect and assist. In addition to fire and emergency skills, the officers must also have the following knowledge and skills:

- Interpersonal communication skills
- Knowledge of basic administrative functions

- Supervisory and leadership skills
- Ability to plan and organize

The terms line and staff have been adopted to describe the relationship created by this distinction:

- **Line functions** — Provide services directly to external customers based on the organization's mission statement and goals.
- **Staff/support functions** — Provide services to the line units (internal customers) based on the objectives established to attain the organization's goals.

In some organizations, the duties and responsibilities assigned to company officers may blur and overlap, resulting in only one level of company officer who performs the activities NFPA® has assigned to both levels. In other organizations, the Level I officer may be assigned to a line function and be in charge of a fire-suppression company, while a Level II officer is assigned additional administrative duties.

All company officers should possess the knowledge and skills that will permit them to safely and effectively provide the services that the authority and citizens expect. Professional development that provides the ability to progress through the ranks should also be available to all personnel. Company officers should remember the old adage that they are *students of the position they aspire to, stewards of the position they hold, and teachers of those who are subordinate to them.*

Knowledge, Skills, and Abilities

The company officer must possess certain knowledge, skills, and abilities (KSA) and have the ability to apply them to their assigned tasks. These tasks include:

- Understanding the structure, policies, and procedures of the fire and emergency services organization and its governing entity.
- Knowing how to effectively communicate orally and in writing in both routine and emergency situations.
- Knowing the fundamentals of human resources management.
- Knowing how to protect the safety and health of company personnel.
- Knowing basic building construction and building systems.
- Understanding the planning process, inspection procedures, investigation techniques, and public fire and life-safety education.
- Knowing how to deliver company-level emergency services to the public.
- Knowing how to deliver company-level training in order to maintain a high degree of company proficiency.

While knowledge and skills can be learned from manuals and courses, abilities are gained through the application of knowledge and skills. Abilities are based on experience and work ethic and develop over time.

This manual provides the knowledge components required to meet the NFPA® 1021 Fire Officer Level I and Level II JPRs. These JPRs are listed at the beginning of chapters where they are referenced. Learning objectives, located at the beginning of each chapter, will assist the reader in focusing on the appropriate topic and knowledge. **Appendix A** correlates the learning objectives and JPRs to the specific page of the chapter that relates to the requirements.

The reader should also be aware of the difference between training and education. Both are essential for safe, effective, and efficient delivery of emergency services, as well as career advancement within the emergency services. They are interrelated, although different in scope, purpose, definition, and application. Officers must also realize the importance of certification.

Training

Training is instruction that emphasizes job-specific learning objectives and traditional skills-based teaching. Some knowledge-based learning occurs in the form of learning about topics, such as fire behavior, symptoms of illnesses, and causes of accidents.

This knowledge is applied toward learning skills, such as fire suppression, patient care, and safe behavior in hazardous environments. Training and practice helps to ensure that fire and emergency services personnel become effective, efficient, and confident in the performance of their duties.

Education

Education involves instruction that emphasizes knowledge-based learning objectives that are not tied to a specific job. Education is related to concepts, such as management styles, budget process, governmental theories, or history.

Because of the shift in responsibilities, new company officers may be required to attend and complete various college-level courses. Continuing education is essential to advancement within the fire and emergency services officer levels.

Fire and Emergency Services Higher Education (FESHE) Model Curriculum

The U.S. Fire Administration/National Fire Academy (USFA/NFA), working in conjunction with universities, created the FESHE model curriculum. Degree-granting institutions are encouraged to use this model curriculum to develop college-level programs for the fire and emergency services. Model curriculums have been developed for Associate and Bachelor's degrees. The model curriculum is a portion of a professional development program that provides a consistent career path for members of the fire and emergency services.

Certification

Certification results from tests or assessments that are given to personnel to determine their abilities to apply knowledge and skills. Career advancement or mobility within the profession can often depend on certification.

All officers should acquire and maintain the appropriate levels of certification required by their organizations. They should also:

- Support professional development for the personnel assigned to them.
- Motivate personnel to attain the required certification, training, and education.
- Continue their own professional development to improve their skills.
- Set the best possible example for subordinates.

Manual Organization

This manual is written to specifically address the requirements set forth in the NFPA® 1021 JPRs for Level I and Level II Fire Officers. It is organized to assist in the creation and use of a curriculum or curriculums for Fire Officer Level I and Level II courses. The manual is divided into two parts: Part A contains information that is specific to Level I certification. Part B contains information that is specific only to Level II certification. **Students who are using this text to certify for Level II Fire Officer are encouraged to review the sections in Part A that relate to the Level II requisite knowledge, such as the chapters on communications, ethics, and leadership.**

Each chapter is preceded by divider pages containing a chapter table of contents, a list of key terms found in the chapter, a list of the JPRs covered by the chapter, and the lesson objectives. The following is a list of the chapter topics addressed in the manual.

Part A Fire Officer Level I

Chapter 1: The Company Officer I

Chapter 2: Organizational Structure

Chapter 3: Leadership and Supervision

Chapter 4: Human Resources Management I

Chapter 5: Communications

Chapter 6: Administrative Functions

Chapter 7: Health and Safety Issues

Chapter 8: Company-Level Training

Chapter 9: Community Relations and Company-Level Inspections

Chapter 10: Preincident Surveys

Chapter 11: Delivery of Emergency Services I

Part B Fire Officer Level II

Chapter 12: The Company Officer II

Chapter 13: Human Resources Management II

Chapter 14: Administrative Responsibilities

Chapter 15: Fire Investigations

Chapter 16: Delivery of Emergency Services II

Chapter 17: Safety Investigations and Analyses

Additional Resources

Additional educational resources to supplement this manual are available from the IFSTA and Fire Protection Publications (FPP). These resources include a study guide that is available in both hardcopy and electronic formats, which will assist readers in mastering the contents of this manual.

A full curriculum is available for instructors and training agencies to facilitate the teaching of the concepts and techniques described in this manual. Clip art, photos, and illustrations that are found in the manual are available on a USB flash drive for use by instructors as well as an instructor's guide for teaching Level I and Level II Fire Officer topics.

Terminology

IFSTA has traditionally provided training materials that are used throughout the U.S. and Canada. In recent years, the sales of IFSTA materials have expanded into a truly international market and resulted in the translation of materials into German, French, Spanish, Japanese, Hebrew, Turkish, and Italian. Writing the manuals, therefore, requires the use of Global English that consists of words and terms that can be easily translated into multiple languages and cultures.

This manual is written with the global market as well as the North American market in mind. Traditional fire service terminology, referred to as jargon, must give way to more precise descriptions and definitions. Where jargon is appropriate, it will be used along with its definition. The glossary at the end of the manual will also assist the reader in understanding words that may not have their roots in the fire and emergency services. The sources for the definitions of fire-and-emergency-services-related terms will be in the NFPA® Dictionary of Terms and the IFSTA Fire and Emergency Services Orientation and Terminology manual.

Due to the many job titles and ranks that are used to describe a company officer, the IFSTA validation committee decided to use specific terms rather than titles to describe Level I and Level II officers. The Level I officer will be referred to by the term supervisor, and the Level II officer will be referred to as manager.

Key Information

Various types of information in this manual are given in shaded boxes marked by symbols or icons. See the following definitions:

Case History

A case history analyzes an event. It can describe its development, action taken, investigation results, and lessons learned. Illustrations can be included.

Company Officer Information

Information boxes give facts that are complete in themselves but belong within the text discussion. It is information that may need more emphasis or separation. They can be summaries of points, examples, calculations, scenarios, or lists of advantages/disadvantages.

Supervisor — A person who is responsible for directing the performance of other people or employees.

A **key term** is designed to emphasize key comcepts, technical terms, or ideas that company officers need to know. They are listed at the beginning of each chapter, and the definition is placed in the margin for easy reference. They are listed at the beginning of each chapter, and the definition is placed in the margin for easy reference. An example of a key term is:

Three key signal words are found in the text: **WARNING!**, **CAUTION**, and **NOTE**. Definitions and examples of each are as follows:

- **WARNING!** indicates information that could result in death or serious injury to fire and emergency services personnel. See the following example:

> ## WARNING!
> Company officers must not attempt a live-burn training exercise without approval from the administration and the training division. They must adhere to the requirements of NFPA® 1500, *Standard on Fire Department Occupational Safety and Health Program*, and NFPA® 1403, *Standard on Live Fire Training Evolutions*, regarding safety during live-burn training exercises.

- **CAUTION** indicates important information or data that fire and emergency service responders need to be aware of in order to perform their duties safely. See the following example:

> ## CAUTION
> Emergency responders should avoid disturbing or destroying potential fire cause evidence during suppression operations in order to preserve evidence. The overhaul process should be delayed until the cause of the fire has been determined and any evidence protected.

- **NOTE** indicates important operational information that helps explain why a particular recommendation is given or describes optional methods for certain procedures. See the following example:

  NOTE: If the evolution involves more than one participant, the demonstration may require the use of an experienced group of responders to perform.

Referenced NFPA® Standards and Codes

One of the basic purposes of IFSTA manuals is to allow fire and emergency services personnel and their departments to meet the requirements set forth by NFPA® codes and standards. These NFPA® documents are referred to throughout this manual. References to information from NFPA® codes are used with permission from National Fire Protection Association®, Quincy, MA 02169. This referenced material is not the complete and official position of the National Fire Protection Association® on the referenced subject, which is represented only by the standard in its entirety.

Metric Conversions

Throughout this manual, U.S. units of measure are converted to metric units for the convenience of our international readers. Be advised that we use the Canadian metric system. It is very similar to the Standard International system, but may have some variation.

We adhere to the following guidelines for metric conversions in this manual:

- Metric conversions are approximated unless the number is used in mathematical equations.

- Centimeters are not used because they are not part of the Canadian metric standard.

- Exact conversions are used when an exact number is necessary, such as in construction measurements or hydraulic calculations.

- Set values, such as hose diameter, ladder length, and nozzle size, use their Canadian counterpart naming conventions and are not mathematically calculated. For example, 1½ inch hose is referred to as 38 mm hose.

- Add metric notes particular to your manual.

The following two tables provide detailed information on IFSTA's conversion conventions. The first table includes examples of our conversion factors for a number of measurements used in the fire service. The second shows examples of exact conversions beside the approximated measurements you will see in this manual. **(Tables on pg. 10 and 11)**

U.S. to Canadian Measurement Conversion

Measurements	Customary (U.S.)	Metric (Canada)	Conversion Factor
Length/Distance	Inch (in) Foot (ft) [3 or less feet] Foot (ft) [3 or more feet] Mile (mi)	Millimeter (mm) Millimeter (mm) Meter (m) Kilometer (km)	1 in = 25 mm 1 ft = 300 mm 1 ft = 0.3 m 1 mi = 1.6 km
Area	Square Foot (ft^2) Square Mile (mi^2)	Square Meter (m^2) Square Kilometer (km^2)	1 ft^2 = 0.09 m^2 1 mi^2 = 2.6 km^2
Mass/Weight	Dry Ounce (oz) Pound (lb) Ton (T)	gram Kilogram (kg) Ton (T)	1 oz = 28 g 1 lb = 0.5 kg 1 T = 0.9 T
Volume	Cubic Foot (ft^3) Fluid Ounce (fl oz) Quart (qt) Gallon (gal)	Cubic Meter (m^3) Milliliter (mL) Liter (L) Liter (L)	1 ft^3 = 0.03 m^3 1 fl oz = 30 mL 1 qt = 1 L 1 gal = 4 L
Flow	Gallons per Minute (gpm) Cubic Foot per Minute (ft^3/min)	Liters per Minute (L/min) Cubic Meter per Minute (m^3/min)	1 gpm = 4 L/min 1 ft^3/min = 0.03 m^3/min
Flow per Area	Gallons per Minute per Square Foot (gpm/ft^2)	Liters per Square Meters Minute ($L/(m^2.min)$)	1 gpm/ft^2 = 40 $L/(m^2.min)$
Pressure	Pounds per Square Inch (psi) Pounds per Square Foot (psf) Inches of Mercury (in Hg)	Kilopascal (kPa) Kilopascal (kPa) Kilopascal (kPa)	1 psi = 7 kPa 1 psf = .05 kPa 1 in Hg = 3.4 kPa
Speed/Velocity	Miles per Hour (mph) Feet per Second (ft/sec)	Kilometers per Hour (km/h) Meter per Second (m/s)	1 mph = 1.6 km/h 1 ft/sec = 0.3 m/s
Heat	British Thermal Unit (Btu)	Kilojoule (kJ)	1 Btu = 1 kJ
Heat Flow	British Thermal Unit per Minute (BTU/min)	watt (W)	1 Btu/min = 18 W
Density	Pound per Cubic Foot (lb/ft^3)	Kilogram per Cubic Meter (kg/m^3)	1 lb/ft^3 = 16 kg/m^3
Force	Pound-Force (lbf)	Newton (N)	1 lbf = 0.5 N
Torque	Pound-Force Foot (lbf ft)	Newton Meter (N.m)	1 lbf ft = 1.4 N.m
Dynamic Viscosity	Pound per Foot-Second (lb/ft.s)	Pascal Second (Pa.s)	1 lb/ft.s = 1.5 Pa.s
Surface Tension	Pound per Foot (lb/ft)	Newton per Meter (N/m)	1 lb/ft = 15 N/m

Conversion and Approximation Examples

Measurement	U.S. Unit	Conversion Factor	Exact S.I. Unit	Rounded S.I. Unit
Length/Distance	10 in	1 in = 25 mm	250 mm	250 mm
	25 in	1 in = 25 mm	625 mm	625 mm
	2 ft	1 in = 25 mm	600 mm	600 mm
	17 ft	1 ft = 0.3 m	5.1 m	5 m
	3 mi	1 mi = 1.6 km	4.8 km	5 km
	10 mi	1 mi = 1.6 km	16 km	16 km
Area	36 ft²	1 ft² = 0.09 m²	3.24 m²	3 m²
	300 ft²	1 ft² = 0.09 m²	27 m²	30 m²
	5 mi²	1 mi² = 2.6 km²	13 km²	13 km²
	14 mi²	1 mi² = 2.6 km²	36.4 km²	35 km²
Mass/Weight	16 oz	1 oz = 28 g	448 g	450 g
	20 oz	1 oz = 28 g	560 g	560 g
	3.75 lb	1 lb = 0.5 kg	1.875 kg	2 kg
	2,000 lb	1 lb = 0.5 kg	1 000 kg	1 000 kg
	1 T	1 T = 0.9 T	900 kg	900 kg
	2.5 T	1 T = 0.9 T	2.25 T	2 T
Volume	55 ft³	1 ft³ = 0.03 m³	1.65 m³	1.5 m³
	2,000 ft³	1 ft³ = 0.03 m³	60 m³	60 m³
	8 fl oz	1 fl oz = 30 mL	240 mL	240 mL
	20 fl oz	1 fl oz = 30 mL	600 mL	600 mL
	10 qt	1 qt = 1 L	10 L	10 L
	22 gal	1 gal = 4 L	88 L	90 L
	500 gal	1 gal = 4 L	2 000 L	2 000 L
Flow	100 gpm	1 gpm = 4 L/min	400 L/min	400 L/min
	500 gpm	1 gpm = 4 L/min	2 000 L/min	2 000 L/min
	16 ft³/min	1 ft³/min = 0.03 m³/min	0.48 m³/min	0.5 m³/min
	200 ft³/min	1 ft³/min = 0.03 m³/min	6 m³/min	6 m³/min
Flow per Area	50 gpm/ft²	1 gpm/ft² = 40 L/(m².min)	2 000 L/(m².min)	2 000 L/(m².min)
	326 gpm/ft²	1 gpm/ft² = 40 L/(m².min)	13 040 L/(m².min)	13 000L/(m².min)
Pressure	100 psi	1 psi = 7 kPa	700 kPa	700 kPa
	175 psi	1 psi = 7 kPa	1225 kPa	1 200 kPa
	526 psf	1 psf = 0.05 kPa	26.3 kPa	25 kPa
	12,000 psf	1 psf = 0.05 kPa	600 kPa	600 kPa
	5 psi in Hg	1 psi = 3.4 kPa	17 kPa	17 kPa
	20 psi in Hg	1 psi = 3.4 kPa	68 kPa	70 kPa
Speed/Velocity	20 mph	1 mph = 1.6 km/h	32 km/h	30 km/h
	35 mph	1 mph = 1.6 km/h	56 km/h	55 km/h
	10 ft/sec	1 ft/sec = 0.3 m/s	3 m/s	3 m/s
	50 ft/sec	1 ft/sec = 0.3 m/s	15 m/s	15 m/s
Heat	1200 Btu	1 Btu = 1 kJ	1 200 kJ	1 200 kJ
Heat Flow	5 BTU/min	1 Btu/min = 18 W	90 W	90 W
	400 BTU/min	1 Btu/min = 18 W	7 200 W	7 200 W
Density	5 lb/ft³	1 lb/ft³ = 16 kg/m³	80 kg/m³	80 kg/m³
	48 lb/ft³	1 lb/ft³ = 16 kg/m³	768 kg/m³	770 kg/m³
Force	10 lbf	1 lbf = 0.5 N	5 N	5 N
	1,500 lbf	1 lbf = 0.5 N	750 N	750 N
Torque	100	1 lbf ft = 1.4 N.m	140 N.m	140 N.m
	500	1 lbf ft = 1.4 N.m	700 N.m	700 N.m
Dynamic Viscosity	20 lb/ft.s	1 lb/ft.s = 1.5 Pa.s	30 Pa.s	30 Pa.s
	35 lb/ft.s	1 lb/ft.s = 1.5 Pa.s	52.5 Pa.s	50 Pa.s
Surface Tension	6.5 lb/ft	1 lb/ft = 15 N/m	97.5 N/m	100 N/m
	10 lb/ft	1 lb/ft = 15 N/m	150 N/m	150 N/m

The Company Officer I

Chapter Contents

chapter 1

Key Terms

NFPA® Job Performance Requirements

This chapter provides information that addresses the following job performance requirements of NFPA® 1021, *Standard for Fire Officer Professional Qualifications* (2014).

The Company Officer I

Learning Objectives

After reading this chapter, students will be able to:

1. Identify the importance of the company officer.
2. Describe the transition into the role of company officer.
3. List the responsibilities of the company officer.
4. Explain the duties of the company officer.

Chapter 1
The Company Officer I

Case History

Fire and emergency services personnel often wonder how personnel become company officers. They ask themselves, "What do they know? Where did they learn all of the things that they know? How did they reach this position?" These questions and others have been echoed over and over by individuals that were mystified by company officers who they respect and desire to emulate. Everyone knows at least one of this type of officer:

- Those officers who communicate with a matter-of-fact response that is complete without being excessive.
- Those officers who others listen to when they speak and are rarely challenged or contradicted.
- Those officers who have built a reputation grounded in knowledge, experience and success.
- Those officers who rarely have to discipline anyone because everyone knows what is acceptable and wants to please.

These company officers learned and developed communication skills that support and reinforce the separate roles of supervisor and subordinate while ensuring that both fulfill their roles as public servants. These company officers must view their world as filled with challenges, expectations, and opportunities. They must inform their personnel about what they want accomplished, train them to perform, provide resources, provide feedback, and focus on the organization's mission.

The transition to the role of company officer is one of the most challenging within the fire and emergency services. Although the promotion may be immediate, the transition from follower to leader occurs over time and requires many personal changes and adjustments. A new officer must:

- Understand the importance of the position of company officer.
- Recognize the challenges, expectations, opportunities, and commitment required.
- Know the responsibilities of a company officer.
- Know the duties of a company officer.
- Act in an ethical manner.

This chapter will address the company officer selection process, transitioning to the role of the company officer, and the important role of the company officer. It also describes challenges, expectations, opportunities, and commitment new company officers may face. Finally, it addresses company officer responsibilities and duties.

NOTE: Throughout this manual, the terms personnel, crew, and member will be used interchangeably to refer to personnel employed by or associated with the fire and emergency services.

National Fire Protection Association® (NFPA®) 1021, *Standard for Fire Officer Professional Qualifications*, Requirements and Prerequisite Knowledge

National Fire Protection Association® (NFPA®) 1021, Standard for Fire Officer Professional Qualifications, sets guidelines for qualification to the Fire Officer Level I. Candidates for this position should meet the following requirements:

- Fire Fighter II as described in NFPA® 1001, *Standard for Fire Fighter Professional Qualifications*

- Fire Instructor I as described in NFPA® 1041, *Standard for Fire Service Instructor Professional Qualifications*

- Chapter 4 job performance requirements (JPRs) of NFPA® 1021, *Standard for Fire Officer Professional Qualifications*

In addition, NFPA® 1021, item 5.1.1 General Prerequisite Knowledge identifies information that candidates should know before promotion or certification to Fire Officer Level I. These items include the following:

- Their department's organizational structure

- The geographical configuration and characteristics of their response districts

- Their departmental operating procedures that relate to administration, emergency operations, incident management system, and safety

- Their department's budget process

- Information management and recordkeeping processes for their department

- The fire prevention and building safety codes and ordinances applicable to their jurisdiction

- Current trends, technologies, and socioeconomic and political factors that affect the fire service

- The rights of management and members

- Agreements in force between their organization and members

- The policies and procedures regarding the operation of their department as they involve supervisors and members

This manual may address certain information relating to the preceding list as it relates to other job performance requirements (JPRs) of NFPA® 1021. Instructors and students should seek local information about their departments and organizations independently.

Importance of the Company Officer

The company officer is at the tip of the fire and emergency medical service "spear," directly overseeing the application of the agency's personnel, training, equipment, and apparatus to the resolution of issues faced by the agency.

Furthermore, they are the first contact with all fire department customers. Therefore, they are in a unique position to have either a positive or a negative effect on the organization's reputation. These roles are important to the personnel they supervise, the administration they support, and the public they serve.

Recognizing and understanding the importance of the position and the responsibilities are critical to the success of a company officer. Filling the position requires competency as a **leader**, ethical behavior, and supervisory skills that many new officers will have to develop. New officers should adopt an appropriate level of humility and respect for those they supervise in order to make the transition to officer less lengthy and difficult.

Leader — A person who leads or directs a unit.

As a Supervisor

Fire and emergency response units are generally close-knit. They look to the company officer as their **supervisor** to make decisions that will provide them with motivation and satisfaction to maximize performance in the workplace **(Figure 1.1)**.

Supervisor — A person who is responsible for directing the performance of other people or employees.

Figure 1.1 Unit members rely on the company officer's knowledge and skills as a leader and supervisor.

The company officer performs many functions including but not limited to:

- Provides leadership
- Acting as a role model
- Giving advice
- Providing representation for members to the administration
- Seeking to resolve interpersonal conflicts
- Applying counseling or coaching when necessary
- Directing the work and ensuring readiness

All of these functions take place continuously with some conflicting with others. The company officer's most important task is to ensure the safety of the unit's personnel. The company officer must balance the acceptable level of risk to the unit while fulfilling assigned objectives.

As a Subordinate

New company officers need to recognize that they are both a supervisor and a subordinate. A company officer is responsible for the members of the unit and their actions while on-duty. The organization's administration expects the company officer to supervise the unit and effectively complete assigned duties.

The company officer is also expected to represent the administration and ensure compliance with administration policies, rules, and regulations. As a subordinate, a company officer is expected to execute the orders of superior officers. A company officer may have to enforce what others perceive as unpopular or unfair policies or orders. Being a supervisor is not a popularity contest! Officers should not publicly question or criticize policies or orders that they believe to be unfair as this provides a negative example for both subordinates and peers. Any criticisms or questions about policies or orders should be discussed privately with the administration in order to search for solutions.

As a Public Servant

The company officer and members of a unit are often the first direct contacts the public will have with the fire and emergency services of a local government. That contact often occurs when citizens are experiencing a crisis. As well, there are numerous non-emergency circumstances that provide the company officer with the opportunity to make a positive impression with the public.

The public sees and may judge the entire organization through the company officer and crew. How that initial contact develops and the results of it are crucial to the impressions that the public will have of the organization. Company officers must understand the role of public servants and ensure that the unit's members understand this role. Customer service concepts should be applied to maintain a positive public perception of the agency.

Fire and emergency services members are held accountable for delivering a service that meets the external customers' needs. The public expects efficient delivery of those services. Company officers should consider the fire and emergency services organization to be customer service-oriented. Customer service applies to volunteer as well as career organizations.

Meeting Challenges and Expectations and Approaches for a Successful Transition

The company officer is the vital link between the unit and the administration of the organization (**Figure 1.2**). The move from the backseat or driver's seat to the officer's seat brings with it challenges and expectations. These challenges and expectations may be external or internal. New company officers, in particular, must be aware of these challenges and how to meet them.

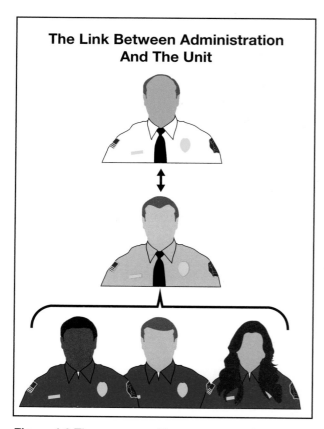

The Link Between Administration And The Unit

Figure 1.2 The company officer represents the administration to the unit and the unit to the administration.

Challenges

Challenges that a new officer will encounter consist of learning and applying concepts such as:

- **Leadership** — Officers must begin to cultivate the leadership skills needed to ensure that a unit operates safely, effectively, and efficiently.

- **Ethics** — Ethical conduct takes on greater importance because the officer is a role model for subordinate members of the unit, peers, and even the public.

- **Supervision** — Company officer level supervision may be the most difficult type of supervision one can encounter. The move from being supervised to supervising while still under the supervision of higher officers can seem overwhelming.

- **Responsibility** — A new officer must assume not only responsibility for his or her own actions, but is now responsible for the actions of subordinates.

- **Authority** — Officers must learn what authority is legitimately assigned to the position and how to apply it in a fair and equitable manner.

New company officers will experience a variety of personal and professional changes during the transition to becoming an officer. Relationships will change because of the officer's newfound authority as will the perception that others have of an individual who recently was a peer. The transition to company officer can also change the dynamics within a group and result in personal changes.

Relationship Changes

For the officer who is promoted or selected from within the organization, the challenge will be to make the change from unit member to unit leader. The relationship between peers and friends will shift to a supervisor and subordinate relationship. The company officer must both develop and use excellent interpersonal skills to satisfactorily communicate with members of the unit and practice a form of leadership that is appropriate to the situation.

Another potentially challenging shift in relationships occurs when the unit must respond to an emergency. During most of the work shift, members of the unit are training or performing routine duties involving station or apparatus maintenance. When the unit responds to an emergency, however, the dynamics of the relationship change. Directions must be given and responded to quickly with appropriate action. It is not a time for questioning or objecting to an assignment. However, when subordinates express safety concerns, the need for authoritative leadership may take a secondary role in favor of addressing the concerns.

In volunteer, combination, or industrial organizations, the relationship may even require the exchange of supervisory roles as the employer and employee leave a place of work and respond to an emergency. The employee may become the company officer, and the employer becomes the firefighter. Mutual respect and the ability to take and give orders are essential for the success of this type of relationship change. It will be necessary for both parties to recognize the change and to react accordingly.

Changes in How One is Perceived

A new company officer will be perceived differently after assuming the new position. Perceptions are subjective, often based on emotions, not facts, and can be difficult to overcome. Members may also have a perception of the relationship between them and the new officer as a result of the previous relationship as friends and peers. They may expect that their friendship will allow them privileges or a freedom from strict policies enforced by the organization.

Unless the officer establishes an understanding regarding the relationship between the officer and the unit members and the enforcement of policy, the unit will suffer. True friendship should never create a situation that places the officer or subordinates in such a negative situation. In such instances, the officer may need to take a more authoritarian approach to establish the new relationship. This is another example of how an officer must use skill and observation regarding the most appropriate method of leading each member of the unit.

Changes to Group Dynamics

Group dynamics may change as the new officer replaces another company officer. Attempting to duplicate the personality and behavior of the previous officer can create resentment and loss of respect for the new officer.

Making sweeping changes to a unit can also be unsuccessful and cause the unit to suffer. The new officer should use the opportunity to verbalize personal expectations, establish priorities, and listen to crew member expectations. The officer must understand the experience-level, educational, and generational differences within the crew.

Traditions

A new company officer may be faced with the challenge that is best expressed as "We never did it that way before." The officer may be tempted to use this same phrase as a response to orders or policies issued by the organization. To overcome this barrier, the officer must be able to explain why it is important to make the change and how the change will benefit the crew and/or the agency and community.

Personal Factors/Personal Changes

New company officers may have to make personal changes to avoid the antagonism, resentfulness, and loss of friendships that can occur if the transition isn't well managed. To overcome these personal challenges, the new officer must:

- **Commit to the responsibilities, duties, and requirements of the supervisory position** — Learn about, be interested in, and be dedicated to the position.

- **Show loyalty to the organization** — Support the leadership team and political authority. Do not openly criticize the organization, management, or decisions that are made by it.

- **Show loyalty toward company personnel** — Share your company's concerns, ideas, opinions, and complaints to your supervisor so that the unit has a voice with management.

- **Act as a liaison** — As a supervisor and part of the management structure in the organization, act as a two-way information agent, expressing agency policies, and listening to and passing on reactions to that policy.

- **Support all types of education and training** — Seek opportunities to learn and also provide them to other members of the organization.

- **Guard conversations** — Never say anything, on or off the job, that would dishonor a person, a position, or the organization. Do not disclose information that is confidential, in particular information concerning subordinates. Consider information confidential unless told otherwise.

- **Accept criticism graciously and accept praise, honors, and advancement modestly** — Admit mistakes and errors and take responsibility for them. Give credit to members of your crew for their accomplishments and their contributions to crew accomplishments.

- **Lead by example** — Set a positive example for subordinates founded on a consistent adherence to a set of moral, ethical, and social values. Such an example is of the utmost importance and is essential to the successful leadership of any organization.

- **Praise in public; discipline in private** — Never discredit subordinates publicly. Point out mistakes or areas for correction to subordinates in private. Causing someone personal embarrassment or humiliation in public can destroy a relationship.

- **Project a professional image** — Project a professional image to the public, elected officials, internal and external stakeholders, and to peers.

Expectations

The expectations of a company officer come from many sources and may be unreasonable or difficult to meet. There are the external expectations of subordinates, peers, family, superiors, and the public at large. There are also expectations that company officers place on themselves. While learning to meet these expectations or to handle unreasonable expectations, a company officer should seek assistance from more experienced personnel or from the administration or training divisions when necessary.

The following individuals may have certain expectations of a new company officer:

- **Family members** — Family members may not realize the added responsibility may result in more work time or increased stress. Their expectations of time and attention from the new company officer may prove to be unrealistic and unattainable, particularly when an officer changes from shift work to day work. The family, and even the officer, may not be prepared for the change.

- **Former peers and firefighters** — An officer's former peers and coworkers may make some assumptions about how they will be treated and have unreasonable expectations. For instance, former close firefighter peers may expect a new officer to overlook policy infractions because of friendship.

- **Administrators** — Administrators may expect a new officer to know how to lead, supervise, and perform the duties of a company officer. New company officers may be developing these skills while still trying to meet administrative expectations.

- **Public** — The public expects every company officer to have all of the answers and be able to mitigate their incident.

Internal expectations may be the most difficult to overcome. Becoming a company officer may cause an individual to improperly use the authority of the position, resulting in an abuse of power. Rank may also be confused with respect, something that must be earned and returned. New company officers may expect to be treated as invaluable to the operation of the organization. They may believe that they can change the world, setting their expectations beyond reach or reason. Realistic company officers know that the only person they can truly change is themselves, creating the opportunity for greater change.

Bringing expectations in line with reality requires the realization that some expectations are unattainable or unreasonable. Reasonable organizational expectations can be met through education, training, and effort. A new officer will learn how to manage the unreasonable expectations and reach a compromise with the people who hold them.

Approaches for a Successful Transition

New officers have the choice to see their new challenges and expectations as either a burden or an opportunity to excel. Successful officers choose to see the transition as an opportunity to grow as a professional. In order to take advantage of the opportunities that becoming an officer provides, a new company officer should try the following approaches:

- Communicate effectively.
- Apply appropriate supervisory techniques.
- Manage effectively.
- Project a command presence.
- Develop an appropriate leadership style.
- Show respect for others.
- Be loyal to the company, organization, and community.
- Be a positive and ethical role model at all times.
- Live by a personal and professional code of ethics.
- Set high yet attainable standards.
- Value diversity in people and situations.
- Praise accomplishments.
- Listen to others.
- Commit to education and training.
- Remain humble.

By applying and practicing the previously listed skills, an officer will provide the type of role model that the company, organization, and profession will recognize and try to emulate. Attaining these skills will require the officer to recognize what is lacking and work to develop it.

A new officer should rarely resort to using rank as a reason for compliance. The officer should establish relationships based on mutual respect for the abilities of members of the unit and the officer. An officer may have already established a reputation for good leadership, strong interpersonal skills, and fair supervision as an acting company officer. This previous relationship can provide a bridge for the new officer.

A new officer should always remember that respect must be earned. It is possible that members of the unit may decide to respect the position and not the person filling it. Then the new officer will have to work to gain the personal respect of the members.

Start Tight, Then Go Light

A new company officer should remember that it is easier to start applying policies and procedures strictly and then ease the restrictions than to become strict after initially being lenient. One way of saying it is 'start tight, then go light.'

There is also the possibility that the officer may be faced with a subordinate who will only respond to strict authority, causing the officer to have to state, 'I am the officer in charge of this company.' This approach should only be used in the most extreme situations and as a last resort.

Responsibilities

By understanding their responsibilities and the people they are responsible to, company officers will be able to perform the duties that are assigned to them. Company officers have responsibilities to all of the following:

- **Subordinates** — Adhere to and enforce safety regulations in order to provide a safe work environment; also represent the needs of their subordinates to the organization and provide:
  - Ethical leadership
  - Fair and just supervision
  - Educational and training opportunities
- **Organization** — Administer all policies and procedures of the organization; represent the organization to members of the unit and the public.
- **Public** — Provide effective and efficient professional service to the public; be aware that the public provides resources to the organization and that officers are stewards of those resources.
- **Profession** — Serve as visible representatives and role models, like all fire and emergency services members. The public and the organization's members judge the profession by the actions of its officers.
- **Family** — Listen to expectations and needs of your family and communicate the expectations of the new position.
- **Themselves** — Live by a set of ethical standards and values that are based on the accepted moral values of the community if they expect their subordinates to live by them; respect themselves and abide by their convictions if they expect the same from others.

NFPA® Officer Levels and Corresponding IFSTA Manuals

Level	IFSTA Manual
I	Fire and Emergency Services Company Officer
II	Fire and Emergency Services Company Officer
III	Fire and Emergency Services Chief Officer
IV	Fire and Emergency Services Chief Officer

Figure 1.3 The International Fire Service Training Association (IFSTA) produces two manuals to meet the training objectives of NFPA® 1021, *Standard for Fire Officer Professional Qualifications.*

Duties

According to NFPA® 1021, the duties of a company officer are divided into general categories that apply to all fire officer levels (I through IV). This manual addresses Level I and Level II while IFSTA's Chief Officer manual contains information that apply to Level III and Level IV Fire Officers **(Figure 1.3)**. The categories listed in NFPA® 1021 are:

- Human resources management
- Community and government relations
- Administration
- Inspection and investigation
- Emergency service delivery
- Health and safety

Each category is further divided into job performance requirements (JPRs) that guide the officer in the performance of the duties. Each JPR lists requisite knowledge and skills used to create officer training programs, establish evaluation and promotional criteria, and create learning objectives like those found in this manual.

Besides the duties identified in NFPA® 1021, additional duties may be assigned to the company officer. Examples of these are included in the Miscellaneous section later in this chapter.

Human Resources Management

Level I Fire Officers must be able to perform the following human resources management duties:

- Provide effective supervision for both emergency and nonemergency activities.
- Assign tasks.
- Evaluate personnel performance.
- Provide company-level training activities.
- Administer policies and procedures efficiently and equitably.
- Recommend actions when situations exceed their authority or ability.
- Act as a project **manager** in certain situations.
- Provide professional development opportunities for members.
- Initiate or assist with personnel transfers, personal benefits (such as annual, sick, injury, and family leaves), changes in those benefits, awards and commendations, disciplinary actions, and labor/management issues (including grievances).

Community and Government Relations

Level I Fire Officers must be able to respond to citizen inquiries and complaints efficiently and courteously. Officers must also be able to present public fire and life-safety educational programs to community members. They must realize that the success of any fire and emergency services organization is directly proportional to its community involvement.

Manager — Individual who accomplishes organizational objectives through effective and efficient handling of material and human resources.

Knowledge of community demographics and cultural diversity, the services provided by the local authority, and the means of processing public requests is essential to all fire officers. Fire officers in small departments may be responsible for reporting to members of the local authority or interacting with managers in other departments within the jurisdiction, such as Public Works, Human Resources, or Finance and Revenue.

Administration

A Level I Fire Officer must administer the organization's policies, procedures, and orders at the unit level. The officer observes the application of these administrative documents and recommends changes to them as necessary. A company officer maintains records of unit activities and prepares reports based on these records. They may also monitor and document the consumption and cost of providing the unit's resources in order to help prepare the organization's budget.

Inspection and Investigation

The Level I Officer may also be assigned fire and life-safety inspections, which requires performing the following duties:

- Understanding building construction.
- Understanding and applying the jurisdiction's building and fire codes.
- Identifying types of hazards and fire protection systems.
- Applying fire and life-safety regulations to all types of occupancies.

When assigned to a fire suppression incident, Level I Officers may also be responsible for the initial fire cause determination or investigation process **(Figure 1.4)**. That duty requires that the following actions be performed:

- Secure the incident scene.
- Preserve evidence.
- Interview witnesses and emergency personnel.
- Notify a fire investigator when the situation warrants it.

A Level I Fire Officer may also supervise salvage and overhaul activities. Officers may supervise salvage and overhaul operations at incidents that involved criminal activity, such as acts of terrorism or the operation of illegal drug laboratories. At these incidents, officers should take the following actions:

- Notify the appropriate law enforcement agency.
- Designate the scene as a crime scene.
- Maintain security of the scene until fire investigation personnel arrive.

Figure 1.4 A company officer may conduct the initial fire cause determination following a structure fire.

Emergency Service Delivery

The Level I Officer supervising the first-arriving unit to an incident is responsible for performing the initial size-up of the situation, establishing the Incident Command System (ICS), and allocating resources to control the incident **(Figure 1.5, p. 26)**.

The Level I Fire Officer may also be responsible for inspecting potentially hazardous sites within the unit's response area, conducting preincident planning, and assisting in the creation of preincident plans. Preincident planning

Figure 1.5 Company officers must be able to quickly and effectively allocate their resources to gain control of an incident.

and the plans that result from that process assist the Level I Fire Officer in evaluating emergency situations. These plans are generally (or should be) shared with other units and command officers (Level II and Level III) who may respond to the same incident.

Upon arrival, the first-arriving company officer must develop and initiate an incident action plan (IAP), an incident safety plan (ISP), and establish the Incident Command System (ICS) in accordance with local policy. Following the incident, the fire officer may conduct a postincident analysis for incidents involving a single unit or participate in an analysis under a command officer's leadership when the situation is appropriate.

Health and Safety

For Level I Fire Officers, ensuring the health and safety of all personnel requires performing the following actions:

- Apply health and safety standards daily.

- Implement safety-related policies and procedures.

- Monitor personnel to ensure that safety guidelines are followed.

- Report all situations that involve job-related injuries or fatalities.

- Act as a role model by personally adhering to accepted health and safety practices.

Safety must become second nature for all personnel in all types of emergency and nonemergency situations. Safety policies are nonnegotiable, and the importance of safety cannot be overemphasized.

Other Possible Duties

Company officers may be assigned other duties that are not specifically mentioned in NFPA® 1021. These duties may include:

- Being assigned to training divisions, medical response units, or specialized rescue or hazardous materials units.

- Performing preconstruction plan reviews.

- Issuing permits or licenses.

- Acting as liaison to other agencies or organizations.

- Report to the local governing body to provide information and advice.

Chapter Summary

The company officer holds a position that is unique in the fire and emergency services and supervisory positions in general. As a working supervisor, the officer must perform the same fire fighting, rescue, or EMS tasks that other members perform. As a member of management, the officer must perform the functions of a first-level supervisor, evaluate personnel, provide training, and develop budget requests, among other duties. The company officer must also be a representative of the unit to the administration, the administration to the unit, and the organization to the public.

In each of these roles, an officer must make decisions, act ethically, and apply supervisory and management skills to provide a professional service to the public and members of the unit. Finally, the company officer must understand and adhere to acknowledged standards of leadership and ethical behavior. Leader, supervisor, manager, and unit member are all roles that a company officer must learn to play effectively and simultaneously.

Review Questions

1. How do the three roles that a company officer plays in an organization differ from each other? (pp.17-18)

2. What are some of the challenges that a new Company Officer I can expect to face? (pp. 19-21)

3. What are the responsibilities of a Company Officer I? (p. 23)

4. What duties will a Company Officer I be expected to perform? (p. 24)

Organizational Structure

Chapter Contents

Key Terms

NFPA® Job Performance Requirements

This chapter provides information that addresses the following job performance requirements of NFPA® 1021, *Standard for Fire Officer Professional Qualifications* (2014).

4.4.4

4.6.2

Organizational Structure

Learning Objectives

After reading this chapter, students will be able to:

1. Describe the basic principles of an organizational structure. [NFPA® 1021, 4.4.4]

2. Explain the purposes of fire and emergency services organizations.

3. Identify classifications of fire and emergency services organizations.

4. List types of organizational staffing in the fire service.

5. Identify the role of a Company Officer I in resource allocation. [NFPA® 1021, 4.6.2]

6. Describe the use of aid agreements in the fire service.

7. Distinguish among the various components of organizational management. [NFPA® 1021, 4.4.4; Learning Activity 2-1]

Chapter 2
Organizational Structure

Case History

A newly appointed captain wanted to make some quick changes to his company. He knew what he wanted and studied all the rules and policies of the organization and decided to put his ideas in place. A week later, he was called into the chief's office and was asked, "Who authorized the changes to the company?" The new captain explained that he decided on those changes based on rules and procedures. By the next shift, things went back to the way they were.

The problem that the new officer encountered was not that he did not know the rules and policies of his organization, but that his decision to change the structure should have involved the organization as a whole. The captain was asked to put his ideas on paper. A few days later, he created a proposal and sent it up the chain of command. The following month, he was called back into the chief's office. The chief told him, "Everyone thought that the recommended changes were positive and should be implemented department wide." Two months later, the proposed changes still had not been implemented. When the captain asked about the delay, he was told that any change requires the approval of the legal, risk management, budget, training, union, and administrative divisions within the organization. The new captain learned that knowing the rules and policies of the organization was not enough. He had to know how each division of the department integrates with the other divisions.

Organizational structure is important to the fire and emergency services because it permits the effective, organized, and efficient use of resources. Teamwork, esprit de corps, quality leadership, personnel development, effective discipline, and efficient operations are all important to emergency response personnel, and the organizational structure must accommodate these traits. In addition, organizational structure helps fire and emergency services organizations provide the highest level of service to their customers at the lowest possible cost.

In most North American public fire and emergency services organizations, the top official is called the fire chief, chief, commissioner, or chief executive officer (CEO). Whatever title is used, this person must ensure that the organization has an adequate structure and management system, including required policies and procedures, to govern the operation of the organization in support of its mission.

Written standard operating procedures/standard operating guidelines (SOPs/SOGs) are used to define organizational policy and describe behavioral and performance expectations of employees. Cooperation among company members is based upon following department guidelines and also on the trust

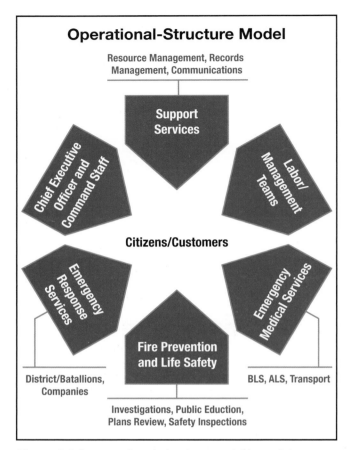

Operational-Structure Model

Resource Management, Records Management, Communications

Support Services

Chief Executive Officer and Command Staff

Labor/Management Teams

Citizens/Customers

Emergency Response Services

Emergency Medical Services

Fire Prevention and Life Safety

District/Batallions, Companies

BLS, ALS, Transport

Investigations, Public Eduction, Plans Review, Safety Inspections

Figure 2.1 An operational-structure model to assist company officers in understanding their organization's structure and their unit's assignment and role within the organization.

that results from the consistent application of sound organizational principles. Company officers must understand their organization's structure, where their units are located in the organization, and how their units relate to other organizational parts **(Figure 2.1)**.

All fire and emergency services organizations must have some type of formal structure to:

- Provide a management framework for the organization.
- Define how it will plan and operate to meet its mission.
- Determine how the organization will interact with other organizations or government agencies, both internal and external to the jurisdiction.

This chapter describes the basic principles of organizational structure, classifications of fire and emergency services organizations, and how organizations are staffed. Resource allocation issues are also discussed.

Basic Principles

Fire and emergency services organizations follow certain basic principles of organizational structure based on organizational theory, research, and practice in both public and private organizations. These principles include:

- Scalar structure
- Line and staff personnel
- Decision-making authority
- Unity of command
- Span of control
- Division of labor

Scalar Structure

The common organizational structure used in the fire and emergency services is scalar, which is defined as having an uninterrupted series of steps or a **chain of command**. Decisions and information are directed from the top of the organizational structure down through intermediate levels to the base of the structure. Feedback and information, in turn, are transmitted up from the bottom through the structure to the top positions **(Figure 2.2)**.

Direct communication at lower organizational levels allows for quicker actions and reactions. Within this scalar structure, certain decision-making authority is delegated to lower levels, and communication is enhanced. Information is generally centralized for decision-making.

Chain of Command — Order of rank and authority in the fire and emergency services.

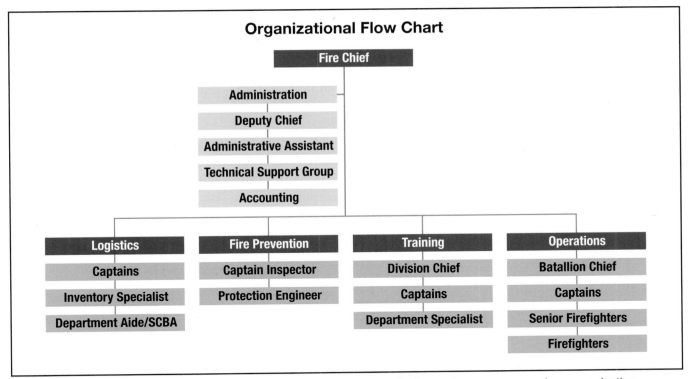

Figure 2.2 An organizational flow chart illustrating the scalar structure of a fire and emergency services organization.

Line and Staff Personnel

Line and staff are terms that refer to an organizational concept that separates fire and emergency services personnel into the following two distinct groups **(Figure 2.3)**:

- **Line personnel** — Those who deliver services to the public or external customers; typical functions include fire suppression, emergency medical services (EMS), inspections, education, and investigations

- **Staff personnel** — Those who provide support to the line personnel or internal customers; typical functions are training, logistics, and personnel administration

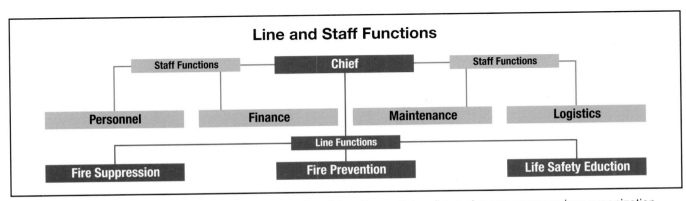

Figure 2.3 Illustrating the differences between line and staff functions within a fire and emergency services organization.

Company officers may report to either staff or line personnel depending upon what duties the company officer is performing at the time. Company officers should also keep in mind that staff duties may also be assigned to line personnel in small organizations, combination (both career and volunteer personnel) departments, and volunteer (all volunteer personnel) organizations.

Decision-Making Authority

Authority refers to the legal ability of an individual to make and implement decisions for which the individual is held accountable. The company officer has changing decision-making roles throughout an incident. There are two types of decision-making models: centralized authority and decentralized authority **(Figure 2.4)**. Authority may also be delegated in either system.

Figure 2.4 Comparison between centralized and decentralized authority within an organizational structure.

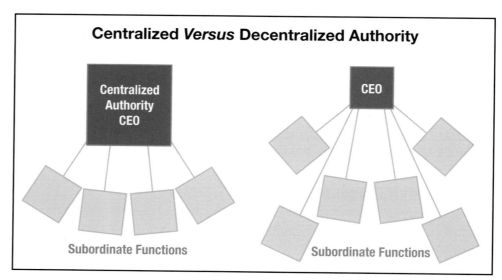

Centralized

Decisions are made by one person at the top of the structure. This model works well in very small organizations, such as an individual fire company. In large organizations, the leader's span of control may be exceeded unless decision-making authority is delegated.

Accountability for decisions is almost always centralized. The chief of the organization delegates to officers the authority to make decisions and implement plans, but the chief is still accountable to the authority having jurisdiction (AHJ) and the public for any decisions made.

Decentralized

Decisions are made at a lower level (basically delegation of authority), with the effects of the decisions reported through the structure. To work effectively, the chief must ensure that all members understand the direction, values, and goals of the organization. Decision-making authority should be delegated to the lowest level possible.

In a decentralized model, decision-making authority is limited to only those tasks over which personnel have been given authority. For example, the chief might give a deputy, assistant, or battalion/district chief the authority to make policy changes while granting a company officer authority over servicing equipment at the company level. The company officer would have full, decision-making authority where equipment service was concerned but would not be able to set policy for the organization, even if the policy applied to equipment.

The chief may also decentralize the authority to make certain decisions only in specific areas. For example, a chief may dictate what tasks are to be performed but delegate to the company officer the authority to decide when and in what order the tasks are performed.

Decentralization of authority allows for the expeditious handling of most matters. With decisions made at lower levels in an organization, upper management personnel are freed to concentrate on other areas of responsibility. The details resulting from a decision do not have to be reported, but the effects of the decision do. For example, depending upon an organization's size and structure, a chief may not need to know what type of maintenance is being performed on an apparatus, merely that the apparatus will be out of service for maintenance.

With decentralization of authority, duplication of effort may occur. To avoid this, policies must define what decisions can be made and under what conditions. A review system should be established to ensure accountability and study the effects of decentralized decisions.

Delegation of Authority

Delegation is the process of providing subordinates with the authority, direction, and resources needed to complete an assignment. The decision to delegate authority to finish a task is often difficult. The officer may worry that the delegated task will not be completed in a manner that meets the organization's standards. Feelings like these are natural and show that the officer wants to do a good job. Concerns about delegating tasks can be alleviated through a training program that builds knowledge, skills, abilities, and trust.

When delegating a task, an officer must ensure that the assigned employee is capable of doing the job. While picking the right person for the right job, officers should look for opportunities to challenge subordinates with tasks to build their knowledge, skills set, and confidence.

Authority and responsibility go hand-in-hand. Delegation of an assignment must be accompanied with appropriate authority and trust that the individual will achieve the desired results using proper methods (responsibility). When assigning a task, the company officer should:

- Describe the task and its relationship to the overall goal or objective.

- Identify available resources.

- Identify time and safety constraints that apply to the assignment.

Unity of Command

Unity of command states that each subordinate must have only one supervisor **(Figure 2.5, p. 36)**. The employee and the supervisors may face a number of problems if an employee is required to report to more than one supervisor including:

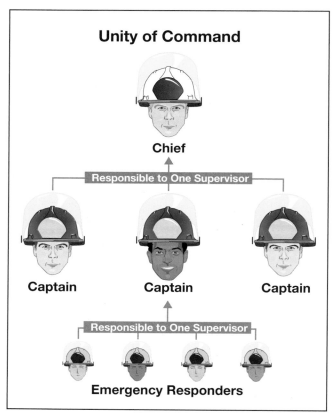

Unity of Command

Chief

Responsible to One Supervisor

Captain   **Captain**   **Captain**

Responsible to One Supervisor

Emergency Responders

Figure 2.5 The basic principle of unity of command is that a subordinate must have only one supervisor.

- The employee follows the last order received, without performing the previous order. The first assignment is incomplete, but the supervisor who ordered it thinks that it has been done.

- The employee executes the tasks poorly while trying to do two (perhaps conflicting) tasks at once.

- The employee plays the supervisors against each other so that neither supervisor knows exactly what the employee is doing, and the employee may do little or no work.

- The employee becomes frustrated while attempting to follow the conflicting orders of different supervisors and gives up both tasks.

Violations of unity of command lead to confusion and frustration by both subordinates and supervisors. Organizations that employ unity of command provide adequate direction and accountability, allowing all workers to be more productive and efficient. Unity of command depends on the use of the chain of command and functional supervision.

Chain of Command

Chain of command is the path of responsibility from the top of the organization to the bottom and vice versa. Although each member reports to one supervisor directly, every member is still responsible to the chief indirectly through the chain of command.

With unity of command, supervisors divide the work into specific job assignments without losing control. The chief can issue general orders that filter through the chain of command and translate into specific work assignments at various levels within the organization.

When a subordinate sidesteps the immediate supervisor and takes a problem to a higher officer, the unity of command is broken. While it is sometimes necessary for a subordinate to do this, it is generally an attempt to circumvent the chain of command. This **sidestepping** can be destructive to organizational unity and cohesiveness.

The superior officer should instruct the subordinate to follow the chain of command and take the problem to the immediate supervisor. Sidestepping could exclude the person best able to solve the problem — the immediate supervisor. There are times when it may be acceptable to bypass a level in the chain of command. For example, if the immediate supervisor is viewed as part of the problem or does not resolve the problem, the subordinate may be justified in bypassing the chain of command (using **skip level notification**). Personnel should always consult local policy prior to taking such actions.

All officers should instruct their subordinates in the proper method of handling problems through the chain of command. They must be willing, prepared, and able to handle their subordinates' problems. To reduce sidestepping the chain of command, officers should:

Sidestepping — The process of going around a link in the chain of command to deal with an issue.

Skip Level Notification — Notifying one's supervisor that one wishes to take an issue to the supervisor's supervisor.

- Be available to listen to their subordinates' problems
- Listen to problems sincerely, give them full consideration, and address their perception
- Take action and notify the employee of your actions
- Take a problem to the next level in the chain of command when it cannot be solved at the officer's level of authority

Functional Supervision

Functional supervision is an organizational principle that allows workers to report to more than one supervisor. Functional supervision deviates from unity of command when personnel are assigned by their supervisor or a senior officer to perform duties that fall under the authority of another supervisor. The subordinates report to the second supervisor on matters relating to that function. For this arrangement to work, both supervisors must communicate with each other and closely coordinate their activities.

Functional supervision is often useful when the distinction between line and staff functions becomes blurred. Company officers may report to a battalion chief or other line supervisor during emergency activities and routine nonemergency activities. Company officers may report to a staff officer when the company is engaged in some specialized activity (such as code enforcement, public education, etc.). For example, company personnel assigned to perform code enforcement inspections may direct their questions to and coordinate their activities with the fire prevention supervisor while they perform those duties. For all other activities, they report to their regular supervisor. For this arrangement to work, both supervisors must communicate with each other and closely coordinate their activities.

Functional Supervision — Organizational principle that allows workers to report to more than one supervisor without violating the unity of command principle; workers report to their primary supervisor for most of their activities but report to a second supervisor for activities that relate to an assigned function only, and both supervisors coordinate closely.

Span of Control

Span of control refers to the number of subordinates and/or number of functions that one individual can effectively supervise. This principle applies equally to supervising the crew of a single company or the officers of several companies under the direction of an incident commander (IC). There is no absolute rule for determining how many subordinates or functions that one person can supervise effectively. The number varies with the situation but is usually considered to be somewhere between three and seven **(Figure 2.6)**.

While a wider span of control can have advantages in nonemergency operations, it is not recommended for the majority of emergency operations. The National Incident Management System-Incident Command System (NIMS-ICS) model is based on a span-of-control ratio of one supervisor to three to seven subordinates or functions. NIMS-ICS suggests an optimum of five. The variables that affect span of control in any given situation include the:

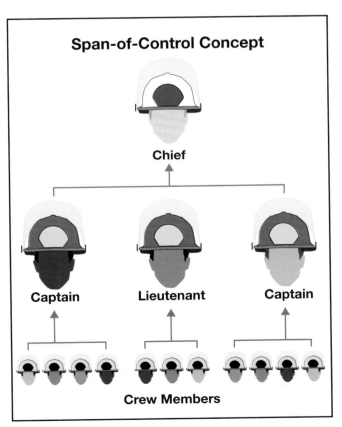

Figure 2.6 Span of control limits the number of personnel each supervisor can effectively control.

- Ability and experience of the supervisor
- Ability and experience of subordinates
- Nature of the task — Characteristics:
  - Urgency
  - Conditions under which it must be performed
  - Complexity
  - Rate at which it must be performed
  - Similarity/dissimilarity to tasks being performed by others
- Proximity of subordinates to the supervisor and each other
- Ease/reliability of communications medium
- Consequences of a mistake

Effective supervision is easier when the tasks are relatively simple and repetitive, all workers are well-trained, and workers are performing the same or similar tasks. Little supervision may be required when subordinates are working near the supervisor or other coworkers so that they can ask questions or get help easily.

Effective supervision is extremely difficult when:

- Tasks being performed are very complex.
- Workers' level of training is minimal.
- Workers are performing dissimilar tasks.
- Workers are widely separated from the supervisor and each other.

These variables may be manageable in some cases. However, when a worker's mistake could result in fatalities or injuries during training or an incident, the effective span of control may need to be reduced to a safe operational level. Examples of proper span of control include when:

- A company officer supervises the members of one company (three to seven subordinates).
- A strike team leader supervises the company officers in charge of the engines in a strike team.
- A division supervisor commands five strike teams and/or task forces, etc.

If an Incident Commander fails to delegate authority properly at a major incident, the span of control may be exceeded. As a result, the IC may attempt to directly control the entire incident, making all decisions at all levels. Making every decision in the absence of good delegation can be quickly overwhelming and can cause:

- Chaos at the incident scene
- Breakdowns in communication and coordination
- Confused, inefficient operations at best and perhaps losses of life and property

Division of Labor

Division of labor consists of dividing large jobs into smaller tasks to be assigned to specific individuals. In the fire and emergency services, division of labor is important for the following reasons:

- Assigning responsibility

- Preventing duplication of effort

- Making specific, clear-cut assignments

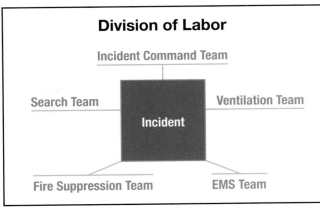

Figure 2.7 Division of labors breaks large jobs at an incident into smaller tasks.

Emergency service organizations are organized in divisions, such as emergency response services, community services, and internal services. Within each work assignment group, subgroups are assigned to complete the specific tasks **(Figure 2.7)**. Work groups may be created based upon the following elements:

- **Type of task** — Organizations commonly place emergency work tasks into similar groups, such as engine, truck, and rescue/EMS companies and assign personnel and equipment to handle these tasks.

- **Geographical area** — Assignments based on the arrangement of districts or battalions within the organization's response area.

- **Time of year or season** — Assignments might include a public education program that focuses on the use of heating appliances in winter.

- **Available resources** — Another consideration is the number of people needed to accomplish the assigned tasks.

- **Skills specialization** — Assignments should be given to the best available personnel for that particular job. An effective way of ensuring the availability of qualified personnel for anticipated assignments is to train individuals to perform particular jobs. Examples of special training and specific jobs include:

  — Emergency medical technicians (EMTs) or Paramedics.

  — Technical rescue teams.

  — Hazardous materials teams.

All positions within the organization must be clearly defined for the division-of-labor principle to be effective. Analyzing each position is the key to identifying all the skills and knowledge necessary for that job. Job analyses and job descriptions are critical to assist personnel in performing their many tasks. All personnel must know what their responsibilities are and understand what is expected of them.

Cross-training should be provided so that company personnel are able to perform a variety of tasks with proficiency. Cross-training enables different companies to work together well because each company officer understands the capabilities, requirements, and needs of the other.

Fire and Emergency Services Organizations: Classifications

Fire and emergency services organizations can be classified as either public or private depending on how the organization is funded. Public fire and emergency services organizations provide services to the public and are funded by the public through the collection of taxes and fees. Private fire and emergency services organizations are funded through the sale of services, contracts, and revenue provided by the parent organization. The services are provided to a single firm or facility and not to the general public. A private fire and emergency services organization may provide services to the general public through a mutual aid agreement with the local AHJ or fire and emergency services organization. The following sections describe some of the common forms of public and private organizations.

Public

The primary means of categorizing public fire and emergency services organizations is by the jurisdiction the organization serves. The fire and emergency services organization may be an organizational unit within a larger jurisdiction or it may be a self-contained entity. For this manual, the term jurisdiction has two distinct connotations:

- The response area served by a fire and emergency services organization.
- The authority that gives the organization the legal right to exist, provide emergency services, and take the actions necessary to ensure adequate protection.

The jurisdiction of a fire and emergency services organization may be tied to a level of government, such as a municipal emergency services department operating within a city's boundaries and with the authorization of its municipal government. Because fires and other emergencies do not recognize territorial and legal boundaries, fire and emergency services organizations are often organized across jurisdictional boundaries.

Some of the more common public jurisdictions that provide fire and emergency service protection include:

- Municpal
- County
- Fire district
- State/provincial
- Federal
- Tribal

Municipal

Municipalities are protected by a variety of types of fire and emergency services organizations. Staffing for any of these organizations or departments may be career, combination/composite, or volunteer. Examples of **municipal** fire and emergency services organizations include traditional departments and public safety **(Figure 2.8)**. In Canadian fire service organizations, there may be some variations to the examples provided of U.S. based fire organizations.

Municipal — Functional division of the lowest level of local government.

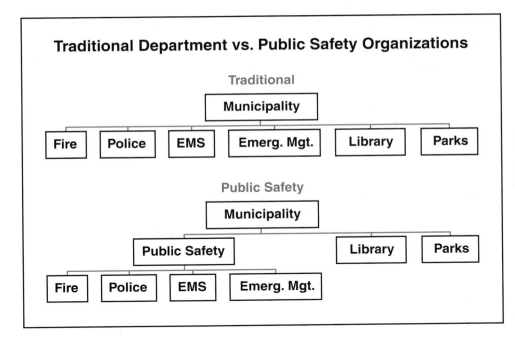

Figure 2.8 Comparison between a traditional department structure and a public safety organization within a municipality.

Most municipal fire and emergency services organizations follow an organizational structure that reflects the local governmental structure. The department head generally oversees the operation of the organization and serves as the principal interface between it and the rest of the municipal government.

The size of the municipal fire and emergency services organization depends primarily on the size of the population and geographic area served. Additional factors that influence its size include special fire protection requirements and the number of services that the local governing body has determined necessary.

Large organizations may operate several stations throughout their service area and have separate facilities for administration, training, and other functions. These organizations may have personnel who specialize in such areas as hazardous materials response, technical rescue, emergency medical care, arson investigation, and fire safety/code enforcement inspections. Combination departments may have career response personnel who are certified as driver/operators, while other responders are volunteers who respond to the incident or station when called.

Large organizations may have administrative and functional subdivisions such as districts, divisions, battalions, companies, and special squads or teams. These subdivisions may be under the supervision of officers with a variety of titles or ranks such as chief officers, majors, captains, or lieutenants.

In small organizations, personnel may be called upon to serve in multiple roles to provide a full range of services. For example, an officer who is in charge of emergency response units may also be the fire marshal in charge of fire and life safety code enforcement.

Funding to support the operation of a career, combination, paid on call, or a volunteer fire department is part of the municipal budget and is usually obtained through the collection of taxes. Some communities also charge subscription fees for fire and emergency services or bill users for at least part of the cost of providing an emergency response — particularly for emergency medical responses and nonemergency (ambulance) transfers. The department's budget generally is set on an annual basis and must address all department expenses, including apparatus and equipment purchases and maintenance, operating expenses, and funding for personnel wages and benefits.

County

The second level in local government is normally the **county**. Fire and emergency services organizations at this level are becoming more common. County fire and emergency services organizations generally protect large areas of unincorporated land that contain large populations, such as Los Angeles (CA) County or Anne Arundel County (MD). The county fire and emergency services organization may exist to augment small town and rural fire departments, or it may consolidate them into a single response organization. Small municipalities within the county may also contract with the county for fire and life safety services.

Fire District

The terms used to describe fire and emergency services organizations that are not under the jurisdiction of a municipal, county, state/provincial, or federal government vary throughout North America. Some common names for these organizations may include **fire district**, fire protection district, and regional fire authority.

Generally, these types of fire districts operate under a board of trustees or commissioners who represent the residents of the district. The board oversees the organization, administers funding, sets policy, and otherwise determines its operation.

Funding may come from a district tax or subscription fee (voluntary fire associations in some states) or may be taken from city, county, state/provincial taxes, special levies, or mill rates. In most cases, the district is established through a vote of the people living in the district, frequently with board members being elected and taxes approved at the same time.

No Man's Land

"No Man's Land" is the term given to an area that lies outside of taxpayer supported or funded jurisdictions. "No Man's Land" areas are generally rural and sparsely populated, or may be too far away from proper fire protection. Citizens living in "No Man's Land" may not be willing to pay taxes for fire protection, gambling that *"This will never happen to them."* Many states continue to struggle with this issue.

Full-time paid, volunteer, or combination personnel may provide the staffing for fire district organizations. Some stations may function in one way while others function differently, especially when the district absorbs existing municipal or county fire and emergency services organizations.

State/Provincial

State/provincial level fire and emergency services organizations may provide either emergency or nonemergency response services. Generally, state/provincial emergency fire suppression companies are organized for forest, wildland, and urban-interface fires. They may include permanently staffed engine and water tender apparatus or on-call aircraft and helicopters to provide aerial support of land-based fire-suppression companies.

Nonemergency services include a state/provincial fire marshal's office that provides inspection and investigation services in areas that do not have municipal- or county-level services. State/provincial training academies provide fire and emergency services training to all departments within the jurisdiction. Training at this level may include certification to a number of NFPA® professional qualification levels and/or specialty training and certification in a variety of fire and emergency services topics.

Federal

Federal fire and emergency services exist to protect federal lands and property. They include forestry units and organizations stationed on military installations. The U.S. government also maintains nationally organized urban search and rescue teams. The U.S. Fire Administration (USFA) provides training courses for all paid, volunteer, and combination/composite organizations through the National Fire Academy (NFA) as well as the Emergency Management Institute (EMI).

The U.S. Department of Defense (DoD) operates fire and emergency services organizations on military installations in the continental U.S. and foreign countries. These organizations provide structural fire protection, airport crash/rescue services, or port facilities and ship board fire protection. **(Figure 2.9)**. These military fire and emergency services organizations may also provide fire protection off base under mutual aid agreements with local civilian fire and emergency services organizations.

Civil service (nonmilitary) personnel, civilian contractors, or local municipal organizations are more and more frequently supplying fire and emergency services protection for the DoD. Military personnel often fill the upper-level positions at these locations.

Figure 2.9 An Aircraft Rescue and Fire Fighting (ARFF) training evolution at the DoD Fire Academy (Goodfellow AFB, TX) prepares firefighters for services at DOD facilities worldwide.

In the U.S., some DoD fire and emergency services organizations are being used during large-scale emergencies for fire protection and emergency recovery operations. These operations include the DoD fire departments and other military personnel working along with local fire and emergency services organizations. These assignments are the results of a presidential order that made DoD serve as mutual aid providers to their neighboring jurisdictions.

The Canadian Defense Department oversees military and civilian fire and emergency services organizations operating in 35 installations in and around North America. These organizations provide structural protection, airfield rescue and fire fighting, vehicle extrication, and hazardous materials response for land-based installations. They also provide fire fighting teams for maritime vessels that carry aircraft. These organizations operate with neighboring communities through mutual aid agreements.

Tribal

Tribal — Term that describes the governmental structure of Native American and Aboriginal Peoples of North America (also known as First Nations, Aboriginals, Inuit, and Metis).

Tribal governments have sovereignty over their designated lands in accordance with agreements with the U.S. and Canadian federal governments. They also have agreements with the state/provincial governments within whose boundaries they exist.

There are 562 federally recognized Native American tribal governments within the U.S. Many reside on the 55.7 million acres of land that the U.S. government holds in trust. The U.S. Bureau of Indian Affairs (BIA) trains, equips, and funds fire and emergency services organizations while members of the tribe living on each reservation staff the organizations. These organizations provide the same types of services that municipal, county, and state fire and emergency services organizations provide.

In Canada, the Department of Indian and Northern Affairs provides similar support to the 633 officially recognized bands of Aboriginal Peoples of Canada (also known as First People). Tribal land and government reserves exist in all provinces and territories of Canada.

Private

While there are fewer private emergency services organizations than there are public ones, they still provide the same types of services . Private emergency services organizations generally fall into one of the following three categories:

- Industrial fire brigades
- For-profit fire and emergency services organization
- Private, nonprofit fire and emergency services organization

Industrial Fire Brigades

Many commercial facilities, such as oil refineries, chemical processing plants, research facilities, marine port facilities, and airports (both public and private), maintain industrial fire brigades or other emergency response teams **(Figure 2.10)**. These teams or brigades may be established in accordance with NFPA® 600, *Standard on Industrial Fire Brigades*, and NFPA® 1081, *Standard for Industrial Fire Brigade Member Professional Qualifications*. Reasons for establishment include:

- Inability or unwillingness of the local community to provide the needed resources
- Need to have a more immediate response than the local public fire and emergency services organization can or will provide
- Need to protect special hazards that require knowledge and capabilities beyond those of the local public fire and emergency services organization
- Remoteness from any public fire and emergency services organization
- Reduced insurance rates
- Reduction of potential liabilities

Figure 2.10 Trained fire brigade members provide fire protection at industrial facilities.

These businesses maintain their own facilities, personnel, apparatus, and equipment to respond to fires and other emergency incidents. Often, such firms are willing to enter into mutual aid agreements and collaborate with public fire officials to develop fire and hazardous materials protection plans involving their facilities.

Because of these agreements, company officers may respond with private industrial fire brigades in order to provide fire protection for these facilities and the surrounding area. Company officers should become acquainted with the mutual aid agreement, facility personnel, equipment, and operating procedures that might be involved in such a response. They should also ensure that equipment and communications are compatible between public and private organizations.

For-Profit Fire and Emergency Services Organizations

The private sector is delivering more and more services that were once considered government functions. Examples of such privatization include delivering mail, collecting refuse, operating correctional facilities, and providing fire and emergency services. Bcause this trend is likely to continue, public fire and emergency services organizations must realize that their very survival as entities may depend on their ability to deliver services to their customers more efficiently.

Nonprofit Fire and Emergency Services Organizations

Nonprofit fire and emergency services organizations consist of both career and volunteer personnel and serve various areas or regions. Funding for nonprofit fire and emergency services organizations must meet the requirements of the U.S. tax code for 501(c)(3) organizations. Funding may come from donations, fundraisers, subscriptions, contracts, or grants. Current U.S. Department of Homeland Security rules permit these organizations to request and receive Fire Act Grant funds and assistance.

Organizational Staffing

Fire and emergency services organizations can be categorized as public or private as described in the previous section. Another way to categorize these organizations is according to how they are staffed. Staffing at fire departments and organiztions may be comprised of **career firefighters** (paid for their services), **paid-on-call personnel** (paid per response), volunteers, or a combination/composite of those three. In this context, the term professional refers to a level of competence or expertise, behavior, and appearance and may also apply equally to career, paid-on-call, and volunteer personnel.

> **Career Firefighter** — Person whose primary employment is as a firefighter within a fire department. *Also spelled* Career Fire Fighter.

> **Paid-on-Call Personnel** — Person who responds to fires and emergencies and is paid for the responses they make on a response-to-response basis.

Career (Full-Time) Organizations

Most large cities and some counties and private industries operate full-time, career fire and emergency services organizations. The municipality, county, or industry maintains facilities and equipment to support fire protection and emergency services and employs firefighters and other personnel to provide those services.

Volunteer Organizations

A volunteer organization may operate as a department of the local government, but many are totally independent from government agencies within the areas they serve. Volunteer firefighters staff approximately 70 percent of fire and emergency services organizations. The organization may be a municipal, county, or nonprofit organization and serve a wide range of geographic areas.

In some cases, a town may provide a facility to be used as a fire station and may even buy and maintain fire suppression equipment. In other cases, the volunteer organization meets its expenses without support from municipal funds. Money may come from donations, subscription fees paid by people in the community, billing for all or part of response costs, and fundraising events such as bake sales, pancake breakfasts, dinners, dances, or fairs.

Oversight of the volunteer organization comes from the local entity that supports the organization or from an independent association or governing board. However, some volunteer organizations are nonprofit corporations governed by boards of directors.

In most cases, volunteer organizations do not maintain fire stations that are continuously staffed. Personnel respond from their homes or workplaces to emergencies when summoned by pagers, telephone calls, or community signals. Designated personnel go to the fire station and drive the apparatus to the emergency scene. Others may report to the fire station or directly to the scene.

Combination Departments

A combination department , whether public or private, is one in which some of its personnel receive pay while others serve on a voluntary basis. For example, a mostly volunteer organization may pay driver/operators or part of the salary of a dispatcher/telecommunicator who is shared with the law enforcement organization. A full-time career department may also maintain a cadre of volunteers trained in fire suppression, rescue, emergency medical care, scene control, or other areas.

Combination organizations provide staffing and receive funding in accordance with the dominant aspect of their organization. Combination departments that are operated primarily as full-time, career organizations tend to staff their stations continuously and fund their operations with tax dollars. Those organizations that primarily use volunteers tend to have few, if any, responders residing in their fire stations.

Paid-on-Call Organizations

Some departments are operated on a paid-on-call basis. These organizations resemble a volunteer organization in that the fire stations are minimally staffed and emergency personnel are normally summoned to the emergency scene or fire station. Fiscally, it resembles a full-time, career organization because most or all paid-on-call organizational funding comes from a local government agency or association.

Resource Allocation

A challenge for most fire and emergency services organizations is allocating the resources available to them while also staying within their fiscal limitations. Many jurisdictions face financial constraints that limit the fire and emergency services protection that can be provided to the public and the methods by which these services are provided. As a result, jurisdictions and the officers who serve them have to be judicious with resources and plan well for emergency responses so that they can adequately provide the protections needed in their jurisdicitions.

Government leaders must distribute their available funds to satisfy a variety of governmental needs and services **(Figure 2.11)**. They must often compromise individual services in order to provide a reasonable overall balance in meeting the jurisdiction's various needs. The following sections discuss the officer's role in resource allocation and the importance of aid agreements to fire and emergency services organizations.

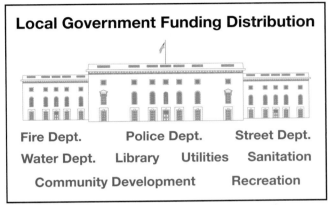

Figure 2.11 Local governments must distribute available money amongst a number of departments and programs.

Officer's Role

One of the roles of the company officer and other fire officers is to make the best possible use of available resources, which involves:

- Protecting personnel and equipment
- Conserving materials and supplies
- Planning for the most cost-effective and efficient use of resources

Performing those actions should result in the fulfillment of the organization's mission at a minimum level of funding. Common techniques for extending the organization's budget include:

- Funding only the minimum number and types of resources needed to deal with those emergencies that are most likely to occur within the jurisdiction

- Relying on mutual aid, automatic aid, or outside aid agreements with other jurisdictions and agencies to supplement the organization's resources for unusually large or exceptional incidents

- Implementing alternative staffing procedures, such as call back, over time, and the closure of certain stations and units

Aid Agreements

Mutual, **automatic**, and **outside aid** agreements are the result of reciprocal agreements between multiple jurisdictions and organizations, both public and private **(Figure 2.12, p. 48)**. These agreements may be verbal but should be written.

Aid agreements should be reviewed periodically to ensure that they remain current and up-to-date. The creation and maintenance of aid agreements require personnel to work with other organizations and other governmental jurisdictions. Aid agreements should be considered contracts and should be reviewed by the legal departments of all affected organizations and approved by the governing bodies of the affected organizations.

Mutual Aid — Reciprocal assistance from one fire and emergency services agency to another during an emergency, based upon a prearranged agreement; generally made upon the request of the receiving agency.

Automatic Aid — Written agreement between two or more agencies to automatically dispatch predetermined resources to any fire or other emergency reported in the geographic area covered by the agreement. These areas are generally located near jurisdictional boundaries or in jurisdictional "islands."

Outside Aid — Assistance from agencies, industries, or fire departments that are not part of the agency having jurisdiction over the incident.

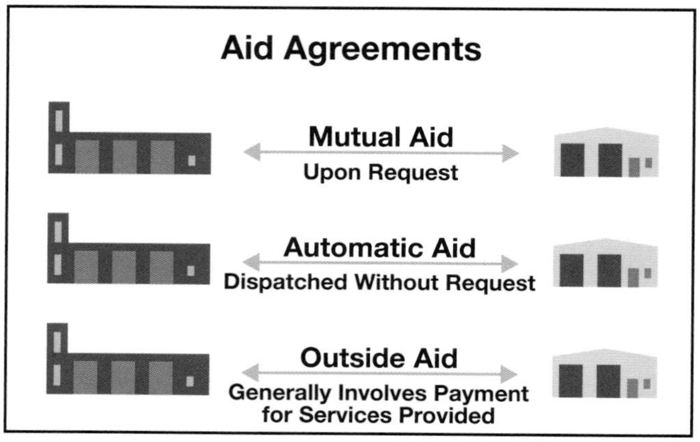

Figure 2.12 Illustrating common aid agreements between fire departments.

Fire and emergency services organizations commonly enter into aid agreements to:

- Receive state or federal funding
- Share limited or specialized resources between neighboring jurisdictions
- Assist neighboring jurisdictions when a response requirement exceeds the primary jurisdiction's capabilities
- Meet operational requirements when its own resources are deployed at an incident and a second, simultaneous emergency occurs
- Assist organizations in meeting NFPA®, Insurance Services Office (ISO), or Center for Public Safety Excellence department accreditation process, and other requirements for staffing, apparatus availability, response times, etc. through shared resources
- Define responses for areas on the boundaries between adjacent jurisdictions
- Define response methods for fire and emergency services organizations within a jurisdiction, such as a military base or corporate fire protection agency (fire brigade) within a city's limits
- Assist neighboring jurisdictions with target hazards or high-risk facilities
- Provide a quicker response when other fire and emergency services organizations are closer to the emergency site than are the primary jurisdiction's resources

Company officers may be asked to assist in the development and maintenance of mutual aid plans. At a minimum, these plans should:

- Define roles of each organization, including incident management and chains of command.
- Establish operating guidelines.
- Define lines and methods of communications.
- Include common terminology, references, specifications, equipment compatibility, and other factors that may directly affect the effectiveness of the different organizations in working with each other.
- Provide maps, evacuation routes, hydrant locations and data, details of potentially affected systems (sewers, railroads, waterways, etc.), and similar information useful in a response outside of one's jurisdiction.

- Address insurance and legal considerations that may affect the agreement.

- Establish additional nonemergency agreements, such as training and routine communications as required.

The implementation of new policies or ordinances may be necessary to support the aid agreements. All fire and emergency services organizations participating in these agreements should conduct joint training exercises so that differences in equipment and procedures may be identified and rectified before a major incident occurs.

Outside aid is similar to mutual aid except that payment, such as a per response or an annual fee, rather than reciprocal aid is made by one organization to the other. Outside aid agreements differ little from the other aid agreements.

Outside aid agreement should define:

- Conditions under which support will be provided: automatic or on request

- Terms for conducting the response: command and communication, standard operating procedures/standard operating guidelines (SOPs/SOGs), legal considerations, among other considerations

Emergency Management Assistance Compact (EMAC) and Mutual Aid Box Alarm System (MABAS)

Two examples of mutual aid agreements that have been created in the U.S. are the EMAC and MABAS. Each provides a framework for responding to major disasters.

The U.S. Congress created EMAC in 1996 as a national disaster-relief compact to link the resources of each state. The compact is designed to provide rapid and flexible deployment of aid to the stricken area.

MABAS is an agreement between the fire and emergency response agencies of Northern Illinois and Southern Wisconsin, and it has spread to other parts of the Midwest. The participating communities, counties, and agencies agree to:

- Maintain a predetermined level of staffing

- Use the Incident Command System (ICS)

- Use common terminology and operating procedures

- Operate on a common radio frequency during mutual aid incidents

Chapter Summary

Fire and emergency services organizations cannot fulfill their missions and achieve their goals effectively and efficiently without a valid organizational base. There are several ways in which emergency services organizations may be organized to achieve their assigned goals: public, private, career, volunteer, and combination.

Regardless of how they are organized, they all function with the same organizational principles: unity of command, manageable span of control, and division of labor. Other principles involve scalar structure, line and staff personnel, and decision-making authority. These principles are important not only at emergency incidents but also in the daily nonemergency routines. For company officers to be effective leaders, they must know and use these principles in both emergency and nonemergency situations.

Review Questions

1. What are the basic principles of organizational structure? (p. 32)

2. How do local, state/provincial, and federal government authorities influence the fire service? (pp. 40-44)

3. How does private fire service differ from public fire organizations? (pp. 44-45)

4. What are the different types of staffing found in fire departments? (pp. 45-46)

5. What is the company officer's role in resource allocation? (p. 47)

6. What are the reasons for entering into aid agreements? (p. 48)

Learning Activities

Learning Activity 2-1

Objective 7: Distinguish the various components of organizational management.

Company officers must be able to identify the purpose of each management position within the organization to which they belong.

For this activity, you will need access to the following resources:

● The organizational chart found in this chapter

● Your department's organizational chart

Develop and give a short, informal verbal presentation that outlines the purpose of each management position outlined on the organizational chart. Make sure to include the following information in your presentation:

● General roles and responsibilities of the position

● The direct supervisor of the position

● Any subordinates that the position may have responsibility for

Answer Key:
See page 33 for answers. If you are using your department's organizational chart, answers for this activity will vary. Check with your supervisor or more experienced personnel for accuracy.

Leadership and Supervision

Chapter Contents

chapter 3

Key Terms

NFPA® Job Performance Requirements

This chapter provides information that addresses the following job performance requirements of NFPA® 1021, *Standard for Fire Officer Professional Qualifications (2014).*

4.2.6

5.2.1

5.4.1

Leadership and Supervision

After reading this chapter, students will be able to:

1. Explain the principles of leadership as applied to a company officer. [NFPA® 1021, 5.2.1, 5.4.1]

2. Describe roles of supervision in the responsibilities of a company officer. [NFPA® 1021, 4.2.6]

Chapter 3
Leadership and Supervision

Case History

A company officer encountered a situation where one individual made unwanted advances to another employee during the officer's shift. To complicate matters, the personnel involved were from different agencies within the jurisdiction.

The officer recognized that this scenario could evolve into a much larger issue, and that he needed to address the issue. An officer in this position should behave professionally, approaching both sides of the conflict while avoiding showing any personal bias. The company officer brought together representatives from each agency to discuss the details of the incident and develop a plan of action. The appropriate individual in the chain of command was contacted to provide a clear description of the issues and propose a plan of action. Once appropriate contacts had been established, a meeting between the officer and the employees on both sides took place to discuss the issues and establish objectives and an expected plan of action, as well as consequences of future occurrences. Finally, to ensure that all parties were clear, the issues and sequences of events were documented to ensure accuracy should the topic arise again in the future.

Leadership has been called a trait, a behavior, a skill, a talent, a characteristic, a science, and an art. Leadership is critical in emergency situations where personal risks are high and hazardous conditions can change rapidly. Motivating personnel is essential to limiting injuries, assuring accountability, and attaining operational goals. In nonemergency operations and during daily work activities, leadership is essential for using resources efficiently and ensuring a safe and healthy environment.

There are many different opinions regarding leadership. Company officers should read and take classes that reinforce their leadership skills as part of their professional development. They should understand the fundamentals of leadership, supervisory methods, and management principles and apply them daily. Along with leadership, a company officer must learn two additional skills — supervision and management. These two skills are different, but are interconnected.

IAFC Professional Development Model Designations

The International Association of Fire Chiefs (IAFC) also divides fire officer ranks into four levels in its Professional Development Model. These levels vary slightly from the NFPA® model shown in NFPA® 1021. The reader should be aware of the following variations in designations:

- **Level I** — Supervising fire officer (all company officers)
- **Level II** — Managing fire officer (battalion, district, and assistant chiefs)
- **Level III** — Administrative fire officer (administrative chiefs in charge of divisions or bureaus within the department)
- **Level IV** — Executive fire officer (chief of the department)

Figure 3.1 Company personnel look to their company officer for leadership.

This chapter provides an overview of leadership, ethics, and their application. It describes supervision and the skills required to execute it effectively. It also addresses management principles that the successful company officer as a supervisor must understand and apply.

Leadership

Company officers serve as leaders to their respective units and must understand key elements of leadership **(Figure 3.1)**. They should understand leadership traits, develop these leadership traits, apply those traits in an ethical manner, and develop a command presence.

Leadership Traits

It is important to understand that no single trait is the answer for every circumstance. Traits are used in combinations that best serve effective leadership. Leadership traits that company officers should cultivate include:

- **Supervisory ability** —Planning, organizing, directing, and controlling in order to coordinate the efforts of the unit to accomplish objectives
- **Decisiveness** — Making decisions quickly and effectively
- **Intelligence** — Using logic and reason in making decisions
- **Self-assurance** — Demonstrating self-confidence when making decisions
- **Initiative** — Accomplishing goals and objectives with a minimum of supervision
- **Desire for professional success** — Gaining additional responsibility and influence within the organization
- **Integrity** — Applying consistently a set of morals or values to the decision-making process
- **Personal security** — Being secure in the leadership position
- **Sense of priority** — Determining an effective order of action to achieve a desired outcome
- **Vision** — Having a dream or concept of the way things can or should be
- **Industriousness** — Working hard to fulfill duties

- **Interpersonal skills** — Working successfully with others to accomplish tasks

- **Empowerment** — Providing support for others to succeed in accomplishing organizational and personal goals

- **Innovation and creativity** — Seeking continuously new and imaginative methods for accomplishing the mission of the organization

- **Consistency** — Applying procedures, policies, rewards, and discipline evenly and fairly over time

- **Preparedness** — Being ready for potential situations

- **Proactiveness** — Anticipating, embracing, and meeting change

Leadership Skills Development

The first step in developing leadership skills is to study successful leaders and develop your own list of leadership traits. This list becomes the personal criteria or benchmark standard that the leader uses to assess him or herself. The company officer also uses the standard as a checklist of personal leadership traits. Individual differences, perceptions, and personal bias can influence the checklist.

Another method involves an anonymous survey of the company officer's subordinates, peers, and superiors in a **360-degree feedback evaluation** that includes objective responses to questions about the officer's leadership traits. This method, too, can be very subjective.

It is common to use a combination of these methods. A disinterested party may compile the results. Once a company officer has determined the characteristics that are present and those that are lacking, it is time to develop a strategy for improving on the weaker skills. Not all leaders are outstanding in all situations.

Depending on the area that appears to need attention, an officer may choose to follow any number of paths to improvement, such as:

- Courses

- Seminars/workshops

- Books or other literature on the leadership topics

- Counselors/mentors

360-degree Feedback Evaluation — an evaluation method that incorporates feedback from multiple sources such as the worker, his/her peers, superiors, subordinates, and customers.

Leadership Skills

Leadership traits may be summarized according to a variety of actions that most good leaders take:

- **Seeing opportunities** — Having a vision that views situations from all angles while still understanding that tradition can provide direction.

- **Identifying challenges** — Recognizing potentially problematic situations ranging from personality conflicts to political intrigue that may confront the workgroup, company, or unit. Recognition requires monitoring both the internal and the external climate of the organization.

- **Communicating** — Being able to express ideas clearly and being able to listen to and interpret feedback from others who are either internal or external to the organization

- **Planning for success** — Generating plans, implementing them, and evaluating their effectiveness. Effective planning saves energy, time, resources, lives, and frustration.

- **Building trust** — Creating an environment of mutual trust within the organization, community, service area, and profession.

- **Understanding the system** — Determining first what needs to be improved.

- **Inspiring a shared vision** — Sharing the vision for your company's success with subordinates and ensuring it is in line with the organization's mission.

- **Enabling others to act** — Giving subordinates the tools and methods to solve the problem or make the change.

- **Modeling desired behavior** — Providing a good personal example, especially when work becomes more difficult.

- **Encouraging subordinates** — Sharing the glory with your subordinates while keeping the troubles to yourself.

- **Establishing priorities** — Examples:
  - The top priority is the emergency response.
  - The second priority is pre-emergency readiness through training, planning, and maintenance.
  - The third priority is administration, including facility maintenance, documentation, etc.

Command Presence

Command presence is the ability to identify the components of a situation, assess the need for action, determine the nature of the necessary intervention, initiate action, and to be perceived as having the ability to take this action. Command presence inspires confidence from subordinates, the administration, and the public.

Effective fire and emergency services leaders can have command presence in all of their assigned emergency and nonemergency duties. To achieve command presence, it may be helpful to have or develop the following attributes **(Figure 3.2)**:

- Self-confidence
- Trustworthiness
- Consistency
- Responsibility
- Acceptance
- Expertise

Along with these personality characteristics, leaders can take the following eight steps to create command presence:

Step 1: Determine what the situation is.

Step 2: Know what resources are available to apply to the situation.

Step 3: Develop the strategy and tactics required to resolve the situation.

Step 4: Listen to all points of view, when appropriate.

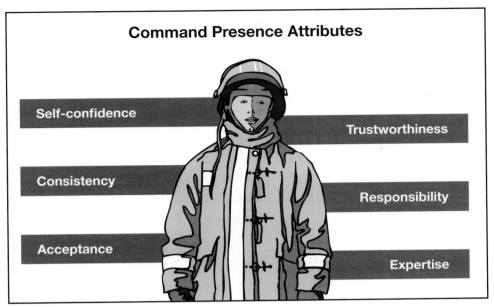

Command Presence Attributes

Self-confidence

Consistency

Acceptance

Trustworthiness

Responsibility

Expertise

Figure 3.2 Company officers must develop the various attributes of command presence.

Step 5: Make the decision.

Step 6: Implement the decision.

Step 7: Evaluate the decision and modify as necessary.

Step 8: Take responsibility for the decision.

Ethics

Ethics (sometimes called moral philosophy) are the agreed-upon philosophical principles that define what is correct and proper behavior for the members of a society. Without ethics, there would be chaos, and civilization (or society) would dissolve. Ethics also define what is right and proper conduct for the individual in all relationships and activities. This conduct may involve relationships with others, the decision-making process, or simply choosing between right and wrong. Not all decisions are clear and may involve many choices that fall into the gray range between the two extremes.

Ethics plays a major role in civilization. Unfortunately, examples of unethical conduct tend to appear more frequently in the news media. The lack of ethical conduct may be the cause of some or all of the following incidents within the fire and emergency services:

- Borrowing (and never returning) fuel, auto polish, or light bulbs from station's supplies
- Shopping for personal items during inspections/pre-fire planning
- Asking merchants for special discounts
- Using the station to conduct a private business enterprise

Fire officers must understand the importance of ethical conduct and how to adhere to it. This section deals with individual and organizational ethical conduct and issues in the fire and emergency services.

Ethical Conduct

Ethical standards express the level of conduct all members of society are expected to follow. Society tends to expect a higher level of ethical conduct from members of the emergency services (i.e. firefighters, police, paramedics, etc). Emergency services members are often seen as heroes when performing their day-to-day duties. As a result of this high standard, the public and the media are very likely to report any unethical behavior on the part of emergency services members. The image of an entire organization can suffer because of the unethical behavior of one member.

Sources of Personal Ethics

Ethical behavior is a trait that individuals learn primarily from their families and secondarily from religious organizations, educational institutions, society as a whole, friends, and peers **(Figure 3.3)**. The values that these sources instill remain with the individual for life unless the person consciously alters them.

Figure 3.3 Personal ethics are developed from a number of sources.

As part of becoming a company officer, the new candidate should incorporate the ethical values of the organization into his or her own set of personal ethics. Generally speaking, most fire service organizations endorse ethical values like honesty, integrity, impartiality, and fairness that most cultures recognize as being important to the existence of civilized society.

Ethics: Three-Step Check

Step 1: *Is it legal?* — *Will I be violating civil law, professional standards, or departmental policy?*

Step 2: *Is it fair to all concerned?* — *Have I based my decision on all the facts as I know them? Will my decision support the mission of the organization?*

Step 3: *How will it make me feel about myself?* — *Will it make me proud? Would I feel good if my decision was published in the newspaper? Would I feel good if my family knew about it?*

Cases of Unethical Conduct

To create an ethical culture within a unit, a company officer must understand what contributes to unethical behavior. Some causes of unethical behavior in fire and emergency services organizations include:

- **Violation of moral principles** — For example:
  - Hiring or promoting based upon favoritism rather than merit
  - Cheating on promotional examinations
  - Taking bribes to influence inspections or plans reviews
  - Misusing department equipment
- **Bottom-line mentality** — For example, focusing on subscription receipts versus performing necessary fire fighting operations.
- **Short-cut mentality** — For example, failing to appropriately complete overhaul because of dinner time or abbreviating training sessions to watch football.
- **Exploitive mentality** — For example:
  - Engaging in sexual harrassment
  - Discriminating against personnel based upon ethnicity, gender, age, or sexual preference
  - Starting and/or spreading rumors
  - Taking credit for the work of others

The Effect of Unethical Behavior on Quality of Service

Providing quality service and maintaining the public trust should be top priorities for the fire and emergency services. Quality service adds value to the individual, company, and organization.

Unethical behavior erodes the public's faith in a fire and emergency services organization. The public is more likely to perceive the organization as providing low quality service. In some cases, unethical behavior has a direct effect on the quality of service when the unethical behavior is directed at members of the public.

A commonly encountered variety of unethical behavior is lying. There are four main reasons for lying. The same reasons can describe most forms of unethical conduct on the part of individuals in general:

- **Basic needs** — Gain objects that fulfill an individual's basic needs, such as food, money, clothing, or other items.
- **Affiliation** — Create, prolong, or avoid social relationships, such as hazing.
- **Self-esteem** — Increase the perceived competence of an individual in the eyes of others, such as falsifying records, cheating to make a higher score on a test, or spreading gossip that belittles another person.
- **Self-gratification** — Increase an individual's personal enjoyment, such as illegal gambling, substance abuse, and theft.

Personal Justifications for Unethical Behavior

When the culture of an organization or society rewards unethical conduct, it is easy to understand why individuals would engage in these types of activities. The individual accepts the benefits of such actions and then justifies them internally.

Justification also occurs when a person is trying to make a decision (whether ethical or unethical). Common justifications for unethical conduct include:

- Pretending that the action is legal or ethical
- Believing that the action is in the best interest of the organization or individual
- Believing that the action is okay because no one will ever find out about it
- Expecting that the organization will support the action if it is ever discovered
- Believing that the action is acceptable because everyone else is doing it
- Believing that the end (result) justifies the means (method) even if the means are unethical

When the individual has justified the unethical action internally, it then becomes easier to commit the action and any similar subsequent actions. To overcome these attitudes, the company officer must create a culture that encourages and rewards ethical conduct and addresses unethical conduct.

Ethics Program

To ensure that the organization maintains an ethical culture, the ethics program needs to include a written code of ethics or ethics policy. This code is a brief, one- or two-page statement of the organization's values and the expected behavior both of the management and the membership.

An essential part of the ethics program is the written code of ethics that is specific to the organization that creates it. Numerous organizations, including the International Association of Fire Chiefs (IAFC), have established codes of ethical conduct. (The IAFC's Code of Ethical Conduct has been included inside the front cover of this manual.) Expressing the organization's code of ethics in written form provides the administration and employees with a visible standard to follow. A code of ethics provides company officers with an idea of what is expected of them, their subordinates, and their organizations.

The responsibility for the development of an ethical culture within the organization belongs to everyone in the organization. The administration and the rank and file must support, communicate, and personally adhere to the adopted code of ethics. Formal training for all personnel should be provided, beginning with entry-level employee training and extending to fire officer training courses.

Annual refresher classes that focus on various ethical questions should be part of the organization's training schedule. At the company level, the fire officer should work to create an ethical culture in the relationship between crew members. Discussions of ethical questions can be used to promote the permanent existence of an ethical culture.

Ethical Issues

A written code of ethics strengthens the ethical culture of the organization but does not guarantee that ethical questions will not continue to challenge the organization or its employees. Training employees in the importance of making ethical decisions, how to make those decisions, and how to recognize and respond to unethical actions on the part of others provides valuable tools for dealing with such issues. In addition, the goals that employees are asked to meet as part of the organization should be ethical.

Behavioral Statements

The following are examples of behavioral statements that might be contained within a fire and emergency services organization's code of ethics:

- Employees must, at all times, conduct themselves in a manner that creates respect for themselves, as public servants, and their jurisdiction.

- Employees must place the public interest above other interests (individual, group, or special) and must consider their jobs as an opportunity to serve the citizens of their jurisdiction.

- Employees must not discriminate because of race, color, creed, sex, age, handicap, national ancestry, or political affiliation.

- Employees must not accept from the public any personal gift, money, service, favor, or anything of value that might influence or be inferred to influence their impartial discharge of their duties.

- Employees must always treat the public with fairness, courtesy, respect, and impartiality.

- Employees must refrain from using their position for personal gain and must maintain the confidentiality of information reserved to the organization.

- Employees must not drink alcoholic beverages or take any incapacitating drug while on duty.

- Employees must clearly distinguish or otherwise identify between all remarks or actions made as an individual and as a representative of the organization.

Company officers must use ethical decision-making to manage issues as they arise, and provide a positive example of how to apply ethics to all decisions and actions. The organization's culture depends in large part on the ethical behavior of officers and others in positions of leadership and authority. Officers must be honest in their presentation of their decisions, both in communicating the decision and results of the decision. Honesty generates acceptance for the decision and builds trust in the officer who made that decision.

The Golden Rule

Of all the axioms for guiding people ethically, Confucius (K'ung Ch'iu) in the sixth century B.C.E. stated the most applicable, "Do not impose on others what you yourself do not want." In Western civilization, that same ethical axiom is known as the Golden Rule: "Do unto others as you want them to do unto you."

Supervision

The definitions of the terms supervision and management are similar and often used interchangeably. This manual uses the terms to describe two distinctly different but associated fire officer responsibilities:

- **Supervision** — Includes the processes of directing, overseeing, and controlling the activities of other individuals.

- **Management** — Refers to the administration and control of projects, programs, situations, or organizations. Level II Fire Officers are often assigned management duties over functions, such as public fire and life-safety education or logistics in a small department or managing an incident scene involving multiple units or agencies.

A supervisor is anyone who is responsible for the activities of one or more subordinate employees. In the fire and emergency services, NFPA® 1021, *Standard for Fire Officer Professional Qualifications*, specifies that Fire Officers I, II, III, and IV are all considered supervisory personnel.

Training in supervision and management techniques is readily available at institutions of higher education and business seminars. Most company officers are responsible for supervising fire company level personnel or small groups. The experience gained at this level creates the foundation for supervising larger and more complex groups as the officer advances to Level II and above.

A company officer has the following basic functions that are common to most supervisory positions:

- Meeting supervisory responsibilities
- Solving problems
- Establishing and communicating goals and objectives
- Building an effective team
- Motivating and supporting personnel
- Applying management principles

The company officer demonstrates sound leadership characteristics. The sections that follow discuss each of the basic supervisory challenges and the responsibilities and tasks that are necessary to meet them.

Meeting Supervisory Responsibilities

All supervisors have specific major responsibilities to an organization regardless of its type. No activity, project, or incident is finished until all assigned tasks have been completed. By accomplishing each of these responsibilities, the company officer can ensure an efficient and cohesive unit.

As part of all their responsibilities, company officers must exhibit strong, positive leadership qualities at all times. A company officer must adhere to a standard of ethical, moral, and legal behavior that motivates subordinates to do the same. Key elements of a successful company officer's supervisory style include:

- Encouraging employee participation in the decision-making process.
- Delegating or involving members of the unit in planning.
- Respecting the judgment of employees.
- Teaching, enforcing, and following health and safety rules.
- Being a coach and mentor to employees **(Figure 3.4)**.
- Showing consideration for diversity within the unit.
- Acknowledging accomplishments.
- Treating each member of the unit fairly and equitably.

- Referring a member to the organization's employee assistance program (EAP) is usually the most effective method for assisting employees on how to resolve personal problems.

- Keeping accurate records.

- Keeping lines of communication open at all times.

- Not contributing to or allowing situations that make other people feel uncomfortable or impose upon their personal dignity.

- Providing positive motivation for subordinates.

A supervisor must be consistent in meeting these responsibilities. Lack of consistency undermines a company officer's authority and ability to lead. Inconsistency can create relationships within the unit that distract attention from the primary goals of the organization and take energy, time, effort, and attention to repair.

Establishing Priorities for the Unit

A company officer's priorities are based primarily on the services provided and the mission of the organization. Having priorities helps the company officer:

- Maintain focus on the important activities.

- Manage time more effectively and direct energy toward the goals and objectives that provide the greatest good for the unit and community.

- Minimize competing priorities to reduce stress and frustration.

- Identify the unit's goals and objectives.

Figure 3.4 Company officers often serve as coaches and mentors to their assigned personnel.

The first line supervisor should categorize activities into three levels of priority: emergency response, preparation for emergency response, and organizational duties. To meet these priorities, the company officer considers the following preparation activities:

- **Indirect preparation for emergency response** — Company officers must be technically and tactically proficient and should ensure unit members are physically and mentally prepared to respond to emergency situations during their work shift.

- **Direct preparation for emergency response** — These activities include training and drilling as a team; ensuring the readiness of the personal protective equipment (PPE), apparatus, and tools; and developing preincident plans for occupancies and hazards within the response area.

- **Application of efficient organizational skills** — This category includes the completion of reports and records, station maintenance, and other administrative duties assigned to the officer.

Company officers who establish priorities for personnel and relate those priorities to their job functions are more likely to frame their expectations clearly. Company officers who adhere to these priorities set strong examples for members of their units.

Solving Problems

As supervisors, company officers should anticipate problems that may occur to prepare themselves for finding effective solutions. Such preparation can aid company officers in brainstorming applicable solutions that can be applied to resolve a problem.

Anticipating Problems

A supervisor must recognize a potential problem, then develop and implement an effective and fair solution. For example, monitoring interaction among unit members is one way to anticipate personnel problems. Company officers should counsel employees when necessary and listen to their concerns and solutions in order to mitigate tension between unit members. The supervisor must be familiar with and follow the organization's policies when handling employee problems. They may need to refer the employee to the organization's EAP or human resources department.

A supervisor should recognize developing situations and attempt to defuse them. A strong command presence can help the supervisor defuse the situation quickly and efficiently. Angry or emotional individuals will not hear rational solutions to problems. Once the individual or involved parties are calm, counseling can determine the root cause of the incident and find a solution. A complete record of the incident and counseling session should be kept to protect all parties involved and the supervisor from unsubstantiated accusations at a later date. This record should be kept confidential in accordance with the organization's policies and procedures.

Brainstorming

Understanding the brainstorming process of problem solving ensures that the team does not limit member participation. If a suggestion is valid and valuable, publicly acknowledge the contribution. If it is not, explain privately to the individual why it will not work or cannot be implemented.

- Encourage team members to be open and honest in their comments to foster an atmosphere of trust and respect within the group.

- Allow the team to have input in establishing measurements for success. The supervisor will then have fair and equitable guidelines on which to base awards or discipline.

- Take advantage of the existing diversity of team members. Capitalize on the strength of each member based on background, education, and experience **(Figure 3.5)**. Diversity of membership assists in obtaining balanced team decisions. Team diversity is the best tool for combating **groupthink**.

- Understand that team members have outside influences that could impact their on-duty performance, such as family, health, finances, and nonwork-related situations. The company officer must be prepared to give the employee guidance regarding organizational priorities.

Groupthink — A pattern of thinking that includes self deception, peer pressure, and conformity to group ethics and values.

Establishing and Communicating Goals and Objectives

A company officer must be able to establish certain short-range objectives, based on established priorities, to meet the long-range goals assigned to the unit.

Figure 3.5 Company officers must learn to rely on the strengths that each company member brings to the unit.

These objectives and the goals of the organization must be communicated to unit members. The acronym SMART can be used to establish objectives that are:

- Specific
- Measurable
- Attainable
- Relevant
- Time-bound

SMART Objectives

SMART (Specific, Measurable, Attainable, Realistic, Timely) objectives are an important aspect of a company officer's duty to manage and lead a crew. An example is:

Using the department's approved assessment tool, the Company Officer will conduct an annual assessment of each crewmember at the end of June.

This objective is:

Specific – conduct an annual assessment

Measurable – can be measured at the end of June.

Attainable – reasonable time has been provided to complete this task

Realistic – this trait should be a regular duty of a company officer

Timely – based on when all assessments must be completed and submitted

Commanding officers must communicate instructions clearly and concisely at emergency incidents, because there may be little or no time for subordinates to ask questions. Subordinates must be able to understand the commander's intent based on the directions that are given.

Groups work more efficiently and effectively toward a common goal when officers communicate goals and objectives clearly and provide periodic progress reports (feedback) to the unit. Employees who are involved in the process of establishing objectives will have more incentives to fulfill the objectives.

Employees should be involved in establishing goals and objectives using one of three methods:

- **Require the employee to accomplish a specific task** — The supervisor knows the best practice to perform the task and has all the information necessary to make the decision, and the employee is thoroughly trained in performing the task as required.

- **Delegate tasks** — Allows employees to select the specific method for accomplishing the task. Involves giving the employee the authority to accomplish the task. The CO must have confidence in the ability of the employees to accomplish the task.

- **Use democratic leadership principles** — Gives members of the unit an opportunity to establish goals and objectives during the planning stage.

Democratic Leadership Approach

For example, in the democratic leadership approach, a company officer may be involved in the decision-making process for purchasing a new fire apparatus. The company officer gathers information from unit members, coordinates efforts with all shifts, and provides input from the standpoint of apparatus users.

The company officer serves as a unit member, facilitator, and coach, guiding the unit toward developing the apparatus specifications. Unit members may also assist in developing operational policies and procedures to include the apparatus' use, care, maintenance, and logistical support. While company officers seek employee involvement, they retain the responsibility for the task being completed regardless of which approach they use.

Building an Effective Team

Company officers usually supervise the smallest subdivision of a department. The unit typically consists of personnel, facilities, apparatus, and equipment appropriate to carry out its assigned duties **(Figure 3.6)**. An effective unit exhibits team work, i.e. working together toward a desired objective.

Team building occurs within any organization and within individual units as personnel promote and transfer, within temporary committees, and in association with people normally outside an organization. Following these basic principles with an assigned crew or a project team, a company officer can create an effective team:

- Inform personnel how they fit into the team, what is expected of them, what to expect of the leader, what the team's objectives are, and how accomplishing the objectives affects them.

- Have frequent planning meetings with the team to determine progress, explain deviations from the plan, resolve problems, and celebrate accomplishments.

Figure 3.6 A heavy rescue company gathering equipment for a high-rise fire exercise.

- Work with individual team members to establish personal goals and objectives. Make certain they understand what responsibilities and authority they have, and they can be comfortable asking for assistance when necessary.

- Encourage team members to make suggestions or provide solutions for problems.

A company officer guides the individuals in the group and focuses their efforts on becoming a cohesive team. This journey usually follows a four-stage development model that includes forming, storming, norming, and performing:

- **Forming** — Employees are initially uncertain of their roles in the group. They are not certain that they can trust or work with the other members. As relationships grow within the group, trust and respect develop, and the members begin to see themselves as part of the group. Group members become enthusiastic about the challenges of a new project or task. This phase is critical within the team-development process and one in which a company officer can have a significant effect.

- **Storming** — Conflict may result at this stage as members jockey for informal leadership or attempt to exert their own influence over the group. Conflict may occur when a new officer joins an existing unit that contains older, more experienced firefighters. The leader is supportive in this stage and actively listens to members and provides explanations for decisions. The most critical aspect of successful team development is to reduce the amount of time the group spends in the storming phase.

- **Norming** — The group establishes and adheres to its own set of norms and values. Members become closer and more cohesive. The company officer again must be aware of team norms and values as much as possible to make sure that those norms don't violate the sense of decency. The leader transitions into the role of team member, allowing other team members to share leadership responsibilities.

- **Performing** — The supervisor works to maintain team spirit as the group accomplishes its objectives. The group is a true team with leadership shared by all members.

Adjourning

This process was born out of the studies of group dynamics and is taught in many leadership and college-level courses. In terms of a project, a fifth stage is added, adjourning. Adjourning is the planned (and sometimes unplanned) termination of the group task. It includes the acknowledgement of the group's accomplishments and participation of individual members. It is an opportunity to debrief group members and determine if any changes in the process should be made.

Motivating and Supporting Personnel

The best way to support and motivate personnel is to create a working environment where personnel can be invested in their work and excel in their positions. The company officer can create this work environment using a number of methods, including:

- Empowering employees
- Providing rewards and incentives
- Coaching, counseling, and mentoring members of the unit
- Celebrating accomplishments

Empowering Employees

Empowering employees requires the supervisor to relinquish some authority and have confidence in employees' skills, judgment, and abilities. The supervisor is helping to increase their self-image and productivity through employee empowerment. Empowering employees is a form of delegation that:

- Allows subordinates to take responsibility for their actions and decisions.
- Helps build self-esteem and motivation within the employee.
- Is based on giving decision-making power to employees instead of the supervisor retaining it.
- Gives employees a vested interest in a project and the organization.
- Allows employees to use special, non-job related skills, such as photography, calligraphy, computer skills, or other hobbies to assist with projects.

The company officer should begin with small attainable projects if unit members have not experienced the empowerment process previously. The following steps can be used:

Step 1: Identify the problem. The solution must be attainable.

Step 2: State that all solutions will be considered, but the best one will be adopted. Tell the unit that it must prioritize the suggested solutions and include a contingency in the event the best choice cannot be used.

Step 3: Explain the reality that outside forces may prevent the adoption of some results.

Rewarding Employees

Company officers usually do not have authority to grant raises or provide monetary rewards for employees. That does not mean that they cannot provide rewards and incentives for good work within the unit.

Rewards are critical as motivational techniques in departments/organizations. Some rewards and incentives company officers may provide include:

- Buying pizza
- Writing a letter for their file
- A simple pat on the back
- Challenge coins **(Figure 3.7)**
- Holding group gatherings or parties to create cohesiveness and spirit
- Making positive statements on the skills and abilities of members of the unit to improve self-esteem
- Making appropriate comments on an employee's job performance evaluations
- Acknowledging a unit's or an individual's accomplishments to the organization's administration

The incentive's size or value is not the critical part of providing incentives for accomplishments; it is that the company officer made an effort to acknowledge an individual's contribution. Reward and award programs are critical to the volunteer staffing component and improve morale in combination and career departments/organizations.

Most organizations have award programs that the company officer should use. Rewards and awards must be earned in order to validate the incentive. When a person is presented with an unearned reward or award, disrespect is shown to that individual and to those who truly deserved the recognition.

Figure 3.7 A challenge coin can be used as a reward for a job well done.

Rewards should be given as soon as possible following the accomplishment. Delaying the award or reward lessens the value of the recognition. Consistency must be applied in the types of rewards given, situations that result in rewards, and justifications for giving them.

Coaching Employees

Coaching is a process of giving motivational direction, positive reinforcement, and constructive feedback to employees in order to maintain and improve their performance. Effective feedback needs to be positive, immediate, direct, and frequent. As a coach, the company officer teaches and directs the subordinate through encouragement and advice.

An effective coach helps a subordinate establish a goal, determine how to reach it, and provides suggestions when they are requested. Telling subordinates what to do and how to do it is not as effective because the subordinates will not feel like taking responsibility for the process.

Counseling Employees

Counseling is a formal process which assists participants in identifying and resolving personal, behavioral, or career problems that are adversely affecting performance. Sessions may be scheduled on a periodic basis, such as annually, before promotional examinations, or when the subordinate exhibits unacceptable behavior.

Counseling should occur in private, and a record should be kept of the session **(Figure 3.8)**. The company officer must adhere to the organization's counseling policies and procedures. The company officer must also be familiar with the labor/management agreement regarding the right to union representation during counseling sessions and the grievance procedures established by the agreement.

The following four-step method of counseling can be used:

Step 1: **Describe the current performance** — Describe levels in a positive manner. Specifically state the required behavior and expectations. Explain how and why current behavior is not acceptable. Use specific examples to identify how behaviors can improve.

Step 2: **Describe the desired performance** — State in detail exactly what action is expected or required in order to provide clear direction for the employee.

Step 3: **Gain a commitment for change** — Ask the employee to agree to the new level of performance. The agreement may be considered a contract and become part of the employee's formal personnel record.

Step 4: **Follow up the commitment** — Observe the employee following the counseling session to determine whether performance improves or schedule a follow-up meeting to discuss progress. If change does not occur, subsequent counseling sessions may be required. If unacceptable behavior continues after subsequent counseling, follow organization policy on disciplinary action.

Figure 3.8 A company officer should counsel subordinates in private.

Mentoring Employees

Mentoring is used to better prepare individuals for their roles and responsibilities within the organization under the direction of a positive role model. Mentoring programs enhance individual skills and improve productivity. Mentoring includes:

- Providing guidance in career choices.
- Assisting in gaining specialized training.
- Providing outside resources.
- Making challenging work assignments.
- Monitoring the achievements of subordinates.
- Encouraging diversity training.

Both mentors and mentees should participate voluntarily and enthusiastically in the program. Mentoring, when approached as a mandatory activity, may make the individuals involved resentful and may limit their participation.

Some business texts suggest that a mentor should not be a direct supervisor to the subordinate. In the U.S. Air Force mentoring model, the immediate supervisor serves as the primary mentor for each subordinate in a unit. Mentoring should not restrict the subordinate's ability to seek additional counseling and professional development advice from other sources or mentors.

Supervisors must make themselves available to subordinates who seek career guidance and counsel. The accomplishments of both the mentor and subordinate should be acknowledged throughout the process.

Acknowledging Accomplishments

Acknowledge the accomplishment of objectives as soon as possible. This acknowledgment signals the completion of a project and shows members of the unit that their contributions are important. Announce the completion of the project to the rest of the organization and congratulate participants on the results. Keep celebrations and acknowledgements appropriate so that they continue to having meaning for unit members and must be earned.

Applying Management Principles

A Level I Fire Officer may be required to manage a single-company incident or project and should be familiar with basic management principles. Level I Fire Officers should be prepared to manage multi-company incidents before the arrival of a Level II Fire Officer. As supervisors, company officers must be able to apply proven management principles. These principles are based on management theories that have been developed, applied, and validated over the past century.

Managing is the process of controlling or directing available resources for the purpose of achieving a goal or objective through the use of authority or persuasion. An effective CO must:

1. Be aware of relevant management functions.

2. Develop and refine the skills necessary to carry out those functions.

All organizational personnel bear some responsibility for the achievement of that organization's goals and objectives. As supervisors, company officers are directly responsible for the effective and efficient use of resources under their command. The primary resources provided by tax (fee) payers through political and economic support are generally considered to be **(Figure 3.9)**:

- Personnel
- Facilities
- Apparatus (vehicles)
- Tools and equipment
- Legal jurisdiction (authority)

Figure 3.9 Common fire and emergency services resources funded by taxes.

NFPA® 1021 uses the term management in conjunction with Level I and II Fire Officer responsibilities, such as information management, incident management, and human resources management. Even though the standard defines the Level I officer as a supervisor and the Level II officer as a manager, it is essential for both Level I and Level II officers to fully understand the theories and methods used in the act of managing.

This section provides the company officer with a basic knowledge of the management functions, the skills required to be an effective manager, and the planning function. The company officer must realize that management, like leadership and supervision, is a broad topic and cannot be completely presented in a single reference.

Management Functions

For this manual, we will address the management process to include the following four functions:

- *Planning* — Encompasses the broadest view of the organization (creation of the mission statement and setting goals and objectives) and the narrowest (development of tactical plans for accomplishing a specific objective).

- *Organizing* — Coordinating tasks and resources to accomplish the unit's goals and objectives as follows:
  - Establishing the internal structure of the unit, system, or organization
  - Creating divisions of labor
  - Coordinating the allocation of resources
  - Taking responsibility for tasks and flow of information within the department
  - Filling of positions with qualified people

- *Directing* — Guiding, influencing, inspiring, and motivating employees to achieve the goals and objectives within a group. Directing is a proactive approach to managing, as the company officer applies the concepts of leading and supervising.

- *Controlling* — Establishing and implementing the mechanisms to ensure that objectives are attained; includes setting performance standards, measuring and reporting the actual performance, comparing the performance standard with the actual performance, and taking preventive or corrective action to close the gap between the two levels of performance.

These four functions are essential to the management of fire and emergency services organizations. Company officers must develop the skills necessary to apply relative functions to the duties assigned to them during both emergency or nonemergency operations and duties.

Management Skills

Proper application of the management functions requires the company officer to possess certain management skills. While most company officers or officer candidates may have the knowledge to perform the technical tasks of the fire and emergency services, they may need to continually develop the interpersonal and management skills to be an effective company officer.

An effective company officer must possess the following management skills:

- *Administrative skills* — Methods and techniques required to perform certain tasks as a manager, such as computer skills; knowledge of laws, codes, ordinances, and labor/management agreements; report writing skills; data analysis skills for problem solving and risk identification, and other skills that will be used to prepare budgets, create reports, or develop specifications. These are in addition to the skills required of the officer as an emergency responder, such as the ability to manage an incident, apply strategic and tactical concepts to situations, and the knowledge of specialized emergency response skills.

- *Human and communication skills* — Interpersonal skills that include the ability to work with other people and supervise subordinates; success or failure often hinges on one's ability to communicate effectively.

- *Conceptual and decision-making skills* — Skills that include the ability to understand abstract ideas and solve problems; also the ability to understand the organization as a whole and recognize how the various parts are interrelated.

Planning Function

Planning determines in advance what an organization, a group, or an individual should do and how it will get done. It is the foundation of the management process. While chief officers and administrative staff develop formal organizational plans, it is the company officers who must plan how to implement them.

Planning should be documented in a timely manner. Documentation provides evidence of the decisions that were made and serves as a guide for future planning. Should the results of the planning fail to meet the required goal, the documentation will assist in determining why the plan needs to be altered and how to do it. Company officers must know the organization's plans, how the planning process works, how to apply it at the company or unit level, and the process for altering existing plans.

Plans are generally classified based on the frequency with which they are used. Two broad categories are established: standing plans and single-use plans. Plans may also be categorized as strategic, tactical, operational/administrative, and contingency. Plan descriptions:

- *Standing* — Policies, procedures, and rules that are used frequently to manage the day-to-day emergency and nonemergency unit activities. These help ensure the consistent and equal application of authority while defining responsibility within the organization.

- *Single-Use* — Accomplish a specific objective, such as the development of a program, project, or budget. These plans are usually intended to reach an objective within a short period of time.

- *Strategic* — Chart the course of the organization over an indefinite future that is divided into definite time components. The plan attempts to take into account the external factors that will affect the organization, such as changes in the economy, demographics, service requirements, hazards, and technology.

- *Operational/administrative* — Focus on how objectives will be accomplished. They deal with those factors that are within the control of the organization, objective, and fact-based while strategic plans are subjective.
- *Contingency* — Create alternative plans that can be implemented in the event of unforeseen events that make original plans unsuitable.

Task Management

The company officer is responsible for completing the tasks or ensuring that delegated tasks have been completed. Planning, organizing, controlling, and evaluating skills are required to complete a task.

- Establishing and communicating the plan for task completion to employees. The plan contains the sequence of steps, the time schedule for step completion, and the assignment of duties, responsibility, and authority.
- Ensuring that the schedule is realistic with attainable objectives. Attainable objectives should be based on the application of available resources to include personnel, funding, time, and materials.
- Organizing employees to work as a team with an objective or a goal in focus. Leadership and the creation of team spirit are essential to the success of the unit.
- Delegating the appropriate amount of responsibility and authority to employees, which gives them a sense of ownership in the project. However, final responsibility and authority always remains with the company officer.
- Evaluating the quality and completion of the task. Monitor progress to determine whether the plan is being followed or a change must be made to resolve unforeseen difficulties. For more complex tasks, the use of such tools as flow charts or **program (or project) evaluation and review technique (PERT) charts** to track task progress may be advisable.

> **Program (or Project) Evaluation and Review Technique (PERT) Chart** — a statistical tool used in project management that is designed to analyze and represent the tasks involved in completing a given project.

Chapter Summary

When a person is selected, elected, or promoted to the rank of company officer, that person's responsibility and authority increase with this new position. Company officers must understand the principles of supervision of individuals and groups. Company officers must know and be able to apply supervisory skills to gain the greatest advantage from subordinates and groups. The development of a team atmosphere and the application of leadership skills will result in the creation of an effective, efficient, and cohesive emergency response or administrative unit.

A company officer must be able to put these skills into action and lead effectively. Leadership based on organizational and jurisdictional policies and procedures and accepted values, morals, and ethical standards ensures that the officer will create a work environment that will foster mutual trust and respect. Company officers must also be familiar with certain management principles. These principles relate to management functions, skills, and planning.

Review Questions

1. How do ethics relate to leadership? (pp. 59-63)
2. What is the difference between management and supervision? (pp. 63-64)

Human Resources Management I

Chapter Contents

chapter 4

Key Terms

NFPA® Job Performance Requirements

This chapter provides information that addresses the following job performance requirements of NFPA® 1021, *Standard for Fire Officer Professional Qualifications* (2014).

4.2.4

4.2.5

4.2.6

Human Resources Management I

Learning Objectives

After reading this chapter, students will be able to:

1. Recognize planning processes as they relate to human resources management. [NFPA® 1021, 4.2.4, 4.2.5, 4.2.6]

2. List human resources organizational polices that Company Officer I is responsible for. [NFPA® 1021, 4.2.4, 4.2.5, 4.2.6]

3. Explain the role of Company Officer I in behavior management. [NFPA® 1021, 4.2.5, 4.2.6]

4. Describe labor/management relations.

5. Organize the completion of a departmental task. [NFPA® 1021, 4.2.6; Learning Activity 4-1]

6. Propose a plan of action to alleviate a member-related problem. [NFPA® 1021, 4.2.4; Learning Activity 4-2]

7. Implement a plan to resolve an administrative problem. [NFPA® 1021, 4.2.5; Learning Activity 4-3]

Chapter 4
Human Resources Management I

Case History

An Apparatus Section supervisor received an anonymous phone call that a subordinate supervisor was believed to be under the influence of alcohol while at work. Additionally, this subordinate supervisor had been involved in an accident with a department vehicle and had directed his staff to make the necessary repairs to the vehicle.

Notifications were made up the chain of command, which resulted in an immediate investigation of the allegations by the Office of Professional Standards. Interviews were conducted and individual statements were taken from all employees onsite. Because a significant amount of time had been taken to start this process, by the time the supervisor was interviewed, there was no indication that he was under the influence of alcohol and no testing was conducted. Following completion of the investigation, it was decided that the subordinate supervisor would be disciplined for failing to report the vehicle accident per standard procedure and abuse of his supervisory authority. The disciplinary action was a two-day suspension for this infraction. Since it was alleged that the supervisor was under the influence of alcohol, it was recommended that it was in his best interest to seek help through the organizations employee assistance program (EAP), if necessary.

The subordinate supervisor did follow up with the organization's employee assistance program and enrolled in a seven-day resident program to address his issue. He served his two-day suspension, and since completion of the program, he has been back to work fully engaged, productive, and has not had any other problems or issues.

Personnel are the most important resources available to the fire and emergency services organizations, and the company officer must always consider personnel safety above all else. Personnel perform emergency or nonemergency duties, tasks, and services for the organization's customers. These personnel may be volunteers or career firefighters, EMS personnel, or officers.

When dealing with personnel, company officers are faced with very similar challenges regardless if it is a career, volunteer, or combination organization. Career fire officers must be familiar with local policies, practices, procedures, and may incorporate labor/management agreements. They should also be familiar with state/provincial and federal human resources laws. Recruitment and retention of volunteers is an additional concern for volunteer officers. Company officers in combination organizations will benefit from the information presented for both situations.

Company officers must communicate with, supervise, train, evaluate, and discipline employees during all unit activities. The company officer plans and prioritizes the activities needed to meet the unit's assigned role in meeting the agency's mission.

This chapter describes the planning process, duty assignments and organizational policies, and behavior management that a company officer should be familiar with. Also included in the chapter are new employee duty assignments, conflict management, specific human resources policies, discipline, promotions, retention, and performance evaluations.

The Planning Process

Throughout the planning process, planning models provide a systematic approach to decision-making **(Figure 4.1)**. A planning model is a five-step approach to problem solving:

Step 1: *Identify* — Identify a problem that requires a response. The problem which may be an emergency situation or a nonemergency incident.

Step 2: *Select* — Choose the appropriate response to the problem according to the desired goals, outcomes, and objectives.

Step 3: *Design* — Determine the steps required to meet the selected goals, outcomes, and objectives.

Step 4: *Implement* — Perform the selected activity or supervise crew members in the activity that will mitigate the problem.

Step 5: *Evaluate* — Determine the effectiveness of the activities in meeting the goals or outcomes. Effectiveness may be immediate, such as the successful extrication of the victim, or it may be prolonged, such as the improved relationship of crew members.

NOTE: Evaluation may indicate the need for some changes in the activities. When changes are identified, a new analysis is used to begin the cycle again.

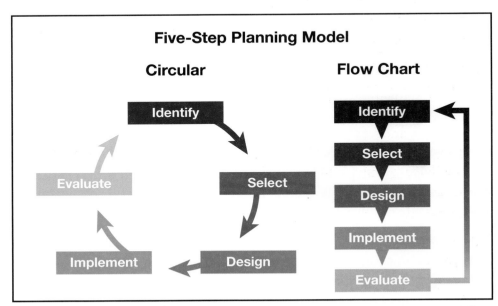

Figure 4.1 The Five-Step Planning Model can be visualized as being circular or as a flow chart.

The Operational Planning "P"

Another helpful planning approach is the Operational Planning "P." The Operational Planning "P" originated with the U.S. Coast Guard based on the Incident Command System. Initially designed for emergency responses, it can be adapted to planned events, which the organization and company officer may participate in. The Operational Planning "P" will be discussed in greater depth in Chapter 11, Emergency Services Delivery I.

Company-Level Planning

Company officers must prioritize their work loads and administrative activities. To accomplish this goal, they must plan effectively, which should improve with practice. Examples of company-level planning can include the following:

- Tasks and activities
- Preincident planning
- Company-level training
- Company-level inspections

Plan Alterations

When a company officer encounters a situation where established organization plans appear inappropriate, an immediate decision may have to be made. In this case, company officers should use their best judgment to formulate a plan or modify an existing plan. To make a recommendation for modification, the company officer should document:

- Situation description
- Recommended alteration
- Justification for recommendation
- Projected outcome of alteration

Organizational Policies

Company officers will have direct involvement with their assigned personnel and should have knowledge of the following organizational policies:

- Duty assignments
- Promotions
- Retention
- Performance evaluations
- Duty exchange
- Leave (vacation, sick, and wellness)
- Substance Abuse
- Absenteeism

Figure 4.2 The company officer should introduce new personnel to other unit members.

Duty Assignments

The company officer will provide new employees with first duty assignments during their probationary period. At this time, the company officer will explain to the new employee what is expected of them while helping them to adjust to their new work environment.

First Duty Assignments

Once a new employee has been given their first assignment, the company officer must begin the training process according to local policies. The company officer must also be prepared to begin the mentoring and socialization process with this new employee in the department culture (**Figure 4.2**). An employee's initial introduction should be as smooth as possible. Initial impressions and experiences can affect a responder's development, motivation, and retention.

Company officers are responsible for establishing work assignments for their units' new personnel. New responders must be told the tasks they will perform at emergency incidents. Specific emergency-incident tasks are assigned to new employees and practiced with other members of the crew who serve as mentors.

The new company member must also learn the duties and tasks required in performing nonemergency activities. These may include but are not limited to:

Figure 4.3 This young firefighter is being supervised by the unit's driver/operator during vehicle cleaning operations.

- Apparatus and equipment care and cleaning
- Facility cleaning
- Standing radio watch
- Interacting with external customers

Some training may be delegated to other company members. Apparatus care and cleaning can be taught and supervised by the driver/operator (**Figure 4.3**). Emergency medical services (EMS) responsibilities can be taught by a senior emergency medical technician (EMT). Infrequent and nonemergency duties can be taught after emergency-response activities are introduced as time permits.

Assigning an experienced unit member as a mentor to new employees helps ensure that knowledge is passed on. Mentors can provide personal instruction and encouragement to a new employee. The activities of new employees should be documented. Some organizations use a sign-off or task book to monitor and account for training.

Probationary Periods

Most fire and emergency services organizations have probationary periods for their new personnel or personnel who have been promoted. These periods are usually from 6 to 18 months and allow the organization to evaluate the probationary employee's ability to fulfill the job requirements for the position.

The company officer is usually responsible for managing the evaluation process for the probationary period. Probationary employees who do not successfully complete the training or are unable to meet minimum job requirements may be terminated or demoted.

During the probationary period, first-line supervisors provide guidance while observing and evaluating the new employee's performance against established standards, policies, procedures, and practices. New personnel may receive additional training that may not have been addressed in the formal entry-level training, such as the location of equipment stored on a unit's apparatus **(Figure 4.4)**.

Figure 4.4 The company officer or other crew members should show new personnel where equipment is stored on an apparatus.

Expectations of New Personnel

When new personnel are hired, the company officer should outline what is expected of them during emergency and non-emergency situations. New personnel should be briefed on the organization's expectations, such as the following:

- Performing assigned emergency duties
- Reporting to work on time
- Performing assigned station duties
- Working as part of a team
- Paying attention to details and following through with assignments
- Respecting authority
- Taking personal responsibility
- Maintaining a positive attitude
- Respecting confidentiality
- Treating others like they want to be treated

These expectations must be explained to the new employee in clear, concise, and understandable terms and should also be provided in written form. To ensure that expectations are understood, an officer must seek feedback from the employee. The company officer must become familiar with the employee's background in order to provide the support and leadership that the probationary responder needs.

Work Environments

Establishing a professional work environment is important to the success of a company officer. Employees must be given the opportunity to fit in and become contributing members. The company officer should help to create an environment that fosters teamwork, communications, and diversity. Because a diverse workforce may be different for some current members, change management is an important part of diversification. The company officer must ensure that the change process occurs smoothly, and employees are properly assimilated into the unit.

The company officer has the responsibility to ensure that the work location/environment is beneficial for all employees. A favorable work environment includes compliance with organizational policies, practices, procedures, and the law.

An unfavorable work environment occurs when employees in a workplace are subjected to a pattern of offensive conduct or behaviors, such as sexual harassment or hazing. The condition is further aggravated if supervisors or managers take no steps to discourage or discontinue such behavior. Policies are established to protect all employees from hostile or abusive actions, and company officers have to be familiar with organizational guidelines that deal with these issues.

Sexual harassment involves both hostile work environments and attempts by supervisors to use their powers to gain sexual favors from employees. Company officers may have to deal with a situation involving a coworker. Failure to follow proper procedures can have legal repercussions on both officers and organizations. Company officers must know and understand the following:

- Laws that govern workplace behavior
- Behaviors that constitute sexual harassment and create a hostile environment
- Local reporting process for sexual harassment charges
- Employee rights in such cases

Eliminating an unfavorable environment and preventing sexual harassment are responsibilities of all members of the organization. Company officers must monitor their own activities as well as those of unit members. Actions include the following:

- Ensure that the organization's sexual-harassment policy is clearly stated to all employees and posted in a highly visible location in the station or facility.
- Be aware of warning signs that sexual harassment is occurring.
- Take corrective action immediately and decisively.
- Inform employees who are engaging in inappropriate behavior that it is an infraction of the organization's policies and will not be tolerated.
- Inform superiors and document all information regarding incidents and attempts to resolve them if behaviors continue.
- Request additional or remedial training in the organization's policy regarding sexual harassment or hostile work environments.

Hostile Work Environment (Title VII of the Civil Rights Act of 1964)

A hostile work environment occurs when there is discriminatory conduct or behavior in the place of work that is unwelcome and offensive to an employee or group of employees. This behavior is a violation of Title VII of the Civil Rights Act of 1964 and other federal authority. There are four criteria for a hostile work environment in Title VII of the Civil Rights Act of 1964, which include:

- The behavior or actions must discriminate against a protected class, such as age, religion, disability, or race.

- It must be pervasive, lasting over time, and not limited to an off-color remark or two that an employee found annoying. The problem becomes significant and pervasive if it is all around an employee, continues over time, and is not investigated and addressed effectively enough by the organization to make the behavior stop.

- The behavior, actions, or communication must be severe and must seriously disrupt the employee's work or interferes with an employee's career progress.

- The employer knew about the actions or behavior and did not sufficiently intervene. The employer may be liable for the creation of a hostile work environment.

Promotions

The company officer should be interested in the career choices of unit personnel and should help subordinates investigate all possibilities of advancement **(Figure 4.5)**. With the help of the organizational or regional training agency, the company officer can provide promotional information on the types of courses subordinates should attend and certifications that would be most helpful.

Retention

All types of fire and emergency services organizations, especially volunteer agencies, are challenged with retaining members. Retention is particularly important to organizations that depend on volunteers because of the ever-shrinking pool of new applicants. Career organizations may lose personnel to jobs with better benefits or wages or to lifestyle changes, such as relocation. The company officer must work to ensure that company personnel are satisfied with their accomplishments and feel needed through continual communication. Company officers can use counseling sessions to assist personnel in selecting appropriate educational and promotional opportunities to reach their career or personal goals.

Figure 4.5 Company officers should assist their subordinates with promotional opportunities and recognize their achievements.

The investment in the training and equipping of new members must be realized through continuous and long-term service. The premature loss of experienced personnel affects the organization due to the loss of knowledge, skills, and leadership ability.

Performance Evaluations

Performance evaluations may be informal or formal. Informal evaluations can be either oral or written; formal evaluations are generally written. Impromptu evaluations are generally informal and enable the company officer to evaluate subordinates during their daily activities. When behaviors warrant, coaching or counseling can be employed to reinforce proper habits or correct improper habits.

Formal performance evaluations are held on a specific schedule, usually annually or semiannually. They can also occur before a promotional examination or when improper behavior that has not improved through informal evaluations needs to be corrected.

According to NFPA® 1021, the responsibility for formal performance evaluations rests with the Level II Fire Officer while in some organizations the Level I officer has this responsibility. Company officers should consult their organization's policies governing performance evaluations.

Leave and Duty Exchange

The interpretation and application of leave and duty exchange policies are an important part of the duties of the company officer. These policies include vacation leave, sick leave, wellness leave, and duty exchange.

Leave (Vacation, Sick, and Wellness)

Company officers may have the authority to approve vacation, sick, and wellness leave for their personnel. Leave is accrued in accordance with the organization's policies. A company officer may have to ensure that personnel have accrued enough leave. Requests may be denied for valid reasons, such as insufficient staffing or mandated training during the period of the request.

Duty Exchange (Shift Trade)

Many organizations permit employees of similar rank and training to exchange duty shifts or portions of shifts. The federal Fair Labor Standards Act (FLSA) requires employers to maintain accurate records of hours worked, which is one of the main reasons that specific requirements for duty exchanges are included in labor/management agreements.

Employee Assistance Programs (EAP)

Company officers must be knowledgeable of the organization's **employee assistance program (EAP)**. These programs are a type of benefit often provided by employers and are designed to help assist employees to deal with stresses in their personal or professional lives. These stresses may adversely affect their work environment, health, or general well-being. EAPs usually provide referral or services for employees in need of counseling or other assistance.

Employee Assistance Program (EAP) — Program to help employees and their families with work or personal problems.

The levels of stress encountered by fire and emergency personnel may be enhanced by certain significant events during an emergency. These events can result in dependence on tobacco products, abuse of alcohol or drugs, domestic violence, excessive gambling, and financial difficulties. Some examples include:

- Death or serious injury of a child
- Death of a colleague
- Cause of unusual human suffering/neglect
- Other high-profile events

Company officers must be able to recognize the signs and symptoms of stress within their personnel and themselves. When the body undergoes normal levels of stress, it responds with increases in heart rate and blood pressure, oxygen consumption, muscle tension and strength, and dilation of the pupils among others. Excessive stress, however, results in further emotional and cognitive responses. Signs and symptoms associated with excessive stress include:

- Difficulty concentrating or staying focused
- Temporary loss of short-term memory
- Obsessive thoughts
- Loss of mental flexibility
- Tendency to withdraw or become isolated
- Invulnerable feelings
- Fantasy or wishful thinking experiences
- Autopilot mind focus
- Abuse of alcohol and drugs
- Sleep disorders

Substance Abuse

Substance abuse includes the improper use of alcohol and drugs which impair judgment and slow reaction times. Their effects are not only on the individual but also on those who work and live with the individual as well as the public.

The symptoms of substance abuse will vary depending upon the type of substance used **(Figure 4.6, p. 90)**. Any one symptom may not be enough to indicate substance abuse but can suggest that there may be a problem. An efficient company officer should be aware of these symptoms and the root causes for substance abuse. However, company officers are not psychologists or professional counselors and must be prepared to refer subordinates to the organization's Employee Assistance Program (EAP).

Absenteeism

Absenteeism may indicate a serious problem, or it may be the result of circumstances beyond the employee's control. The first step is for the company officer to gather all the information concerning a particular incident through communication with the employee.

If an absence was due to severe weather, severe illness or injury, or a missed airline flight, the company officer should counsel the employee on the importance of contacting the supervisor or other officer in these circumstances. The company officer should let the employee know that the organization will, within its policies and procedures, work to assist the employee.

If an absence was due to a personal problem, the company officer should refer the employee to the EAP for counseling. If the situation cannot be resolved or the employee is absent repeatedly, the company officer may recommend some form of discipline. Records of the incident and subsequent interviews should be maintained.

Figure 4.6 Common symptoms of substance abuse.

Symptoms of Substance Abuse

General Substance Abuse:

- Change in circle of friends
- Reclusive behavior — long periods spent in self-imposed isolation
- Long, unexplained absences
- Lying and stealing
- Involvement on the wrong side of the law
- Deteriorating family relationships
- Obvious intoxication, delirium, incoherence, or unconsciousness
- Changes in behavior and attitude
- Decrease in job or school performance

Specific to Opiate and Narcotic Abusers:

- Accelerated heart rate
- Constricted pinpoint pupils
- Relaxed or euphoric state that may lead to a dangerous level of respiratory depression resulting in coma or death

Others:

- Dilated pupils
- Restlessness
- Hyperactivity
- Euphoria
- Slurred speech
- Disabled coordination
- Decreased attention span
- Impaired judgment

Source: Government information from the U.S. National Library of Medicine in the Public Domain.

Behavior Management

Personal differences can result in many types of conflict that must be resolved if personnel are going to live and work together. The company officer is responsible for ensuring that unit members can overcome these differences and learn to resolve conflicts.

Behavior management consists of conflict management processes, discipline activities, and strong leadership skills on the part of the company officer. These activities require the company officer to be familiar with the organization's human resources policies and procedures and any existing labor/management agreement.

Conflict Management

Company officers are responsible for managing conflicts, which occur when people are in opposition or disagreement. To be able to control or resolve these situations, company officers should understand conflict management styles, methods of negotiating internal conflict resolution, and steps to resolving conflicts.

Management Styles

Each generally accepted conflict management style is based on the concern for the other party and oneself. These concerns result in three types of behavior that are defined as follows:

- *Passive (nonaggressive)* — Occurs when people hide their own emotions so that others do not know how they feel. The goal of passive behavior is to appease others and avoid conflict at any cost.

- *Aggressive* — Occurs when people express their emotions openly and use threatening behaviors toward people or objects, which results in the violation of others' rights. The goal is to dominate the situation or other person and "win," which forces the other person to "lose" (win-lose situation).

- *Assertive* — Occurs when people express their emotions honestly and defend their rights without hurting others. The goals of assertion are communication and mutual respect, fair play, and compromise between the rights and needs of the two parties involved in the conflict. The personal rights of other people are not violated, while the thoughts, feelings, and beliefs of the individual are expressed in an honest and appropriate manner.

Methods of Resolving Conflict

Resolving conflict may include any one or more of the following five methods **(Table 4.1, p. 92)**:

1. *Avoiding* — Taking a nonassertive or passive approach; people may deny that a problem exists, refuse to take a stand on a situation, or mentally or physically withdraw from a situation. The result is a lose-lose situation because the conflict is never resolved.

2. *Accommodating* — Appeasing other persons by passively giving in to their positions. The result is a lose-win situation because the second person's needs are met at the expense of the first person.

3. *Forcing* — Relying on an aggressive and uncooperative approach to conflict management, resulting in a win-lose situation. The forcing style can damage relationships, create animosity, and result in a single-solution response to problems.

4. *Negotiating* — Reaching a compromise solution that all parties can agree upon. The supervisor is moderately assertive and cooperative. The result is a decision that causes everyone to compromise on some things while benefiting on others. The conflict is resolved relatively quickly, and relationships are maintained.

5. *Collaborating* — Sharing of information openly and honestly, which usually results in the best solution to the conflict (also referred to as the problem-solving style). While the previous styles involve the personal interests of the parties involved, this style is focused on the best interests of the organization, community, or service area.

Conflict Resolution Steps

It is best to resolve conflict as soon as it occurs. The longer the company officer waits to confront a problem, the harder it will be to find a solution. The decision-making process can be used as the basis for managing conflict. Some

Table 4.1
Conflict Management Styles

Number	Style	Description	Example Situations
1	**Avoiding Conflict** (taking a nonassertive or passive approach)	• Although it may appear that the benefit of avoiding conflict is to maintain relationships, the relationships will suffer in the long term. • The longer the conflict goes unresolved, the greater the strain on the relationship and the lower the work efficiency of those involved. • All conflict should be resolved as soon as possible.	Some situations in which avoidance may be necessary and acceptable are as follows: • The conflict is trivial and does not affect the tasks being done. • The company officer or supervisor does not have a high stake in the issue that is causing the conflict. • There is no time to attempt to resolve the conflict due to other priorities. • The conflict may damage or compromise an important relationship. When the relationship is important, avoidance provides the time necessary to balance the importance of the conflict with the importance of the relationship and determine a logical resolution to the conflict. • The emotions involving the conflict are very high. The avoidance approach will permit both parties to gain control of their emotions before attempting to resolve the conflict.
2	**Accommodating Conflict** (appeasing others by passively giving in to their positions)	• While the initial benefit may be maintaining relationships, the result may be counterproductive. • It is possible that the person who is giving in had the better solution for the situation. • Continuing to accommodate others also results in the loss of leadership and influence in the group. • Too much accommodation on the part of anyone involved in a conflict might result in a compromised solution and the potential for animosity or resentment.	Situations that may be appropriate to the accommodating style of conflict management are as follows: • The person employing it prefers to be a follower and not a leader in this situation. • The company officer or supervisor does not have a high stake in the issue that is causing the conflict. • There is limited time to resolve the conflict. • The conflict may damage or compromise an important relationship. It may be appropriate to balance the importance of the relationship with the importance of the situation that is causing the conflict. • The senior person involved in the conflict is an autocratic manager who uses the forcing style of conflict management.

Continued

Table 4.1

Number	Style	Description	Example Situations
3	**Forcing Conflict** (relying on an aggressive and uncooperative approach)	• If the person using this style is correct, the solution may be the best possible one. • However, if the opposite is true, the solution may be disastrous. • In any event, the potential for damaged personal relationships is very high for the person using this style.	Some situations that may require the forced style of conflict management are as follows: • The issue is extremely important, and the final decision will be an unpopular one. • The support of others is not important to the outcome of the decision. • Maintaining relationships is not important. • Conflict resolution is urgent, and there is no time for debate or discussion.
4	**Negotiating Conflict** (reaching a compromise solution that all parties can agree upon)	• The disadvantage is that the solution may not be the best one for the organization or unit. • Also, if this style is used too often, it causes the people or groups involved to ask for more than they need, knowing they will not get it. • This approach has become symbolic in some labor-management negotiations.	The appropriate uses of the negotiating style are as follows: • The issues are complex and critical. • There are no clear or simple solutions to the situation. • All parties to the conflict are interested in different solutions. • All parties have similar power within the organization. • The resulting solution will be temporary. • The time to resolve the conflict is short.
5	**Collaborating Conflict** (also called the *problem-solving* style) (sharing of information openly and honestly)	• The advantage of this style is that it usually results in the best possible solution. • The disadvantage is that it takes mutual trust, time, skills, and effort to use it. • It is the most difficult of the styles to implement, yet it is also the most rewarding. • Collaboration requires that all parties are willing to work for the goals of the organization or unit and provide all the information that is necessary to make the final decision. • In most organizations, this style requires a change in culture, which has to originate at the highest level.	Situations that can be addressed with the collaborative style are as follows: • The situation demands the best possible solution without a compromise. • The parties involved are committed to cooperation for the good of the organization. • The maintenance of relationships is very important. • There is sufficient time to implement the collaborative process. • The conflict is a peer-based conflict.

guiding principles to resolving conflict include separating the involved parties from the issues and focusing on common interests. The six steps of conflict resolution are as follows:

Step 1: *Classify/identify the problem* — Determine what type of conflict is involved and identify participants.

Step 2: *Define/diagnose the problem* — Determine the amount of time, skills, effort, and resources required to resolve an issue. Determine whether a conflict is a symptom of a deeper and more involved problem.

Step 3: *Determine the right response/appropriate conflict management style* — Determine whether an issue should be resolved through collaboration, negotiation, force, accommodation, or avoidance. Determine which conflict management style is most appropriate to the problem.

Step 4: *Determine alternative options* — If the selected style is not effective, determine which style is the next best choice. Knowing the advantages and disadvantages of each style and the situations that are appropriate to each will help in making this decision. If possible, base the decision on common ground, such as overlying goals of the organization.

Step 5: *Convert the decision to an action* — Implement the chosen conflict management style. If a situation requires an immediate and forceful response, give direction to those involved and expect them to follow it. If there is time, gather information and pursue a negotiated or collaborative agreement. The result of the process must be a decision that all parties will adhere to either through force, when necessary, or through agreement.

Step 6: *Test the action against the desired outcome* — Implement the decision and test the results against the agreed-upon outcome.

The company officer may not be able to resolve a conflict or may even be a part of the conflict. In these instances, another approach will be required. If the conflict is not resolved internally, it may result in a loss of unit team spirit, transfer of personnel, or a costly and time-consuming legal confrontation.

The alternative to this situation is an internal conflict or dispute resolution process. One of the most effective has been the peer-mediation process. The conflicting parties voluntarily appear before a team of organizational employees who are specially trained in the mediation process.

Some benefits of this process include:

- *Relationships are maintained* — Results are consensus-based and tend to be long lasting.

- *External publicity is avoided* — Conflict remains within the organization. Confidentiality is maintained among the participants.

- *Costly litigation is avoided* — Process occurs outside the judicial system and depends on mutual agreement for enactment of the resolution.

- *Organization and participants control the process* — Participants and the organization control the selection of the type of mediation, topic of the mediation, and resolution of the mediation.

- *Participants control the resolution* — Outcome of the conflict is determined by the membership and not by an external group.

Discipline

Personnel may break the rules or not comply with procedures, and this behavior can lead to a need for discipline. Some of the possible reasons that people break the rules include the following:

- *Resentment* — Created when wages and working conditions are (or are perceived to be) substandard, bitter labor/management disputes have occurred, difficult contract negotiations have occurred, or rules are being unfairly or inconsistently applied

- *Boredom* — Caused when there is too little work or too little interest in the work

- *Ignorance* — Created when there is a lack of knowledge of the job requirements and/or the rules of conduct

- *Stress* — Caused by personal problems (on or off the job) that affect job performance

If personnel break the rules, the company officer may be responsible for carrying out corrective discipline. Discipline has been defined as *training that corrects*; thus, the main purpose of discipline is to educate. Discipline should be imposed to correct inappropriate behavior and not to punish persons, but to educate them. It is a formal process that requires the company officer to provide appropriate documentation as required by the authority having jurisdiction (AHJ). Discipline in the fire and emergency services is designed to:

- Provide positive motivation.
- Ensure compliance with established rules, regulations, standards, and procedures.
- Provide direction.

Corrective disciplinary actions should be taken in a manner that is progressive and lawful. Corrective action is required when an employee disobeys established rules or performance requirements or adversely affects the safety of its members. All discipline should start with gathering information regarding the situation or behavior that appears to require a change. Employee rights may be established by local policy or state/provincial laws.

Progressive Discipline

Most public entities have policies, guidelines, or practices requiring some form of progressive discipline. Progressive discipline starts with training/education to correct the first instance that an employee fails to meet performance standards or violates the rules of conduct. Discipline then progresses to punitive (formal sanction) measures if there are additional offenses.

A sufficiently serious first offense (theft, assault, gross negligence) may result in termination. The action should always fit the offense, so the initial response may be corrective (written notice) or punitive. Progressive leadership and participatory management can help to ensure that punitive discipline is seldom used within the organization.

Figure 4.7 Company officers should be prepared to take preventive action to correct inappropriate behavior.

Progressive discipline usually involves the following three levels:

- **Preventive action** — Hold an individual counseling interview to correct the inappropriate behavior as soon as it is discovered and prevent it from becoming a pattern or progressing to a more serious offense **(Figure 4.7)**. The following process should be applied during the counseling session:

  — Ensure that the employee understands both the rule that was violated and the organizational necessity for the rule during the interview.

  — Explain exactly what is expected of the employee in the future and what may happen if the rule is violated again.

  — Document the interview in a written record.

- **Corrective action** — Use corrective action when an employee repeats a violation for which preventive action was taken, commits a different violation, or commits a serious violation as a first offense. Corrective action differs from preventive action primarily in that it is always done in writing. Give the employee a letter in person or send one by certified mail with a return receipt requested to guarantee that it is received. The letter includes the following information:

  — Description of what transpired in the preventive interview if one was held

  — Description of what the employee is or is not doing that violates organizational rules

  — Review of organizational policy regarding the possible consequences if the behavior continues or a change in behavior fails to meet organizational standards

  — Statement informing the employee that a copy of the letter will be placed in the employee's personnel file

- **Punitive action** — Give the employee notice of possible sanctions. Use this action when an employee either continues to exhibit inappropriate behavior, despite earlier corrective efforts, or commits a very serious violation of organizational rules as a first offense. Put the employee on notice that this behavior cannot and will not be tolerated. After meeting all mandated procedural rules and employee protection requirements, consider the range of possible sanctions as follows:

  — Formal written reprimand

  — Fine (specific monetary payment)

  — Suspension (time off without pay)

  — Demotion (loss of rank)

  — Termination (dismissal from organization)

  — Prosecution (legal action that may result in a large fine or jail time)

The company officer is most likely to use preventive action. It is unlikely that the company officer will have the authority to apply either corrective or punitive action, but the company officer should understand corrective or punitive actions. The officer will have to recommend to higher authorities the appropriate action based on documented evidence of misbehavior by the employee.

Legal Aspects of Discipline

All discipline must meet legal requirements. If there is no valid requirement, there is no basis to discipline an employee. Discipline that is administered for any other reason may result in the action being overturned. Discipline may only be administered for violations of the following:

- Written policies
- Procedures
- Rules
- Regulations
- Standard operating procedures/standard operating guidelines (SOPs/SOGs)
- Verbal orders

Not every possible violation by an employee must be covered by a specific written policy or regulation. Most SOPs/SOGs include a general duty clause that simply prohibits actions or behaviors that are considered unprofessional or inappropriate.

Grievances

A **grievance** may be lodged by the subordinate or the labor representative if the company officer does not follow the agreement procedures when administering a disciplinary action (even a minor one), potentially preventing any future action against the employee on that issue. Potential issues that may be cited in a grievance include but are not limited to:

- Demotion
- Suspension without pay
- Work assignments that violate the labor management agreement, law, or organizational policy
- Conditions of work or employment that violate the labor management agreement, law, or organizational policy

Grievance — A complaint against management by one or more personnel concerning an actual, alleged, or perceived injustice.

Labor/Management Relations

In many career organizations, the company officer may belong to a public labor union. Although there are differences between public and private unions, the goal of a union is still the same: improvement in employees working conditions. This goal is usually carried out through collective bargaining negotiations and employee involvement and participation.

Collective Bargaining Negotiations

During the collective bargaining process, negotiations are carried out. These negotiations are open communications between representatives of the public union, organizational management, and the local governing body. After negotiations are concluded, the labor/management agreement is formulated and this agreement determines the working conditions, wages, and benefits for the duration of the agreement.

Employee Involvement and Participation

A company officer may be a member of the union, but at the same time may also be an active participant in the negotiating process. Involvement in negotiating the process and an understanding of the labor/management agreement can help the company officer's relationship with other personnel. It can lead to increased morale and retention among personnel and will help the company officer to be more aware of the rules governing personnel.

Chapter Summary

Supervising a fire and emergency services company or unit demands that company officers have strong leadership qualities and interpersonal skills, an understanding of the planning process, and an ability to apply these skills to the human resources management process. The process includes developing plans for the most effective use of personnel in both emergency and nonemergency operations, supervising new employees during their probationary periods, administering human resources policies, and applying behavior management techniques for conflict management and discipline. Because human resources issues involve the organization's members, it is essential that the company officer know both the human resources policies and procedures and the existing labor/management agreement.

Because company officers represent management as supervisors but are also eligible for union membership, they must often walk a very fine line. They must know what contracts and agreements are in effect between their organization and the labor union and what each side's rights and responsibilities are under those agreements.

Company officers should also have some knowledge of labor relations in general and about local unions' procedures in particular. They should have knowledge of typical contract issues and the various means available for resolving those issues. Company officers should also be prepared to be active participants in any initiative directed toward building a cooperative relationship between labor and management in their organization. Finally, company officers must be aware of the grievance process in their organization, whether it is based on policy or a labor/management agreement.

Review Questions

1. What are five steps in the planning process? (p. 82)
2. What aspects of human resources management is a Company Officer I directly involved with? (p. 83)

3. In what ways can a company officer help to resolve conflicts among his or her subordinates? (pp. 91-94)

4. What role does the Company Officer I play in labor/management relations? (p. 98)

Learning Activities

Learning Activity 4-1

Objective 5: Organize the completion of a departmental task.

Company officers must be able to recognize any and all actions necessary to complete a task and be able to delegate those actions to crew members when necessary.

Using the following scenario, create a short, informal written document that outlines a plan for completing the task and assigning these actions to crew members.

Scenario:

Your fire station is scheduled to have an open house one week from today in order to dedicate the purchase of a new apparatus. This event was to be supervised and organized by Tom, your public information officer, but he has been called away suddenly on a family emergency. The only scheduled event is a short dedication speech from the mayor, but the event has also advertised free hot dogs, events for children, and tours of the station.

The following crew members are available to help prepare for this event:

- Driver/operator Burke: Burke has twenty years of experience in the department and is easily the department's elder statesmen. He takes special pride in maintaining and cleaning the station and its equipment.

- Firefighter Tipton: Tipton is the rookie of the department and is still very reserved around the crew, although she is one of the hardest workers you've ever encountered. She is currently taking certification classes and will be back in two days.

- Firefighter Ramirez: Ramirez has been with your department for six years now. He is good at his job and well-liked, but he can get distracted by socializing with fellow firefighters when he is assigned minor tasks.

Answer Key:

Answers for this activity will vary; however, your outline should address:

- What tasks are necessary to complete before the event
- The priority for each task
- Which tasks should be assigned to which personnel
- Justifications for those assignments
- Any safety considerations
- A timeframe for completion of each task
- A method for evaluating the completion of those tasks

Learning Activity 4-2

Objective 6: Propose a plan of action to alleviate a member-related problem.

Company officers must be aware of personal or professional problems that may affect the work and lives of their crew members, and must be willing to address these issues when they arise.

For this activity, you will need access to the following resources:

- A copy of your department's employee assistance program OR the sample employee assistance program provided below

Using the scenario below, develop a short, informal oral presentation that outlines a plan for speaking with and assisting a subordinate in finding solutions with any problems that may be affecting his or her professional or personal life.

Scenario:

Ramirez, a driver/operator in your department, is normally very outgoing and talkative, but has become more withdrawn and gloomy for the past two weeks. Yesterday, he was absent from his shift. He is back at work today, but still seems distracted.

Answer Key:

Answers for this activity will vary. Answers should address how to determine if there is a problem, what types of problems might be encountered, as well as possible ways that a company officer can help the subordinate find solutions.

Home Town Fire Department

Policy: Employee Assistance Program (EAP)

Policy #: 100.1

Effective: September 1, 20XX

Policy

The Home Town Fire Department shall make available counseling assistance to employees and their families who are in distress from financial, emotional, medical, or professional problems.

Procedure:

1. It is the responsibility of the company officer to identify the need for employee assistance based on family financial, emotional, medical or professional problems.

2. Once a company officer suspects a problem may exist, the company officer shall review the EAP resource information with the employee. The company officer shall explain each benefit and the method for accessing the assistance.

3. At all times the company officer shall avoid providing advice to the employee.

4. If requested by the employee, the company officer may make the initial contact with an EAP counselor to schedule a meeting with the employee. The EAP help line is 555-7000.

5. The company officer shall follow-up with the employee within five calendar days to determine if further assistance is required.

6. All information provided by the employee shall be confidential.

Learning Activity 4-3

Objective 7: Implement a plan to resolve an administrative problem.

Company officers must be able to put into action any human resources policy or procedure that may be required of them.

Using the following scenario, create a short, informal written document that outlines a plan for implementing a new or changing human resources policy. Make sure that the document addresses in detail how the change should be implemented.

Scenario:

> The fire chief has just sent out the following memo:
>
> Date: October 1, 20XX
>
> To: Company Officer
>
> From: Fire Chief
>
> Subject: Shift trading policy
>
> The Home Town Fire Department will begin a new policy that will take effect on January 1st. This new policy states that:
>
> - Any trades in shift must be requested at least a month in advance
> - All requests must to be made in writing
> - All requests must be approved by the fire chief
>
> Please communicate this new policy to your department as soon as possible.

Answer Key:

Answers for this activity will vary; however, it should address questions such as:

- Will training be necessary? If so, how much training?
- Can the policy be communicated verbally or in writing?
- What will the time frame be for implementing this policy?
- What is the anticipated reaction to this change? How should you plan for that reaction?

Communications

Chapter Contents

chapter 5

Key Terms

NFPA® Job Performance Requirements

This chapter provides information that addresses the following job performance requirements of NFPA® 1021, *Standard for Fire Officer Professional Qualifications* (2014).

4.1.2	4.3.3
4.2.1	4.4.1
4.2.2	5.2.1
4.2.3	5.4.4
4.2.5	5.4.5
4.3.2	

Communications

Learning Objectives

After reading this chapter, students will be able to:

1. Define the components of interpersonal communications. [NFPA® 1021, 4.2.1, 4.2.2, 4.3.2]

2. Recognize the importance of listening skills in interpersonal communications. [NFPA® 1021, 4.2.5, 4.3.2]

3. Explain the role of oral communications in company officer duties. [NFPA® 1021, 4.2.1, 4.2.2, 4.2.3, 4.3.2, 4.3.3, 4.4.1, 5.2.1]

4. Explain the role of written communications in Company Officer I duties. [NFPA® 1021, 4.3.3, 4.4.1, 5.4.4, 5.4.5]

5. Describe the importance of incident scene communications. [NFPA® 1021, 4.2.1, 4.2.2]

6. Compose a written document relating to the fire service. [NFPA® 1021, 4.1.2; Learning Activity 5-1]

7. Apply the interpersonal communications model to common firefighter scenarios. [NFPA® 1021, 4.2.1, 4.2.2; Learning Activity 5-2]

Chapter 5
Communications

Case History

In early 2010, due to the regionalization of smaller fire departments in Eastern Canada, the Sandy Point Fire Department evolved into a six station fully career department. The fire chief soon realized that all maintenance of equipment and inspections of some 13 pumpers and four heavy rescue units created a major challenge for this new department.

After evaluating several incident reports, the chief recognized an ongoing problem of missing equipment from the various apparatus and rescue vehicles. Some of these were minor in nature (such as medical gloves) and some major (such as power saws). Expecting growing pains associated with the regionalization of the departments, the chief launched a project to build a computer program to link the stations to the newly formed city's Communications and Supplies Store Departments. The chief and the city's Information Technology department developed the program, nicknamed "CIMS." It enabled shift captains to enter apparatus and rescue vehicle daily inspection logs. All vehicles were set up in the system with an acceptable and minimum equipment inventory requirement. Once a shift captain entered information into the Daily Inspection Sheet Data, the system would automatically send an email to the chief and the Stores Supply Office to indicate equipment required. All necessary supplies were normally sent to the required station within hours, ensuring that all apparatus and units were properly stocked.

Over time, monitoring of equipment costs has proven the system to be a budgetary saving tool. It has streamlined both minor and major purchasing to a minimum. In addition, it has eliminated duplication of orders and information and has become a great consumable tracking device.

Company officers must communicate effectively with their supervisors, subordinates, and the public. Most of the daily tasks company officers perform involve some form of continual communication, such as:

- Receiving orders from superiors and communicating them to subordinates
- Communicating with others at an emergency scene
- Dealing with citizens
- Making public fire and life-safety education presentations
- Writing reports and record keeping
- Communicating electronically
- Facilitating training and instruction

The four most common forms of communication within the fire and emergency services are informal interpersonal, oral, written, and incident scene communications **(Figure 5.1, p. 106)**. This chapter provides a brief overview of interpersonal communication through communicating effectively and listening skills. It addresses oral communications and making oral presentations to groups of people. This chapter also describes the writing process. It introduces company officers with the issue of interoperability, and the types of communications equipment they will be expected to use and proper procedures for using this equipment.

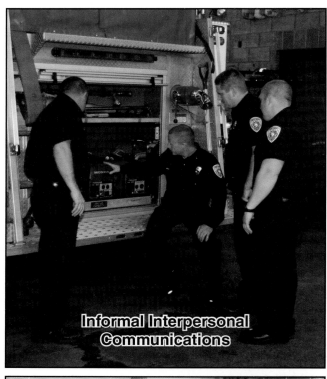

Informal Interpersonal Communications

Oral Communications

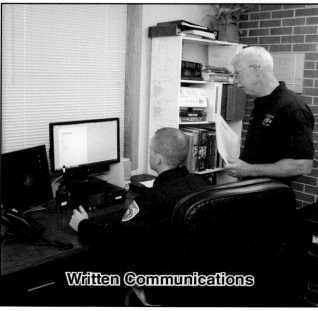

Written Communications

Incident Scene Communications

Figure 5.1 Company officers will use informal interpersonal, oral, written, and incident scene communications during the performance of their duties.

Interpersonal Communications

Interpersonal communication takes place between individuals every day in casual conversation and has the following characteristics:

- Casual language
- Casual nonverbal clues
- Frequent changes of the speaker and listener roles
- Spontaneity

Numerous college courses teach the dynamics of interpersonal communication. Such courses include learning and applying the concepts as well as practicing them through role-play situations. The following sections explain the basic concepts and principles of interpersonal communication in a brief overview, give interpersonal communication purposes, and discuss both verbal and nonverbal components.

Communication Basics

The tone of the conversation can change based on the perceptions of the two parties. All individuals need to understand, develop, and/or master the skills involved in interpersonal communication. Company officers must understand the importance of the message and feedback from their company personnel. Interpersonal communication consists of the following five basic elements **(Figure 5.2)**:

- **Sender** — The person who initiates the message using both verbal and nonverbal communication.

- **Message** — The content that the sender is trying to communicate. The message may consist of information intended for multiple human senses (sight, hearing, taste, smell, touch).

- **Receiver** — Individual or individuals to whom the sender is attempting to communicate.

- **Feedback to the sender** — Reaction of the receiver to the message and its tone. If this feedback is verbal, the receiver becomes the sender and relates a new message to the original sender, who becomes the receiver. Receiving feedback allows the original sender to confirm reception of the message and to assess the receiver's level of understanding.

- **Interference** — Anything that may prevent the receiver from completely understanding the message.

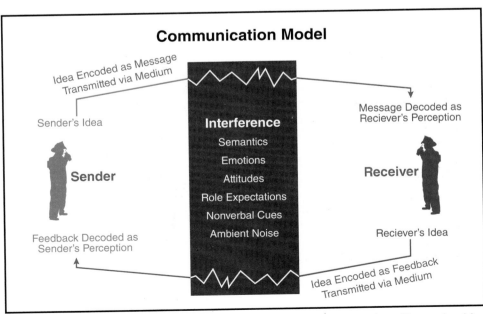

Figure 5.2 To better understand the communications process, company officers should become familiar with the components of the Communication Model.

Clear-Text (Plain English)

Clear-text (plain English) should be used in radio transmissions to replace the numerous, contradictory 10-codes. The National Incident Management System strongly encourages the use of plain English for all emergency messaging. Electronic communications (text messaging and e-mails) have become popular communications mediums.

Fire and emergency services personnel frequently use the term "roger" during radio communications to acknowledge that a transmission has been received and understood. "Roger" implies that if a command message is sent, it is received and will be carried out.

It is the sender's responsibility to communicate the information in such a manner that receivers will understand it. All communication takes place within a larger frame of reference. Senders encode their messages based on their education level, position of authority, personal or ethnic background, and other characteristics. The receivers will then decode the messages based upon similar characteristics of their own. When senders take these characteristics into account, the receivers are more likely to understand the message clearly.

Receivers respond to senders through feedback. Feedback may be verbal, such as someone asking a question, or nonverbal, as when a person appears bored and unmotivated. When senders pay attention to receiver feedback, they can modify the message to improve the communication.

Interference can be encountered when sending or receiving a message so it is important to pay attention to feedback. Failure to actively monitor feedback can be a major cause of interference. Senders need to pay attention to their receivers, and receivers need to pay attention to their senders.

For communication to be effective, both the sender and receiver must agree on its purpose. A shared purpose can create agreement. In some cases, the purpose must be explicitly stated to ensure that both parties understand it fully. A situation that involves influencing the actions of a subordinate would require that the subordinate understands that the purpose of the conversation involves a change in their attitude or behavior.

There are five general purposes for interpersonal communication: to learn, to relate, to influence, to play, and to help. Brief descriptions of these purposes are as follows:

- **Learning** — Acquire knowledge or skills.

- **Relating** — Establish a new relationship or maintain an existing one.

- **Influencing** — Control, direct, or manipulate behavior.

- **Playing** — Create a diversion and gain pleasure or gratification, as with positive humor.

- **Helping** — Attend to another person's needs or console someone in a time of tragedy or loss.

The sections that follow focus more specifically on the verbal and nonverbal components of communication. Both of these components have strengths and weaknesses and inherent interference that company officers must overcome.

Verbal Component

To be effective communicators, company officers must select and use words that accurately symbolize the image that they are trying to convey. They should always be aware of their audience or receiver. Word selection is particularly important when speaking to people who do not have a shared experience with the speaker. Explaining how a smoke detector works to someone who does not have a background in fire science requires fewer technical terms than explaining the concept to another emergency responder. The terms that are common to the fire and emergency services may have another meaning or no meaning at all to the general public. Avoid technical language and fire service jargon when speaking with the public, elected officials, media, and others from outside the profession. Also avoid language that might be considered offensive, gender biased, racist, or otherwise stereotyped.

Strong verbal communication is an important skill to cultivate as an officer. Practicing the following guidelines will help company officers to hone their verbal communication skills:

- **Engage in dual perspective** — Be aware of the receiver's frame of reference. Recognize the listener as having a different culture and attempt to relate to it rather than diminish it or make fun of it.

- **Take responsibility for personal feelings and thoughts** — Use language that is I-based, such as "I believe . . ." or "I think . . . ." Avoid phrases such as "You hurt me" or "You disappoint me." Focus instead on language that owns one's feelings and concentrates on the cause of those feelings, such as "I am disappointed by your actions."

- **Show respect for the feelings and thoughts of the other person** — Avoid trying to apply personal feelings to another person, such as saying, "I know how you feel." Instead, understand and respect others' positions and build upon those concepts to create strong relationships. A better way of responding in this type of situation is to say, "I'm sorry you have to go through this."

- **Try to gain accuracy and clarity in speaking** — Avoid the abstract language that can cause misunderstandings. Avoid generalizations that result in stereotypes, such as "All lawyers are crooks." Generalizations are, in themselves, false. Be clear and accurate in all types of communication.

- **Be aware of any special needs of the receiver** — Be sure to speak slowly and clearly while facing a person when the person is hearing impaired, for example. This procedure makes it easier for the person to read lips. Do not exaggerate lip or mouth movements because this action is not helpful and may even make the words more difficult to understand.

- **Avoid speaking or addressing a problem while angry or emotional** — Pause and place the conversation on hold until emotions are under control.

Nonverbal Component

Speech communication research indicates that nonverbal communication transmits 93 percent of any message: 55 percent is body language while 38 percent is vocal tone and inflection **(Figure 5.3, p. 110)**. Only 7 percent of the transmitted message is actually verbal communication.

Nonverbal communication consists of the following elements:

- Body language
- Vocal tone and volume
- Personal appearance

An understanding of the importance of each of the elements of nonverbal communication assists the company officer in recognizing and interpreting those nonverbal signals, which improves nonverbal communi-

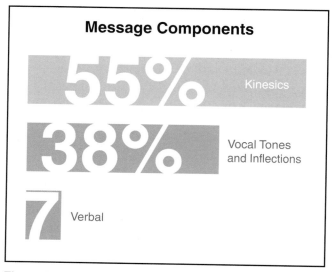

Message Components

55% Kinesics

38% Vocal Tones and Inflections

7 Verbal

Figure 5.3 Nonverbal communication (kinesics and vocal tones and inflection) transmit 93 percent of a message.

cation. Nonverbal communication can project a person's self-perception, emotional state, approachability, or cultural background. Brief descriptions and recommendations are as follows:

- **Eye contact** — Learn to maintain eye contact while speaking and modify the amount or duration of eye contact when appropriate. In some cultures, good eye contact can convey self-confidence, honesty, trust, and credibility. Averting one's gaze can indicate deceit, dishonesty, insecurity, or anxiety. However, eye contact is also a function of cultural background, so it must be appropriate to the situation, the relationship, and the culture. Examples:

  — In the wrong context, too much eye contact can be as damaging as too little. Staring into the eyes of a member of the opposite sex can be considered too personal or intimidating.

  — Many Native American and Asian societies believe that it is disrespectful to make direct eye contact with a person who is not of the same status.

- **Facial expression** — Learn to match the facial expression to the message. The face can show the six basic emotions: happiness, sadness, surprise, fear, anger, and disgust. To effectively communicate the correct message in a relationship, the facial expression must match the verbal message.

- **Gestures** — Identify and control gestures that are annoying or distracting to others. Learn to use gestures to emphasize and illustrate the message. In situations where noise prevents verbal communication, gestures are effective for sending messages such as *come here* and *stop*.

- **Posture** — Maintain good posture when standing or sitting in front of a classroom or assembly. Sitting or standing erect can create the impression of a person with self-confidence and authority. Slouching or standing with stooped shoulders makes a person appear insecure, disinterested, or intimidated.

- **Poise** — Present an image of self-confidence and authority through nonverbal elements, such as good posture and a sense of calm. Company officers develop poise gradually as they become more confident and less nervous when speaking publicly.

- **Vocal characteristics** — Learn to use vocal characteristics that are appropriate for the message and the situation. Practice speaking slowly and using variation in pitch to provide emphasis. Use volume appropriate to the situation and proper diction to ensure that words are clearly understood.

- **Vocal interferences** — Eliminate filler words such as *um, er,* or *like,* and empty phrases such as *you know* or *and things like that.* Company officers with a regional or cultural accent may also need to closely monitor their speech to make sure their audience can understand them.

- **Personal appearance** — Maintain a professional appearance at all times. Set an example for subordinates, and require the same level of professionalism from other members of the organization.

- **Touch** — Become conscious of the effect that touch can have on others, both positive and negative.

- **Proximity** — Be aware that different cultures have different interpretations of how close people should be when they interact. Apply this knowledge appropriately.

NOTE: What has been presented in this section is a brief description of nonverbal communication. Company officers are encouraged to seek out other sources of information on the topic.

Listening Skills

As role models for their personnel, company officers must practice good listening skills. Improving listening skills is essential to effective communication within the crew.

Listening, unlike simply hearing, is an active process that includes attending to, understanding, remembering, evaluating, and responding to the speaker **(Figure 5.4, p. 112)**. Paying close attention to these aspects of the listening process will help company officers become better listeners. Descriptions of listening components are as follows:

- **Attending** — Focusing on the speaker while ignoring any other distractions. Company officers should ensure that the environment provides as few distractions to the listeners' ability to attend as possible. Some suggestions for improving the attending step are as follows:

  — Look at the speaker when possible. Think about the speaker and what is being said.

  — Visualize the situation or event that the speaker is talking about.

  — Wait until the speaker has finished delivering the message before responding.

  — Listen to the verbal message and observe nonverbal messages.

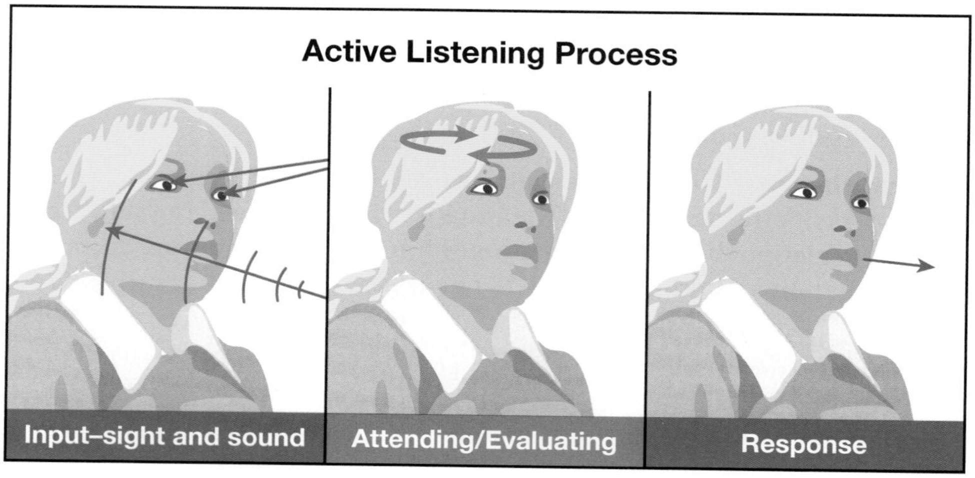

Figure 5.4 The components of the Active Listening Process.

Active Listening Process

Input—sight and sound | Attending/Evaluating | Response

- **Understanding** — Decoding the message and assigning meaning to it involves the following actions:
  — Organizing the message into a logical pattern
  — Interpreting nonverbal cues
  — Asking questions to clarify meaning
- **Remembering** — Retaining information in short term and then long term memory; taking notes, repeating information back to the sender, using **mnemonic devices**, and asking questions about unclear information are all ways to aid remembering.
- **Evaluating** — Critically analyzing information to determine how accurate it is, or to separate fact from opinion. To effectively evaluate a message, listeners must draw on their own personal experience, assess the credibility of the speaker, and interpret nonverbal cues.
- **Responding** — Indicating to the sender that the message or information has been understood or requires more explanation; responses may be verbal, such as asking questions or requesting more information, or nonverbal, such as sleeping in class.

Company officers should listen to speeches or presentations and assess the speaker's strengths. Repeating the key elements of the speeches or presentations is good practice and a great way to develop better listening skills.

Before small group meetings or individual counseling sessions, remove barriers to listening in the rooms where the meetings will take place. These barriers may include noise-producing equipment or visual distractions, such as posters on the walls. Wall decorations in classrooms should supplement the course material and not distract from it. During training exercises, try to identify barriers to communication that take place over the radio and at the command post.

Oral Communications

Oral communication is the process of engaging with individuals or groups using a verbal medium. Company officers utilize oral communications to communicate with their crews, conduct training sessions, deliver presenta-

Mnemonic Device — Any learning technique that assists in memory retention. Mnemonic devices may be used on various forms of information such as lists, short poems, acronyms, memorable phrases, and images.

tions, and communicate during emergency situations. While most people can speak easily with small groups of people, many fear speaking to large groups. The fear of public speaking can be overcome through:

- Practice
- Public speaking classes
- Organizations such as Toastmasters
- Instructor training programs

Communicating with the Crew

Company officers communicate orally with members of their crews on a daily basis. The basic rules of interpersonal communications apply to these communications. Daily oral communications with the crew include:

- Issuing crew assignments **(Figure 5.5)**
- Assigning tasks
- Passing along information
- Receiving reports
- Career counseling

Figure 5.5 Crew assignments are often made through oral communications during shift change/roll call.

Conducting Training Sessions

Company officers frequently organize and conduct company-level training sessions for their personnel and may be assigned to training duties with the departments training division **(Figure 5.6, p. 114)**. Oral communications skills are critical to imparting:

- Knowledge.
- Describing skills.
- Issuing commands.
- Critiquing the training.

Figure 5.6 A company officer detailed to his organization's training division during a Fire Officer I training class.

State and federal agencies and local community colleges provide instructor training programs for company officers. These courses cover such topics as:

- Learning principles
- Instructional planning
- Development and use of training materials and equipment
- Presentation methods and skills
- Classroom instruction
- Conducting training evolutions
- Testing and evaluation

NOTE: These courses also provide the opportunity for company officers to practice speaking to groups of people. Additional information on conducting company-level training sessions can be found in Chapter 8, Company-Level Training.

Delivering Speeches and Presentations

Company officers may make such presentations as giving reports to governing boards, public relations talks to community groups, and providing public information to the news media **(Figure 5.7)**. Each type of speech or presentation requires a different approach.

Types of Speeches and Presentations

The primary types of formal speeches and presentations for company officers include:

- Persuasive
- Informative
- Instructional

The company officer will most often make persuasive, informative, and instructional types of speeches. Chapter 8, Company-Level Training, will address the instructional speaking.

Figure 5.7 A company officer may be assigned to provide public information to news media during an incident. *Courtesy of Steven Baker, New South Wales Fire Brigades.*

Persuasive speeches may be difficult to develop and yet can be the most important speeches an officer can give. Describing a problem and supplying a solution is intended to cause change. The following can serve as the basic outline for persuading a group:

I.   Gain the audience's attention with an introduction.

II. Describe the problem and demonstrate a need for a change in the current situation.

III. Present the best solution, provide information and evidence to illustrate how it accomplishes the goal.

IV. Describe the best solution, where it has been successfully used before (if that is the case), example of the results, and how it will affect members of the audience. You may also visualize the results that might occur if the action were not taken.

V.   Provide the audience with the basic steps needed to accomplish the change, which is the basis of the conclusion of the speech. The action steps must be easy and manageable.

Informative speeches are the easiest to develop when supporting data is compiled and analyzed. Company officers use these speeches to:

- Provide status reports.
- Describe events.
- Give project updates.
- Provide unit-level training.
- Educate the public and media.

The topics a speech covers classifies them as informative. These topics include:

- **Ideas** — to explain principles, theories, and concepts.
- **Objects** — to explain a tangible object.
- **Procedures** — to describe how something works or outlines a process.
- **People** — to provide a general overview of a person's life or may focus on one specific event.
- **Events** — to describe an actual event.

Using certain principles, a speaker effectively conveys the informative message to an audience. The informative speech principles are:

- Adapt the topic to the audience.
- Motivate the audience to listen to the speech.
- Use redundancy (Tell them what you're going to tell them, tell them, then tell them what you told them!).
- Use the simple-is-better concept.
- Organize the topic in a logical manner.
- Use clear transitions to move the listener through the topic.
- Use both verbal and nonverbal reinforcement of ideas.
- Use an even flow to deliver the information.
- Build on the familiar.
- Use visual aids sparingly.

Report Presentations

Report presentations provide information, such as a project status report or proposed policy changes. Persuasive speech skills may also be used during budget request presentations to persuade the appropriate governing board to adopt it.

Public Relations Speeches

An organization's public image depends on the quality of service it provides and maintaining a positive image and relationship with the community. Public relations speeches help keep the public informed and address community concerns. These speeches may be informative or persuasive in nature. The speaker must be prepared and maintain a positive, noncombative attitude throughout the presentation.

Public Information Speeches

Company officers may be called upon to speak with the media during prearranged press conferences or impromptu interviews at incident scenes. Media interviews can be a challenge. Company officers should work with the media, be honest and forthright, and follow organizational media relations policies and procedures. Some organizations have a designated public information officer (PIO) assigned to answer media questions on large incidents. At these incidents, company officers should politely direct questions and interview requests to the PIO.

Speech and Presentation Preparation Process

When preparing a speech or presentation, the speaker must remain focused on the intended audience. Canned speeches or presentations prepared can be ineffective because each audience and each occasion is different. However, previously given speeches can be modified for similar audiences and occasions and reused. When preparing a speech or oral presentation, a logical sequence should be followed. The steps of the speech preparation process include:

Step 1:   Select the topic.

Step 2:   Determine the purpose.

Step 3:   Generate ideas.

Step 4:   Develop the central idea.

Step 5:   Gather supporting evidence.

Step 6:   Organize the speech.

Step 7:   Rehearse the speech.

Step 8:   Deliver the speech.

Step 9:   Evaluate the speech.

Written Communications

Company officers may have to prepare written communications, such as reports, press releases, letters, memorandums (memos), electronic mail (e-mail) messages, meeting agendas, minutes, personnel evaluations, policies, and procedures. Written communications must be accurate, concise, and professional in appearance.

The appearance and quality of the document gives the reader an impression of the ability and credibility of the company officer and the organization. Some officers may have clerical staff to assist with the development and writing of a final document. Most company officers have to research, draft, finalize, and edit each document that carries their signature.

Documents are written to educate, persuade, inform, or enlighten. Effective writing helps to ensure that the intended purpose is attained. Technical or business writing courses at local colleges or vocational schools can help company officers assist in mastering effective writing skills. Company officers should be aware that any form of written communication can be considered public record and may be used in legal proceedings.

Social Media

In some organizations, company officers may be tasked with communicating information through social media sites. Although shorthand is common in social media, official communications require the use of formal spelling and grammar conventions. While these sites have become a more common method of communication, it is important to realize that there may be strong organizational restrictions placed upon this usage.

Document Organization

The first step in writing any document is to determine the audience, scope, and purpose. The basic organization of the document is then outlined using an audience definition and scope and purpose statements. Company officers must be familiar with their organizations' policies and procedures for organizing written documents as some organizations have very specific directions for document organization.

Audience, Scope, and Purpose

The audience may be an individual, internal group, or external audience. Knowing the audience helps to keep the writer and the document audience-focused. An audience-focused document is written to the needs, concerns, and levels of understanding of the readers. The document's scope is the subject (topic or thesis statement) and how broad or narrow the coverage of it is. The purpose is why the document is being written. It establishes what the writer wants to accomplish, such as informing the audience of an event or describing a new method or procedure.

Outline

Lengthy or highly technical documents may require an outline. An outline for a written document may follow the same format as one for a speech or for a standard training lesson plan to include an introduction, a body, and a conclusion **(Figure 5.8)**. This outline can be expanded to include additional main points that support the topic sentence. Smooth transitions should be used to tie the parts of the document together. The authority having jurisdiction (AHJ) may have templates that company officers may use to submit important information in a generalized and structured manner. Also, many word processing programs have built-in outlining functions that can help company officers develop an outline.

Outlining the document helps the writer establish the logical flow of the material, placing the strongest points at the beginning and then supporting each point with additional data. Common technical writing practices require that outlines must be balanced with a minimum of two points under each heading. If there is only one point, it becomes part of the heading and is not included as a separate entry. Balance also applies to the use of bullets, numbers, or letters (if there is no 2, then there is no 1).

Headings should be expressed in parallel form. For example, nouns need to be made parallel with nouns, verb forms with verb forms, and so on. Although parallel structure is desired, logical and clear writing should not be sacrificed simply to maintain parallelism.

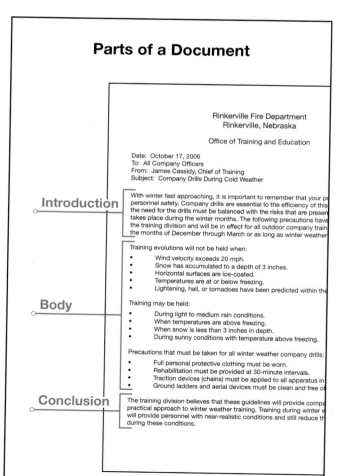

Figure 5.8 The Introduction, Body, and Conclusion are the three main parts of a written document.

Document Writing Guidelines

Once the outline is developed, the text is created within the framework of the outline. Each paragraph needs to contain a topic sentence that announces and controls the content of the paragraph. The topic sentence may occur at the beginning, in the middle, or at the end of a paragraph.

The number of paragraphs depends on the number of subdivisions in the outline. Very long paragraphs tend to slow the reader, while short ones create an impression of a choppy and disjointed document. The average paragraph is 75 to 125 words long, equating to a topic sentence and four or five supporting sentences. Transitional ideas are used to tie paragraphs together and help to maintain the flow and rhythm of a document.

Paragraph Transitions

Transitional words usually come at the end of one paragraph and then at the beginning of the next paragraph. Some common transitions used at the end of a paragraph to indicate summation include the following:

- Briefly
- Finally
- In any case, in any event, in brief, in conclusion, in short, and in summary
- On balance and on the whole
- To summarize

Transitions used at the start of a paragraph include the following categories:

- Showing contrast or qualification — Examples: on the contrary, however, yet, but, nevertheless, in spite of.
- Indicating continuity — Examples: besides, furthermore, in other words, next, to begin with.
- Showing cause and effect — Examples: thus, consequently, as a result, so that, therefore.
- Indicating exemplification — Examples: for example, for instance, to illustrate, namely.

Text Development

Some generally accepted writing guidelines that assist in the development of the text are:

- Be clear
- Get to the point
- Use a minimum of words to convey the message
- Write in a conversational tone, but avoid slang or colloquial expressions
- Use a friendly and positive tone
- Use current and understood words, terms, and phrases
- Avoid jargon
- Avoid long sentences and the use of numerous commas within sentences
- Write in an active voice
- Use parallel structure

- Always proofread a document before finalizing it
- Have someone else proofread it
- Use bullets, numbers, or other indicators for key points
- Use appendices for additional information
- Retain a copy of the written document

Specific Document Types

Generally, the document organization and writing guidelines mentioned earlier can be applied to all company journals/diaries, memos and e-mail messages, letters, press releases, reports, and executive summaries. Agendas and minutes of meetings take a slightly different form because they use a chronological format to either schedule or report the results of a meeting.

The authority having jurisdiction (AHJ) requires a more formal style of procedures, policies, and requests for proposals (RFPs or bid specifications). If the AHJ does not have a formal style for these documents, model forms may be found in technical writing manuals, on the Internet, or acquired from other organizations. Manufacturers usually supply model bid specifications formats upon request.

Company Journal/Diaries

Company officers routinely make written entries into a company journal or diary **(Figure 5.9)**. These may be written in hard copy form or completed digitally. These journals perform a variety of functions, such as:

- Documents the activities of the company for each shift
- Serves as a pass-along log
- Identifies equipment tagged out of service
- Identifies public concerns that need to be forwarded to senior staff
- Documents internal occurrences requiring further action
- Keeps an ongoing record of the company

Figure 5.9 A company journal allows information to be passed from one company to another on a different shift.

Memos and E-mail Messages

A memo is a quick and simple way of transmitting a message within an organization. It is brief and describes what, where, when, who, why, and sometimes how. Memos are valuable because they commit the writer to a certain course of action and provide a chain of communication and evidence of action on a specific topic. Modern memos are generally written digitally, saving time and creating direct communication between the writer and audience. Company officers should remember that memos and e-mails are also considered to be **public record** documents.

Memos are generally sent digitally rather than as hard-copy documents in interoffice mail. The methods for writing memos and e-mails are generally the same. New company officers should take a course in business communication or attend a workshop on memo or e-mail writing to become effective memo creators. Company officers must remember to stay within the organization's chain of command when sending electronic communications.

Organizations may have an e-mail policy that includes information on proper e-mail etiquette, enforcement, training, and monitoring elements. Important reasons for an organization to have such a policy include:

- **Professionalism** — Proper creation and use of e-mails help to convey a professional image.

- **Efficiency** — E-mails provide the necessary information and do not need further explanation.

- **Liability protection** — E-mail content, use, and distribution guidelines can prevent unnecessary legal actions. Avoiding the use of personal e-mail accounts for business related e-mails can eliminate a liability for both the individual and the organization as these e-mail accounts are open for public record and available through the **Freedom of Information Act (FOIA) requests**.

A memo or an e-mail may have one of several purposes, such as requesting information, providing a situation report, issuing a hazard warning, and notifying personnel about a meeting. It should be short and to the point. Lengthy or wordy e-mails may be ignored. An e-mail should only address one issue and never use string e-mails to address issues not identified in the original communication. The majority of memos or e-mails can be written to give the following six pieces of information **(Figure 5.10, p. 122)**:

- **Who** — Assigns responsibility for the task or action.

- **What** — Identifies the task or action that is expected or has been accomplished.

- **When** — Identifies the date and time for and action to take place or it may set a deadline.

- **Where** — Identifies the location of the task or action.

- **Why** — Explains the reason for the action.

- **How** — Describes the steps for implementing the task or action.

General formats. Preprinted memo forms allow the writer to simply fill in the blanks. Computer-generated templates allow the writer to insert information into the form, save the finished product under an appropriate name, mail it electronically, or print it for distribution.

Public Record — Any writing containing information relating to the conduct of government or the performance of any governmental or proprietary function prepared, used, or retained by any state or local agency regardless of form or characteristics.

Freedom of Information Act (FOIA) request — A petition to a federal, state, or local agency for access to records concerning a specific topic, individual, or organization.

Sample E-mail

From:	DeputyChief@clearwater.org	**11/11/2014 8:32:13 AM**
To:	Captain Tim Michaels	
CC:	Station 3 B-Shift Personnel List	
Subject:	Visitors from Philips Fire Department	

Tim,

Just a reminder that Chief Pike, Captain Forbes, and Driver/Operator Moreland will visit Station #3 on December 2, 2014. The purpose of their visit is to inspect Engine 31. Their department is considering purchasing a similar model from the manufacturer and they would like to look one over in person before going to bid.

I know that you and your personnel will ensure that the station and apparatus are prepared for the visit. We want them to see Clearwater FD at our finest!

Let me know if you have any questions.

Thanks!

Rich

Rich Hoff
Deputy Chief
Clearwater Fire Department

Figure 5.10 Modern electronic communications allow fire and emergency services personnel to communicate quickly and effectively by using e-mail.

Value. Ensure that the memo or e-mail carries a strong and professional image of the writer. The writer needs to proofread the memo or e-mail before issuing it. When proofreading, look for:

- Correct spelling
- Correct punctuation
- Correct grammar
- Neatness
- Consistent format
- Concise/accurate content

Cautions about contents. Memos and e-mails can also be a source of embarrassment and legal difficulties. Consider the following cautions about their contents:

- Never put into writing anything that cannot be made public.
- Do not use memos or e-mails for criticisms, reprimands, or personal communications that are best communicated in person.
- Never use sexist, racist, or inappropriate language in memos or e-mails.

- Have memos and e-mails proofread.
- Remember that e-mails cannot be withdrawn once they are sent and will exist forever.

Letters

Letters are generally used with persons, groups, and agencies outside the organization. They are longer, more formal, and often represent the entire organization rather than a specific branch or section. The contents of letters may be similar to memos and e-mails or include information that is normally found in a report.

Comparing the Memo or E-mail and Letter

Memo or E-mail	Letter
Brief	Long
Internal Audience	External Audience
Formal/Informal	Formal
Represents Subunits	Represents the Total Organization

Letters are official documents that should be professional and flawless and require the attention that a report or executive summary gets. To ensure that the letter properly reflects the image of the organization, the writer should:

- Proofread the letter
- Review the letter for accuracy in the content
- Have the superior approve the letter when necessary

Most organizations provide some form of official stationery. Letters may then be printed directly onto the stationery or onto a separate page. A number of general considerations apply to letters to ensure that they reflect the proper image. The organization may require various types of letters, and most have an accepted format.

Accepted format. The physical arrangement of the letter's elements depends on the organization's letterhead stationery and its policies or procedures. The accepted format for most business letters consists of the following parts **(Figure 5.11, p. 124)**:

- Heading
- Opening
- Body
- Closing

General considerations. The following general considerations should be taken into account when developing a letter:

- Consider the tone of the letter.
- Be sincere in the message.

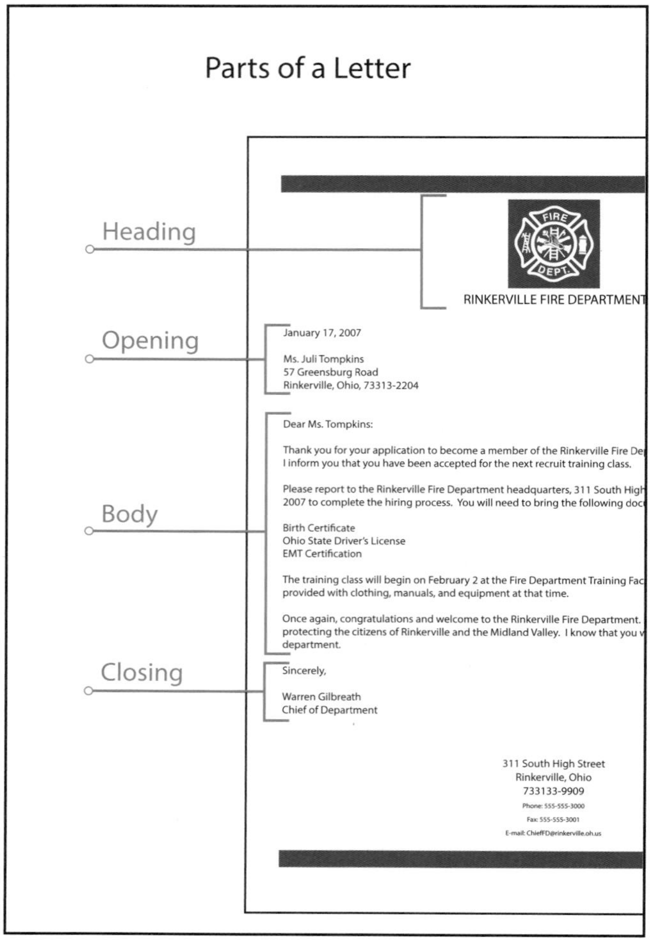

Parts of a Letter

Heading

RINKERVILLE FIRE DEPARTMENT

Opening

January 17, 2007

Ms. Juli Tompkins
57 Greensburg Road
Rinkerville, Ohio, 73313-2204

Body

Dear Ms. Tompkins:

Thank you for your application to become a member of the Rinkerville Fire De[...]
I inform you that you have been accepted for the next recruit training class.

Please report to the Rinkerville Fire Department headquarters, 311 South High[...]
2007 to complete the hiring process. You will need to bring the following doc[...]

Birth Certificate
Ohio State Driver's License
EMT Certification

The training class will begin on February 2 at the Fire Department Training Fac[...]
provided with clothing, manuals, and equipment at that time.

Once again, congratulations and welcome to the Rinkerville Fire Department.[...]
protecting the citizens of Rinkerville and the Midland Valley. I know that you v[...]
department.

Closing

Sincerely,

Warren Gilbreath
Chief of Department

311 South High Street
Rinkerville, Ohio
733133-9909
Phone: 555-555-3000
Fax: 555-555-3001
E-mail: ChiefFD@rinkerville.oh.us

Figure 5.11 The four common parts of a letter: the Heading, Opening, Body, and Closing.

- Make the letter reader-centered (audience-focused).
- Express praise easily and always say "please" and "thank you".
- Make the letter personal when possible.

Reports

Reports constitute a significant amount of a company officer's writing. Reports are public record so company officers should stick to the facts of an incident so that the information is accurate and properly documented. Because reports are subject to being reviewed as a part of litigation, the writer needs to retain a copy of the report and any other notes made at the time of the incident. Personal notes can be subpoenaed and may prove beneficial if the writer is called to testify.

Some reports are simply forms that are completed with specific information concerning an incident or event. Other reports are more like essays, written in narrative, paragraph form and requiring greater thought and organization than form reports.

Form-based. Most company officers complete form-based reports on a daily basis **(Figure 5.12)**. These may include incident reports, injury reports, fire investigation reports, training reports, internal or external inspection reports, or attendance reports. The officer is required to write specific information into spaces or fields in the digital form or on the hard-copy form.

A

| MM | DD | YYYY | | | |

FDID ☆   State ☆   Incident Date ☆   Station   Incident Number ☆   Exposure ☆

☐ Delete
☐ Change
☐ No Activity

NFIRS–1 Basic

B   Location Type ☆   ☐ Check this box to indicate that the address for this incident is provided on the Wildland Fire Module in Section B, "Alternative Location Specification." Use only for wildland fires.

Census Tract ⬚⬚⬚⬚ - ⬚⬚

- ☐ Street address
- ☐ Intersection
- ☐ In front of
- ☐ Rear of
- ☐ Adjacent to
- ☐ Directions
- ☐ US National Grid

Number/Milepost   Prefix   Street or Highway   Street Type   Suffix

Apt./Suite/Room   City   State   ZIP Code

Cross Street, Directions or National Grid, as applicable

C   Incident Type ☆

Incident Type

D   Aid Given or Received ☆   ☐ None

1. ☐ Mutual aid received
2. ☐ Auto. aid received
3. ☐ Mutual aid given
4. ☐ Auto. aid given
5. ☐ Other aid given

Their FDID   Their State

Their Incident Number

E₁   Dates and Times   Midnight is 0000

Check boxes if dates are the same as Alarm Date.

	Month	Day	Year	Hour	Min

ALARM always required
Alarm ☆ ⬚ ⬚ ⬚ ⬚ ⬚

ARRIVAL required, unless canceled or did not arrive
☐ Arrival ☆ ⬚ ⬚ ⬚ ⬚ ⬚

CONTROLLED optional, except for wildland fires
☐ Controlled ⬚ ⬚ ⬚ ⬚ ⬚

LAST UNIT CLEARED, required except for wildland fires
☐ Last Unit Cleared ⬚ ⬚ ⬚ ⬚ ⬚

E₂   Shifts and Alarms   Local Option

Shift or Platoon   Alarms   District

E₃   Special Studies   Local Option

Special Study ID#   Special Study Value

F   Actions Taken ☆

Primary Action Taken (1)

Additional Action Taken (2)

Additional Action Taken (3)

G₁   Resources ☆

☐ Check this box and skip this block if an Apparatus or Personnel Module is used.

	Apparatus	Personnel
Suppression		
EMS		
Other		

☐ Check box if resource counts include aid received resources.

G₂   Estimated Dollar Losses and Values

LOSSES: Required for all fires if known. Optional for non-fires.   **None**

Property $ ⬚,⬚,⬚ ☐
Contents $ ⬚,⬚,⬚ ☐

PRE-INCIDENT VALUE: Optional

Property $ ⬚,⬚,⬚ ☐
Contents $ ⬚,⬚,⬚ ☐

Completed Modules
- ☐ Fire–2
- ☐ Structure Fire–3
- ☐ Civilian Fire Cas.–4
- ☐ Fire Service Cas.–5
- ☐ EMS–6
- ☐ HazMat–7
- ☐ Wildland Fire–8
- ☐ Apparatus–9
- ☐ Personnel–10
- ☐ Arson–11

H₁ ☆ Casualties   ☐ None

	Deaths	Injuries
Fire Service		
Civilian		

H₂   Detector   Required for confined fires.

1. ☐ Detector alerted occupants
2. ☐ Detector did not alert them
U. ☐ Unknown

H₃   Hazardous Materials Release   ☐ None

1. ☐ **Natural gas:** slow leak, no evacuation or HazMat actions
2. ☐ **Propane gas:** <21-lb tank (as in home BBQ grill)
3. ☐ **Gasoline:** vehicle fuel tank or portable container
4. ☐ **Kerosene:** fuel burning equipment or portable storage
5. ☐ **Diesel fuel/fuel oil:** vehicle fuel tank or portable storage
6. ☐ **Household solvents:** home/office spill, cleanup only
7. ☐ **Motor oil:** from engine or portable container
8. ☐ **Paint:** from paint cans totaling <55 gallons
0. ☐ **Other:** special HazMat actions required or spill > 55 gal (Please complete the HazMat form.)

I   Mixed Use Property   ☐ Not mixed

- 10 ☐ Assembly use
- 20 ☐ Education use
- 33 ☐ Medical use
- 40 ☐ Residential use
- 51 ☐ Row of stores
- 53 ☐ Enclosed mall
- 58 ☐ Business & residential
- 59 ☐ Office use
- 60 ☐ Industrial use
- 63 ☐ Military use
- 65 ☐ Farm use
- 00 ☐ Other mixed use

J   Property Use ☆   ☐ None

Structures
- 131 ☐ Church, place of worship
- 161 ☐ Restaurant or cafeteria
- 162 ☐ Bar/tavern or nightclub
- 213 ☐ Elementary school, kindergarten
- 215 ☐ High school, junior high
- 241 ☐ College, adult education
- 311 ☐ Nursing home
- 331 ☐ Hospital

- 341 ☐ Clinic, clinic-type infirmary
- 342 ☐ Doctor/dentist office
- 361 ☐ Prison or jail, not juvenile
- 419 ☐ 1- or 2-family dwelling
- 429 ☐ Multifamily dwelling
- 439 ☐ Rooming/boarding house
- 449 ☐ Commercial hotel or motel
- 459 ☐ Residential, board and care
- 464 ☐ Dormitory/barracks
- 519 ☐ Food and beverage sales

- 539 ☐ Household goods, sales, repairs
- 571 ☐ Gas or service station
- 579 ☐ Motor vehicle/boat sales/repairs
- 599 ☐ Business office
- 615 ☐ Electric-generating plant
- 629 ☐ Laboratory/science laboratory
- 700 ☐ Manufacturing plant
- 819 ☐ Livestock/poultry storage (barn)
- 882 ☐ Non-residential parking garage
- 891 ☐ Warehouse

Outside
- 124 ☐ Playground or park
- 655 ☐ Crops or orchard
- 669 ☐ Forest (timberland)
- 807 ☐ Outdoor storage area
- 919 ☐ Dump or sanitary landfill
- 931 ☐ Open land or field

- 936 ☐ Vacant lot
- 938 ☐ Graded/cared for plot of land
- 946 ☐ Lake, river, stream
- 951 ☐ Railroad right-of-way
- 960 ☐ Other street
- 961 ☐ Highway/divided highway
- 962 ☐ Residential street/driveway

Look up and enter a Property Use code and description only if you have NOT checked a Property Use box.

➡ Property Use ⬚⬚⬚ Code

Property Use Description

NFIRS–1 Revision 01/01/05

Figure 5.12 An example of a form-based report. Company officers only need to fill in the blanks to complete the report.

Form-based reports require certain writing skills that may be taken for granted. Some of these skills are as follows:

- **Legibility** — Text must be printed or typed rather than in script.
- **Accuracy** — Times, addresses, names, quantities, and events must be correct.
- **Completeness** — All available information must be included.
- **Objectivity** — Text must express facts and not opinions; it cannot be subjective.

Narrative. A narrative report may be the result of a form report or it may be generated as part of a project or analysis. Topics may include staff reports, technical reports, detailed incident reports, resource allocation analyses, or business, master, strategic, or work plans. Narrative reports are written in essay form.

The first step in preparing a narrative report is to determine the purpose of the report. The purpose may be to supply required information needed at a specific time or at a predetermined schedule. In other cases, the company officer may decide to provide a report that informs the audience of progress on a project.

Next, the writer must decide who the intended audience will be. Knowing the audience determines the amount of detail used, format, and tone of the report. Annual reports will be formal with details of costs, services, and needs. Brief project updates will be short and informal and include only information that has developed since the last report. Professional jargon should be limited to internal audiences and not used for readers outside the organization.

The writer then determines the format for the report. Types of narrative reports include:

- **Justification** — Focuses on why a certain course of action was taken or should be taken. The report begins with the situation or problem and then provides the solution to the problem and steps taken (or that should be taken) to gain the solution. Example: budget request.
- **Recommendation** — States the problem, provides a variety of solutions, and then recommends the best solution based on the available criteria. Example: station-location report.
- **Progress** — Provides an overview of the current status of a project. It is chronological in nature, beginning with a description of the project and proceeding through the steps to the current point or actual completion. Example: Progress reports required on long-term projects.
- **Progress and justification** — Combines the two forms into one. Provides justification for the project, describes the steps to project completion, and includes justification for any changes in the project development.
- **Description** — Describes a process, project, or item that gives the audience a detailed image of the subject. Examples: Describe a new apparatus design.

With the purpose and format determined, the topic is then thoroughly researched. Background data is assembled from previous reports, personal experience, interviews, analysis, and other documents. Include source citations in the form of footnotes and endnotes and direct the audience to the original material. Footnotes keep the information on the same page and make it easier for the reader to find. Endnotes keep all the notes and citations together in one list at the end of the paper. Endnotes may also contain a larger amount of information, including graphs or tables that will not fit in a footnote.

Once the subject has been researched, an outline is developed based on the format. At least two subtopics support each main topic in the outline. Reports should follow the basic introduction, body, and conclusion format. The narrative report also includes a brief review or executive summary.

Policies and Procedures

A policy is a guide to organizational decision-making. Organizational policies originate with top management and are disseminated to lower levels for implementation. A procedure is a detailed plan of action that is similar and closely related to a policy. Procedures detail in writing the steps to follow in conducting organizational policy for some specific, recurring problem or situation.

Company officers may be called upon to assist in the development or revision of their organizations' policies and procedures. The majority of fire and emergency services organizations have written policies and procedures. These documents may be called different names, including but not limited to: standard operating procedures (SOPs), standard operating guidelines (SOGs), policies and procedures manual (PPM), or general orders (GOs). They contain the mission statement, responsibilities, and authority of the organization and each of its branches and functional positions.

NOTE: Information on the administration of policies and procedures is found in Chapter 6, Administrative Functions.

Rules and Regulations vs. SOPs/SOGs

Rules and regulations are generally written to preclude deviation from the standard being set. SOPs/SOGs are usually written to allow deviation based upon conditions found at an incident.

In the context of this manual, policies define what must be done and procedures describe the steps required to comply with the policies. Procedure manuals may include but are not limited to training manuals, operational manuals, and maintenance manuals.

Basic format. All policy and procedures documents have some basic similarities and generally contain the following:

- Statement of purpose
- Statement of scope
- Contents page
- Procedures or policies organized by specific topic or function
- Appendices containing copies of forms that are referred to in the body of the text

Each agency identifies the basic information to be found at the top of each page to assists the reader in navigating the document. This basic information usually includes the following:

- **Subject** — What the policy or procedure is about
- **Policy or Procedure number** — Number assigned to the specific policy or procedure for tracking purposes
- **Dates** — Original date of implementation plus any revision dates
- **Supersedes** — Procedure number that is replaced with the current page
- **Approvals** — Initials of the authority approving the policy or procedure
- **Distribution** — List of persons or groups to whom the policy or procedure is issued
- **Applicability** — Persons or groups to whom the policy or procedure applies
- **Pages** — Number indicating the position within the document
- **Revision** — Indication of whether the current page is original or a revision
- **Forms used** — Indication of the appropriate form used to fulfill the policy or procedure

Revisions. Policy and procedures manuals must be revised periodically. A master list of the manuals should be created and maintained that includes the individual tracking numbers and locations. Some agencies require that when new pages are distributed, they are signed for to verify receipt and all personnel are notified that changes have been made. Training should be accomplished prior to any new policy or procedure involving major changes or additions is implemented. Organizations that distribute revisions through e-mail need to establish a tracking method to ensure that all personnel and sites have received, read, and understand the material.

Another method for maintaining and updating the PPMs is to load them onto an organization's computer network server, if available, to which all personnel have access. Personnel are then assured of having access to the current version of each policy or procedure. A notice is sent to all work units whenever a policy or procedure is added or updated to ensure all personnel are made aware of the change.

Requests for Proposals and Bid Specifications

Company officers may assist with the development of requests for proposals and bid specifications. A request for proposal (RFP) defines the needs of the organization and allows manufacturers or authorized distributors to decide if they can meet bid specifications. Bid specifications include the organization's specific equipment requirements plus the AHJ's legal requirements. Writing RFPs and bid specifications is a very technical skill. Errors in writing bid specifications can result in the purchase of equipment that does not meet the needs of the organization. The persons assigned the task of writing RFPs or developing bid specifications should be thoroughly trained in the process. Each organization will identify the policies and procedures to be followed in developing RFPs and bid specifications.

Communicating in Emergency Situations

At an emergency scene, the preferred method of communication is direct, face-to-face voice communications; however, effective scene communication usually requires the use of radio or some other form of electronic communication.

Equipment

Company officers must be able to use the communications equipment they have at their disposal and know their jurisdiction's standard communications procedures. Common types of communications equipment that company officers are expected to operate may include:

- Radios
- Pagers
- Telephones
- Fax machines
- Wireless broadband connections
- Mobile data systems
- Geographic information systems (GIS)
- Global positioning systems (GPS)
- Citizen's Band (CB) radios
- Amateur radio systems

Radios

Radios provide instantaneous communication among emergency response companies, between those companies and the telecommunications center, and between companies and the rest of the emergency scene organization. The safety of emergency responders is greatly increased through effective radio communication **(Figure 5.13)**.

Figure 5.13 Radio communications play a critical role in many emergency operations.

Common types of radios used in the fire and emergency services include:

- **Base Radios** – Base radios are normally operated from the jurisdiction's telecommunications center, stations, and other facilities. At large-scale incidents with relatively long durations, a scaled-down base radio may be assembled at an incident command post (ICP) or incident base.

- **Mobile Radios** – Mobile radios are mounted in emergency response vehicles. Modern apparatus design usually includes the primary radio in the cab with remote stations at the pump panel, on the aerial device turntable, or in the basket of an elevating platform. Radios in aircraft may also be used on special incidents, such as wildland fires, airport operations, or medical evacuations.

- **Portable Radios** – (sometimes referred to as walkie-talkies, handy-talkies, or simply portables) Handheld radios that allow personnel to remain in contact with each other while they are away from an apparatus' mobile radio. Portable radios may be operated on multiple channels.

- **Repeater systems** – Repeater systems receive a signal from a radio, boost its power, and then transmit the signal to the receiver. The two primary types of repeater systems include apparatus mounted and those prepositioned in specific geographical areas.

While a small-scale emergency operation can work effectively using a single radio frequency, this practice is not recommended for larger incidents utilizing multiple companies. Additional frequencies may be needed when multiple units from one organization are assigned to an incident or units from different organizations are assigned together.

The number of frequencies needed on an incident depends on the resources involved and size of the incident command function. Each may require one or more radio frequencies on large incidents:

- Command
- Tactical operations
- Support operations
- Air-to-ground communications (aircraft fire/rescue, wildland, or medical evacuation)
- Air-to-air communications (wildland)
- Medical services

Fire and emergency services organizations may have multiple radio frequencies available for their use. Normally, all emergency dispatch functions are on one frequency, routine operations are handled on a second frequency, and additional frequencies (tactical channels) are available for large-scale incidents.

Pagers

Pagers are most often used to notify volunteers, paid-on-call and off-duty career personnel, and staff officers to respond to the station or emergency incident scene. Dialing a specific telephone number activates some pagers. A transmitter tone from the telecommunications center activates most pagers used in fire and emergency services. Pagers provide information to the user in one of two modes: voice message or text message. Many communication centers can send text messages to smart phones and eliminate the need for pagers. With certain smart phone applications (apps), the individual can pull up call information and maps.

Alternative Communications Methods and Technologies

Alternative communications methods and technologies may be required during large-scale, long-duration emergency incidents or if the primary communication system is disrupted or must be abandoned. Their use depends on the level of preparedness of the organization involved in the incident. Examples of alternative communications methods include but are not limited to:

- **Land-Based Telephones** — If radio communications break down, public telephones or field telephones may be used to communicate at large-scale incidents, high-rise incidents, and shipboard and other confined-space incidents. Telephones can be used to send lengthy routine messages instead of tying up emergency radio frequencies.

- **Cellular Telephones** — Cellular telephones that can capture and transmit photos, videos, and access the Internet directly can provide company officers with rapid retrieval of information while not dominating a command radio frequency. Heavy media and public usage may block cellphones and/or smartphones during large-scale incidents. Company officers should be knowledgeable of areas within their jurisdictions where cellular telephone will not work due to a lack of signal coverage.

- **Satellite Telephones** — These wireless telephone systems can provide reliable communications that are free of the limitations and interference that characterize the other types of telephonic communications. Some satellite telephones can operate as radios, communicating with other units within the coverage area.

- **Fax Machines** — Fax machines normally transmit signals over land-based telephone lines, but they may be operated through cellular telephone systems. Fax machines can be very useful for transmitting and receiving written documents, such as situation status reports, building plans, hazardous chemical data, and weather updates. At major emergency scenes, the incident base or ICP may have one or more fax machines.

- **Wireless Broadband Connections** — Modern computer technologies allow voice and image transfer, allowing real-time photo and video images to be transferred rapidly though this system. Broadband connections (high-speed Internet access) are at least 10 times faster than modems. These connections allow easily viewed, full-screen images, such as preincident maps and photos, to be transferred and viewed on a computer screen rather than smaller, postage stamp size images. Web-based software programs and online file storage can be accessed from remote locations.

- **Mobile Data Terminal** — An MDT is a radio-operated data terminal that allows a telecommunications center to transmit dispatch information, incident/patient status information, confidential messages that are not appropriate for verbal transmission over a radio, chemical information, and maps and charts to units at or en route to an incident scene.

One style of MDT looks like a small personal computer mounted on a pedestal near a vehicle's dashboard. Another style resembles a laptop computer that can be pulled from the vehicle and used in a remote location if needed. Many MDTs are also equipped with status buttons that allow the telecommunications center to be aware of the unit's status (en route, on scene, or available) without the need for verbal radio transmissions.

- **Mobile Data Computer** — An MDC has all of the features of an MDT with the addition of a keyboard that allows two-way communication between the mobile units and the telecommunications center **(Figure 5.14)**. An MDC allows complete messages to be transmitted and received in the vehicle, facilitating two-way communications that are not appropriate for radio transmission.

- **Geographic Information System** — A GIS is designed to provide a computer-readable description of geographic features in a given area. A mobile computer can store data and display that data in suitably equipped apparatus throughout the jurisdiction. Information such as addresses and occupancy information on

Figure 5.14 Company officers should become familiar with using mobile data computers installed in their apparatus.

individual structures may be stored in a GIS. This information may be useful to telecommunicators, responders, incident commanders, planning personnel, and technical specialists assigned to an incident.

- **Global Positioning System** — Common uses of GPS devices include: dispatching the closest available units to an emergency, tracking units at emergency scenes, and determining specific coordinates during emergencies, such as wildland fires. GPS may also be used to track individual responders at incidents, making it easier to locate lost or unconscious personnel.

- **Citizens Band (CB) Radios** — Used in some small, rural jurisdictions, CB radios are relatively inexpensive and many small organizations do not have the financial resources to purchase standard mobile radios for their apparatus.

- **Amateur Radio Networks** — Volunteer ham radio operators have access to extensive radio communications networks and equipment. Through their base stations and mobile and portable radios, ham operators can access repeaters, satellites, and telephone systems. Drills should be held with ham operators to practice notification and mobilization procedures.

Interoperability

Interoperability is the ability of a system to work with and use the parts or equipment of another system **(Figure 5.15)**. Communications interoperability means that agencies should be able to coordinate their response and activities within the organization and with other responding organizations through compatible communication devices. This interoperability is a vital part of implementing the National Incident Management System (NIMS) during emergency response.

Organizations that routinely work together on emergency incidents should have the ability to communicate with each other using portable or mobile radios on common or mutual aid frequencies. If that capability does not exist, it

Figure 5.15 Interoperability can expand an organization's communications abilities to other agencies or organizations during emergency operations.

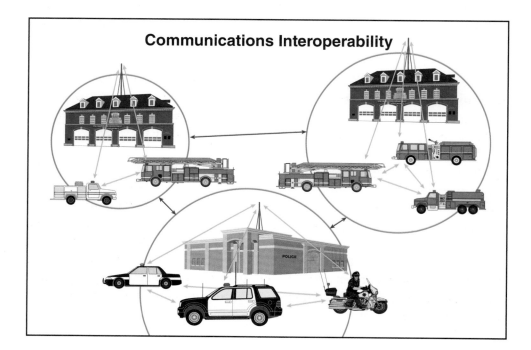

may be necessary to provide mutual aid companies with portable radios once they are on the scene to ensure proper communications.

Four key objectives in the development of the standards were to:

1. Provide enhanced functionality with equipment and capabilities for public safety needs.
2. Improve spectrum efficiency.
3. Ensure competition among multiple vendors through open systems architecture.
4. Allow effective, efficient, and reliable intra-agency and interagency communications.

Procedures

Incident communications procedures are often agency specific. Each organization should have a communications management policy that defines the procedures and language to be used during routine activities and emergency operations. Company officers and personnel must be knowledgeable about their organizations' policies and procedures for incident communications.

Communication procedures must accomplish two objectives:

1. Establish the use of specific common terms (clear text) that mean the same thing to all emergency response personnel.
2. Establish a system of transmitting periodic progress reports to keep all units current on the progress of an incident.

Company officers have an obligation to learn and use correct radio terminology. The term "clear text" is meant to encourage the use of plain English and refrain from codes such as "ten-codes" that can differ between agencies. Specific terms are used to describe apparatus and standard operational modes and functions. Many other terms have specific meanings and applications in clear text. Despite the fact that clear text has been in use for decades, some of the most common misuses of radio terminology occur in the area of resource identification. A common confusion is the use of the word "tanker" rather than "water tender."

The NIMS-Incident Command System (NIMS-ICS) made the adoption and use of clear text radio communications mandatory. This adoption is intended to increase the interoperability between all emergency services organizations. At major interagency incidents, all agencies must adhere to the NIMS-ICS communications procedures in states that have adopted NIMS.

Radio Communications

Radio communications allow units in the field to exchange critical or pertinent tactical information during emergency operations. The information exchanged can be task-related; for example, *Command, Engine 7; we need an additional supply line to support Truck 37's ladder pipe*. The information can also be a direct order based upon the decision of the incident commander; for example, *Communications, Penn Command; dispatch an additional pumper and rescue unit to this incident. Have all companies report to Staging at 5th and Penn Streets.*

The news media, the public, and the FCC can monitor all radio communications. Radio operators should always be careful to not transmit any message that might reflect badly on the organization or provide confidential patient information. Company officers are responsible for the radio discipline and conduct of their crews. Company officers and their subordinates must be careful around any radio and consider all microphones as open (activated) and transmitting.

Effective communications require a knowledge of basic radio communications, the ability to recognize and transmit essential information, and how to give direct orders over the radio. These topics are addressed in the sections that follow.

The Five Cs of Radio Communication

During an emergency, there is no time for company officers to stop and think about the correct method of radio communication. The five Cs of radio communication include:

- **Conciseness** — Messages should be as concise as possible to avoid congesting assigned frequencies. Company officers must plan their transmissions before keying the microphone. Messages should be specific, task-oriented, and directed at companies, not individuals.

- **Clarity** — Company officers should combine clarity with simplicity and describe only one task at a time. Orders issued to different units must be sufficiently spaced to avoid any question that separate orders are being transmitted.

- **Confidence** — Company officers must show confidence (also known as command presence) when using communication equipment. Using a calm, natural tone and speaking at a controlled rate, they can communicate confidence.

- **Control** — The incident commander and telecommunicator should follow established radio protocols. Requiring the receiver to repeat the message back to the sender reduces the chances of misunderstanding.

- **Capability** — Effective communication depends on capable (well-trained) senders and receivers. Capability is not limited to technical proficiency; it also includes the abilities to communicate, listen effectively, and initiate effective messages. Company officers must be able to exercise emotional control, remain calm under stress, and follow established communication procedures.

Basic Radio Communication Procedures

Emergency responders must train with their radios as much as they train on their SCBA, rope systems, hose streams, and ladders. Failure to understand how to use the radio can lead to catastrophic outcomes for individuals, the company, and the agency. Every crew member must be trained on the following topics:

- Basic radio operation
- Radio frequency assignments and usage

- Organizational radio procedures to be followed in both routine and emergency activities
- Radio safety (such as using intrinsically safe radios in potentially explosive atmospheres)
- Radio care and maintenance (such as keeping radios clean and changing or recharging batteries)

//

CAUTION

Using an incorrect frequency could result in a delay of assistance or total communications failure. In some cases, help for trapped firefighters was delayed because their mayday calls were transmitted over the wrong radio frequency and units at the scene did not hear the calls.

Company officers must also know the limitations of their radio equipment. Some types require a *line-of-sight* between transmitter and receiver, while others may benefit from the use of a repeater system that strengthens the transmission **(Figure 5.16)**. Some systems cannot penetrate structural members of certain buildings, making transmissions impossible between radios within the building and those outside the building. When limitations exist, alternate communication methods should be located. Protocols should be established for working in areas that may obstruct transmissions.

Essential information. One potential problem with the use of clear text is that some radio operators may ramble while transmitting. Company officers should monitor their crews' radio usage and ensure that personnel follow procedures and keep radio messages short and to the point. Only essential information should be transmitted, and proper radio formats should be used.

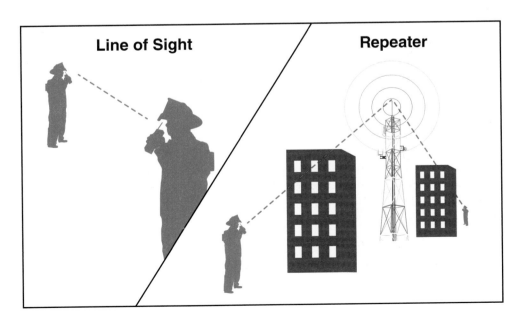

Line of Sight

Repeater

Figure 5.16 The use of repeater systems can help overcome line of site communications problems.

Direct orders. An example of a direct order: *Ladder 65, Operations — ventilate the roof.* A direct order can provide extra information, such as who is to carry out the task and why, how, when, and where it must be done. The officer issuing the order must consider the urgency of the task and capabilities of the individual or unit to whom the order is given.

Chapter Summary

Having a thorough understanding of effective communication during nonemergency and emergency situations is important to all company officers. Nonemergency communications can include interpersonal communication, making presentations, or providing written communications with employees and customers that are external to the organization. Emergency communications can include transmitting and receiving messages during an emergency event.

When delivering nonemergency communications in written form or through an oral presentation, it is important to be accurate and provide a professional appearance are critical elements. It is important to remember that with all forms of communication, the company officer must deliver the information so that the audience understands and acts upon the presentation.

During emergency events, proper communications are an essential part of operational effectiveness and safety. Company officers play a pivotal role in distributing information during these incidents, including orders to crews and situational status reports. It is essential for the company officer to know what communications equipment is available to them, how to use it effectively, and how to be a positive role model for their crew members.

Review Questions

1. What are the components of verbal and nonverbal communication? (pp. 109-111)

2. What components of verbal and nonverbal communication are involved in the active process of listening? (pp. 111-112)

3. What are the differences between persuasive and informative presentations? (p. 115)

4. What are some basic differences between common written document types? (pp. 120-128)

5. What are the five Cs of radio communication? (p. 134)

Learning Activities

Learning Activity 5-1

Objective 6: Compose a written document relating to the fire service.

Company officers must be able to write letters, memos, and other reports that have clear purpose and organization.

For this activity, you will need access to the following resources:

- A computer with a word processing program
- A printer, e-mail access, or other way to transfer the document

Using the following scenario, compose a short, formal letter that demonstrates good written communication skills that include accuracy, concision, and professionalism.

Scenario:

Your station's open house celebrated the dedication of a new apparatus on October 5th. A few days later, you and your chief are discussing the event's proceedings. The mayor gave a short speech at the ceremony that praised the fire department's work and stressed the importance of fire safety to the attendees. Your chief wants to properly thank the mayor and asks you to write a letter to formally do so.

Answer Key:

Answers for this activity will vary; however, your letter should include the following:

- Clear purpose and organization
- A formal and professional tone
- Proper grammar, and error-free punctuation and spelling
- Accurate information

Learning Activity 5-2

Objective 7: Apply the interpersonal communications model to common firefighter scenarios.

Company officers must be able to assign tasks and responsibilities to crew members clearly, concisely, and completely in both emergency and nonemergency situations.

For this activity, you will need access to the following resources:

- Another student or partner to whom you can present your information.

Using the following scenarios, verbally assign any necessary tasks to crew members clearly, concisely, and completely, and answer any questions or comments that may arise.

Scenario 1:

Today is cleaning day at the station. Firefighter Ramirez and Driver/Operator Burke are normally assigned to cleaning the new apparatus, but you realize that Firefighter Tipton, the rookie, has been sweeping the bay on cleaning day for a long time. You feel that she deserves to learn some new skills, and you contemplate having her help clean the apparatus today. However, Ramirez enjoys washing the apparatus, doesn't like sweeping, and has seniority.

Answer Key:

Answers for this activity will vary; however, your instructions should address the following:

- Which tasks are assigned to which crew members
- A timeline for completion
- Any safety considerations
- Any special instructions to individual crew members
- The reasons for your assignments
- Answers to any anticipated questions or comments you may encounter

Scenario 2:

You are first to arrive at a fire scene involving a local restaurant in Engine 3. Several customers and employees are already outside, and you can see black smoke coming from the back of the building. As you come to a stop, Engine 5 radios that they will be on scene in one minute.

Answer Key:

Answers for this activity will vary; however, your instructions should address the following:

- Which tasks are assigned to which crew members
- A timeline for completion
- Any safety considerations
- Any special instructions to individual crew members
- The reasons for your assignments
- Answers to any anticipated questions or comments you may encounter

Administrative Functions

Chapter Contents

chapter 6

NFPA® Job Performance Requirements

This chapter provides information that addresses the following job performance requirements of NFPA® 1021, *Standard for Fire Officer Professional Qualifications* (2014).

4.4.1

4.4.2

4.4.3

4.4.5

4.6.3

5.6.2

Administrative Functions

Learning Objectives

After reading this chapter, students will be able to:

1. Explain the customer service concept in relation to the fire service. [NFPA® 1021, 5.6.2]

2. Describe the function of policies and procedures in administrative duties. [NFPA® 1021, 4.4.1, 4.4.2, 4.4.3, 4.6.3]

3. Identify the budget process. [NFPA® 1021, 4.4.3]

4. Define the role of records management in administrative duties. [NFPA® 1021, 4.4.2, 4.4.5]

5. Propose a revision to existing departmental procedures. [NFPA® 1021, 4.4.1; Learning Activity 6-1]

6. Develop a budget request for a specific departmental need. [NFPA® 1021, 4.4.3; Learning Activity 6-2]

7. Maintain a log of routine, unit-level administrative functions. [NFPA® 1021, 4.4.2, 4.4.5; Learning Activity 6-3]

Chapter 6
Administrative Functions

Case History

A group of assistant chiefs and company officers of a large fire and emergency services organization was assigned to review and update the organization's policies and procedures manual. The task proved difficult due to the size of the organization and its extensive geographic area. It was difficult for personnel to attend meetings due to their routine and emergency response duties and responsibilities. Suggested changes were made and discussed only during the occasional meetings. These and other impediments put the project behind schedule.

While attending a fire and emergency services conference, one young company officer from the group learned of online programs that might be of assistance. Upon returning to work, he suggested using two online collaborative programs. One program allows the sharing of the documents digitally with the team, and the other program provides online meetings to allow team members to attend the meetings more often. The team's collaborative process improved dramatically, major improvements were made to the organization's policies and procedures, and the project was soon ahead of schedule. Use of these and other online programs became part of the organization's policies and procedures. The young company officer was rewarded with a new role in the organization's administration section with additional authority and responsibilities.

Company officers may often be assigned a number of administrative functions. These functions may include but are not limited to:

- Providing customer service
- Preparing and administering policies and procedures
- Preparing or assisting in the preparation of the organization's budget

Over the last couple of decades, the fire and emergency services organizations have had to adopt a customer service focus. Company officers and their personnel play a vital role in their organization's customer service concept. These personnel are often the first to meet with the public who rely on the organization's services, both non-emergency and emergency.

Company officers must deal with written policies and procedures on a daily basis. They must comply, enforce, and educate their personnel on the policies and procedures in effect and may participate in the revision of these or the development of new ones. Company officers should be thoroughly familiar with their organization's policies and procedures and with the methodologies their organizations use to revise and develop them.

Company officers should know the types of records that they are required to develop, maintain, and store and how to access these records. They should be familiar with electronic data storage and recovery and the computer system and programs their organization uses.

This chapter describes the customer service concept, policies and procedures, the budget process, and records management. While these topics could each fill numerous books, this book will focus on how the company officer manages these topics.

Customer Service Concept

The groups of people the fire and emergency service organizations serve are often referred to as customers. Fire and emergency services organizations provide services to internal employees, external beneficiaries, and stakeholders **(Figure 6.1)**.

The customer service concept is valuable to any organization. In the private sector, the bottom line is the profit or loss of the business. In emergency services organizations, customer satisfaction and the value you bring to the community is the bottom line.

The public must believe that they are getting quality service for the taxes and fees they pay. A dissatisfied public can demand change in leadership or how the service is provided.

In order to ensure that the proper level of customer service is being provided, company officers should strive to meet the following objectives:

- Generate productive professional relationships with the customers and implement organizational strategic plans.
- Form individualized relationships with stakeholders within organizational policies and procedures.
- Educate their personnel about the community's expectations.

Figure 6.1 Examples of a fire and emergency services organization's customer base.

Customer Base

It is important to define who the customers are and monitor their changing attitudes. All fire and emergency services organizations have the following types of customers:

- **Internal customers** — Employees and members of the organization, including emergency personnel, administrative staff, and officers. Each group will have its own wants and needs.

- **External customers** — Members of the general population within the service area who are beneficiaries of the services provided and people responsible for providing the majority of the funds needed to operate the organization. They are not a homogeneous group of people who have the same needs, wants, and desires.

Needs, Wants, and Desires

Humans have basic needs, general wants, and very specific desires. These three terms are often confused with one another. A comparison of needs, wants, and desires is as follows:

- I need transportation.
- I want a car.
- I desire a luxury sport utility vehicle (SUV).

The needs, wants, and desires of people are not constant or static. They vary with the individual customer from day to day and even moment to moment. Many organizations or municipalities have suffered revenue shortfalls, limiting the amount and method for raising funds while still being expected to maintain or increase the previous levels of service. It is beneficial to company officers to identify the customers, monitor their changing expectations, and communicate this information to their organization.

Internal Customers

Internal customers are those within the organization. Their wants include but are not limited to:

- Fair compensation
- Reasonable benefits
- Position security
- Rewarding experiences
- Safe working environments
- Ethical leadership
- Dignity that comes from respectful management
- Feeling of being an integral part of an organization

In career and combination organizations, the labor/management agreement and/or civil service process where one exists satisfies most of the tangible needs. Chief officers, company officers, and members who compose the workgroup supply the intangible needs.

External Customers

While the specific needs of external customers vary, the basic needs are generally protection of their lives and property from the effects of fires and other hazards and access to competent emergency medical care. As the demographics of the service area change, services need to keep pace with them.

Information-Gathering Methods

Information on the needs, wants, and desires of customers can be gathered through a passive method where the organization simply waits for a customer to express a specific need, want, or desire. This approach takes very little effort in terms of time or money. The problem with this approach is that it is reactive, is crisis-oriented, and can be biased. When a customer has finally expressed an opinion, the problem may already exist and will require an immediate change.

A second, more active approach takes the initiative and seeks information on a regular basis from internal and external customers and stakeholders. This approach may be accomplished through periodic meetings, surveys, and informal interviews **(Figure 6.2)**. Each of these ways is based on the concept of feedback. Listening to feedback is a primary method for determining the needs, wants, and desires of any of the three groups of customers. The company officer may be involved in the collection of information using the feedback approach.

Meetings

Allowing customers to be involved in the decision-making process at meetings benefits the organization. Internal customers view this involvement as empowerment that can improve their morale and productivity. Examples of meetings include:

- Supervisor and an employee
- Division manager and subordinates
- Administration and labor organization representatives

Surveys

Company officers may provide or conduct surveys, which are another method for gathering information from customers. These surveys may be conducted following an emergency response (for example, a fire or an EMS response) to determine the customer's satisfaction with the service provided. Customer surveys also identify the services that external customers believe should be provided.

Informal Interviews

Company officers may conduct informal interviews with their subordinates. The interviews are opportunities to determine if changes are needed in the work environment, policies, or other work-related issues. These interviews may identify the first indicators of potential trends that may affect others in the workgroup.

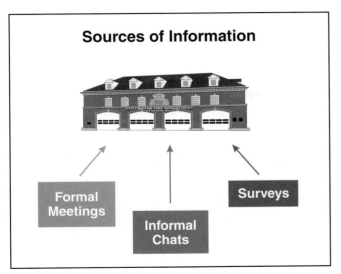

Figure 6.2 Information can be gathered through formal meetings, informal interviews or chats, and surveys.

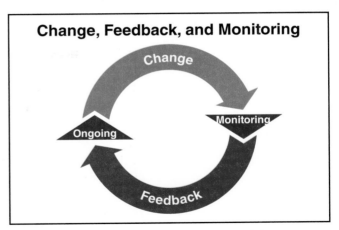

Figure 6.3 An example of a change-feedback loop.

Information Interpretation

Gathering information on customers and their needs/wants/desires is only the beginning of the customer service process. Those needs/wants/desires must then be analyzed to determine operational change suggestions, fiscal requirements, and priorities.

Service-Delivery Monitoring

To determine the success or failure of any change in service, the organization monitors the outcome of the change. This monitoring occurs over the life of the change, usually at specified periods, such as monthly, semiannually, or annually. Meetings, interviews, and surveys are used to monitor the change. When feedback indicates that needs are being adequately and efficiently met, monitoring will then be used to determine whether they change over time, requiring an alteration in the service level in the future **(Figure 6.3)**.

Policies and Procedures

Written policies and procedures are essential for the effective and efficient operation of any fire and emergency services organization. They document the organization's expectations based on its organizational model and strategic and operational plans. An organization may use the following methods to ensure that policies and procedures are fully understood and complied with:

- Distribute in written or electronic format.
- Post in a conspicuous place in all facilities.
- Verify that personnel have received the communication.

  Policies and procedures are also known as:

- Standard operating procedure (SOP)
- Standard operating guideline (SOG)
- Administrative policies and procedures
- Policies and procedures

Policies and procedures must contain information that is current and appropriate. The organization should have an established process to evaluate the need for creating new policies and procedures and revising existing ones. Policies and procedures are continually monitored for effectiveness.

Company officers must explain organizational policies and procedures to subordinates and new employees as part of their training. Whenever company officers learn of a new relevant law or regulation from any level of government, they have an obligation to inform their superiors about it. This information helps determine if new organizational policies and procedures are needed to comply with the new legislation. In some jurisdictions, accepted practices that deviate from written policies or procedures may legally become a policy or procedure.

Policies

As previously stated, a policy is a guide to organizational decision-making. Organizational policies originate with top management and are disseminated to lower levels for implementation. Policies not only aid in decision-making, but they also define the boundaries and standards that the administration expects company officers and members to use.

Policies are created when formal written guidelines or criteria are needed for the operation of the organization. Policies are placed and maintained in physical (manuals) or electronic forms (organization's intranet). Some policies are the result of government regulations. A policy analysis is performed when changes in operations require changes in policies.

Some policies result from an appeal to management for guidance in making decisions about exceptional situations. This appeal is moved upward in the organization's hierarchy until it reaches someone who has the authority to make the decision. The decision-maker may write a policy for handling similar cases in the future. A company officer may make a decision in order to resolve a problem, and this decision serves as a precedent that evolves into organizational policy.

The company officer's duty regarding policies is to understand and apply them fairly and consistently. Correct interpretation and application of organizational policies may require consultation (through the chain of command) with the administration. Formal instruction in organizational policies and their interpretations is necessary for all members of the organization (**Figure 6.4**).

Policy Analysis

A policy analysis determines if current policies are effective and enforceable, or if the lack of policies caused problems. This analysis often occurs when an organization is experiencing internal difficulty. The analysis process takes time and effort and may require the assistance of an outside agency such as the authority's legal department or human resources department. If the problems are not severe, the organization can form an internal committee or task force to provide the analysis.

Figure 6.4 Senior officers need to ensure their subordinates fully understand organizational policies and procedures.

Government Laws or Ordinances

Federal mandates, state/provincial regulations, local government laws, codes, and ordinances sometimes impose policies upon fire and service organizations. For example, the federal government imposed equal employment opportunity practices.

Policy Manual

Policies must be communicated throughout the organization to make the administration's intent clear. Written policies give members of the organization a reference point for decision-making. Collectively, these policies form the organization's policy manual. Organized, well-drafted policies promote consistent, uniform practices throughout the organization and more predictable outcomes in the field.

Procedures

A procedure details in writing the steps to follow in conducting organizational policy for some specific, recurring problem or situation. Procedures may be developed with input from the company level because these individuals will be responsible for following and implementing procedures to meet corresponding policies.

Most organizations provide personnel with detailed information for handling specific situations. SOPs provide a consistent point of reference that helps all members of the organization perform to a measurable standard. They can reduce misunderstandings about techniques, responsibilities, and procedures. SOPs are the basis for company-level skills training, such as initial fire attack, use of the Incident Command System (ICS), rapid intervention crew (RIC) procedures, fire ground search and rescue and more. It should be noted that in emergency services it is impossible to create an SOP for every situation that may be encountered.

Revision and Monitoring Process

The organization should establish a process for revising policies and procedures. The company officers should be familiar with the process. A decision-making model described earlier in this manual may be applied to this process. Examples of when policies and procedures should be revised include:

- Is there a specific timetable for revision?
- Do conditions or circumstances cause a policy or procedure to need revision?
- Do the policies or procedures require any revisions?

Indications that a policy or procedure needs to be revised may include the following:

- Internal/external customer complaints
- Increase in policy or procedure infractions
- Injuries or property loss due to a failure of the policy or procedure
- Change in the resources used to accomplish the task
- Change in the problem that the policy or procedure was intended to solve
- New technology
- Legal mandates

Company officers must communicate any concerns or problems with the policies and procedures to their supervisors. As the first level of supervision within the organization, company officers are responsible for administering policies and procedures and reporting any problems that occur when using or enforcing them.

Figure 6.5 Company officers assign tasks at an emergency by issuing orders.

Orders and Directives

Orders and directives can be used interchangeably depending upon the organization and are based upon the authority delegated to the company officer. Company officers may issue many verbal or written orders and directives. At an emergency incident, they are both considered mandatory because of the situation.

Issuing orders at an emergency incident is an important company officer supervisory duty **(Figure 6.5)**. Orders also aid in training and developing cooperation. Properly given orders result in the need for less supervision in the future as members learn what is expected of them.

Company officers must control their emotions when issuing orders at emergencies. Detection of any anxiety, uneasiness, or extreme excitement in company officers can influence the emotions and performance of firefighters in their companies. Emergency incident orders must be issued calmly, clearly, concisely, and completely. This duty requires strong leadership abilities and a command presence on the part of the company officer.

Another supervisory duty of company officers involves issuing and enforcing unpopular orders. Sometimes the administration establishes policies and procedures that may adversely affect firefighters. It falls to company officers to implement and enforce these orders.

To develop support for an unpopular order, company officers should find out why the order was issued. Chief officers do not issue orders frivolously, so they must have good reasons for issuing a controversial one. Company officers should make every effort to find out what those reasons are so they can explain the necessity for the order and answer any questions that their subordinates might have.

Budget Process

Every fire and emergency services organization must have a budget with which to operate. In this manual, budgets refer to the narrow financial budget that lists both proposed expenditures (personnel pay, benefits, facilities, apparatus, materials, utilities, and insurance) and expected revenue sources.

The revenues that fund the organization's budget may come from a variety of sources. Common revenue sources include but are not limited to:

- Taxes
- Fees
- Fundraising events
- Private and corporate donations
- Government subsidies and grants

Company officers must be able to prepare budget requests to obtain the items needed to operate their particular companies or sections. They must understand the types of budgets normally used in their organization, types of revenue sources available, and the steps of the budget process itself. While local laws and ordinances vary, basic budgetary theory remains the same among jurisdictions.

Historically, company officers have not had direct control over the budget allotted at the company level. More recently, an increasing number of jurisdictions have assigned budget responsibilities to the company officer. The benefits to the organization include the reduction of delays in performing general maintenance and obtaining disposable items. It also provides some experience for company officers to work with a budget and make decisions accordingly.

Budget Types

Company officers may be responsible for preparing budget requests to obtain the items needed to operate their unit, station, or section. Public organizations use two types of budgets: capital budgets (projected major purchases) and operating budgets (recurring expenses of day-to-day operation). It's important to understand that in most cases funds cannot be transferred between capital and operating budgets based on governing authorities.

Capital

A capital budget includes projected major purchases — items that cost more than a certain specified amount of money and are expected to last more than 1 year (usually 3 or more years). Fire apparatus and vehicles, equipment, and facilities are typical capital items for fire and emergency services organizations.

Operating

An organization's operating budget is used to pay for the recurring expenses of day-to-day operations. The largest single item in the operating budget of most career organizations is personnel costs — salaries and benefits. Personnel costs (sometimes called personnel services) may represent as much as 90 percent of the operating budget. Considering that noncash (fringe) benefits cost some jurisdictions an amount equal to 50 percent of a person's base salary, it is easy to understand why the personnel-services category represents such a high percentage of the budget. Operating budgets also pay for the following:

- Utilities
- Office supplies
- Apparatus and vehicle fuel
- Janitorial supplies
- Contract services for the maintenance of apparatus and facilities
- Other items needed on a daily basis

Process Steps

Budget development is an involved and ongoing process. The steps involved in the budget process are planning, preparing, implementing, monitoring and evaluating, and revising **(Figure 6.6)**.

Planning

The budget planning process continues throughout the current fiscal year. Budgets are planned for the next fiscal year using:

- Tax projections
- Expected grants and subsidies
- Expected fees for services
- Bond sales
- Funds from other sources

Preparation

Estimated revenues from all sources are translated into preliminary budget priorities. Organizations may be informed of general fiscal conditions and what parameters to work within during department budget planning and preparation sessions. Preparation sessions will take into account the types of spending (fixed cost, discretionary, and emergency). Other considerations in preparation include:

- **Justifications** — Justifying a budget request requires documentation and supporting evidence that proves the request is valid. Thorough research and internal records are the basis for this documentation. This information is not only used to justify the budget request, it is also used to prepare the budget.

- **Internal reviews** — The organization's administrator, the chief/manager of the department/organization, or staffs of both organizations thoroughly review the fire and emergency services budget request. After the internal review, the budget is incorporated into the combined budget request for the entire parent organization and submitted to the jurisdiction's governing body for an external review.

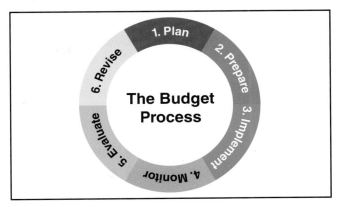

Figure 6.6 Illustrating the steps in the budget process.

- **External reviews** — The external review is the final review that the budget-request document receives. The governing body of the jurisdiction schedules one or more public hearings so that citizens of the jurisdiction can have input on the budget. The budget may be revised in light of citizen interests or concerns.

Implementation

The approved and adopted budget represents a plan for the organization's operation for the fiscal year. Once approved and adopted, the administrator, department heads, managers, and supervisors will have the funds to turn budgets into reality. The budget identifies whether new personnel can be hired, staff cuts will be necessary, vacant positions can be filled, and new equipment can be purchased. Company officers can explain the adopted budget to subordinates and clarify any misconceptions that may exist.

Monitoring and Evaluating

The budget process does not end with the implementation of the budget. The budget must be monitored and evaluated in order to determine its effectiveness and prevent a budgetary crisis in the event of a change in the economic environment. The processes for monitoring and evaluating a budget are often identified in the organization's policies and procedures.

Revision

A budget may have to be revised during the budget cycle. Causes may include:

- Decrease in revenue

- Increase in operating costs

- Underestimation of actual costs

- Increase in service requirements

- Change in labor/management agreement

- Unforeseen or catastrophic occurrence

Records Management

Company officers must also be familiar with *records management*, which is the systematic control of an organization's records to ensure quick access to information. Records management programs need to allow personnel to input and extract information effectively. Supervisors must understand the records management process of an organization. An organization's records management system may perform the following actions:

- Operate efficiently and effectively.
- Prepare short-, medium-, and long-range plans.
- Meet legal and AHJ obligations and requirements.
- Meet the expectations of internal and external customers and stakeholders.
- Identify and safeguard historically important records.
- Assign tasks and identify responsible individuals.

Systematic management of records assists the organization in performing the following actions:

- Know what records the organization has and how to locate them easily.
- Save administrative costs, both in staff time and storage capacity.
- Support decision-making processes.
- Be accountable.
- Monitor the accomplishment of strategic goals and objectives.
- Provide administrative continuity in the event of a disaster.
- Protect the interests of internal and external customers and stakeholders.

Company officers generate raw data and create reports that become part of the system. They may also be responsible for analyzing information for the purpose of assisting in decision-making, establishing, or monitoring trends. Company officers must follow their organization's record management system and strive for accuracy in the collection of data used in records and reports.

Record Types

Fire and emergency services organizations primarily maintain budget, inventory, maintenance (preventive and corrective), activity, and personnel records. Personnel records include categories such as:

- Training
- Performance
- Attendance
- Hazardous materials or biological/medical exposures
- Medical

Budget

Budget records may include all information used to create them, budget status reports, past budgets, and budget requests that were not funded. Purchasing records, contracts, surplus sales, and other similar records should also be retained with this information.

Company officers should maintain the data they used to create their budget requests, justifications for requests, and processes used to generate requests. They should also maintain all records relating to purchases or purchase requests that they make and what has been spent on each item. This information is necessary when federal grants are reviewed.

Inventory

The administration or logistics branch of the organization generally maintain inventory and fixed-assets records. These records should be accurate and include information on all materials, equipment, facilities, land, and apparatus in the possession of the organization.

A copy of all inventory records for the unit's apparatus, personnel, and facility should be maintained. Company officers may be responsible for performing periodic inventories of their areas of responsibility. Any changes in inventory must be noted, reported, and, in some cases, justified.

Company officers may need to establish and maintain an inventory of necessary supplies at each station. The facility may be stocked with disaster preparedness supplies in the event of a natural disaster or other uncontrollable circumstances. Each station should be prepared to operate for a number of hours without the ability to procure certain items.

Officers can often order supplies through an on-line program arranged through the organization or they may work with local vendors and companies to maintain the supplies in the station. The organization may already have certain vendors of choice that officers can utilize. Supplies can be obtained with a purchase order or with an organizational credit card. Some organizations (based on their size) place the responsibility of operating a department purchasing program to company officers under the direction of a chief officer.

Maintenance

Fire and emergency services organizations keep maintenance records on stations, other facilities, vehicles, tools, and equipment. These records are usually kept in two distinct categories: preventive and corrective **(Figure 6.7)**. Both sets of records hold significant legal value when an organization has to go to court over an incident involving a piece of its equipment. The logistics chief/manager usually maintains and analyzes records.

Preventive maintenance is performed to prevent damage, reduce wear, and extend the useful life of an item, vehicle, or facility. Records that are compiled during the preventive maintenance of apparatus, facilities, or pieces of equipment can provide the information necessary to predict a trend or justify a replacement so it is usually performed according to a predetermined schedule. Past experience, industry standards, and manufacturers' recommendations combine to form the basis for a schedule of periodic inspection and maintenance. Frequent

Figure 6.7 Drivers/operators complete daily checkout forms to identify damage, problems, or discrepancies for maintenance personnel to correct.

inspection and cleaning often reveal incipient problems that are relatively easy and inexpensive to correct. Examples of preventive maintenance include but are not limited to:

- Periodic inspection, cleaning, and maintenance of fire station floor coverings, heating and air-conditioning systems, fire extinguishers, appliances, and septic systems.

- Apparatus engine oil changes and chassis lubrication.

- Annual fire pump tests.

- Periodic tests and calibrations of electronic meters (pump panel gauges, monitoring devices, and air-quality testing instruments).

- Fire hose inspections and annual testing.

- Annual and after-each use inspections of ground ladders, respiratory breathing equipment, and personal protective equipment (PPE).

Corrective maintenance (repairs) is always possible due to an unforeseen event. Damage may occur because of an accident, overuse, operator error, or even abuse. When an item is damaged or ceases to function, it must be repaired or replaced as soon as possible.

Deciding to repair or replace an item is often based on its maintenance record and life expectancy. The corrective maintenance record is a critically important part of the decision-making process in the following ways:

1. Showing that an item is relatively new would probably indicate that the item should be repaired

2. Showing that an item is old and has a history of increasingly frequent failures or breakdowns may indicate the need to replace the item with something newer and more reliable

Activity (Incident Reports)

Activity records are the basis for planning and justifying budget requests. These records provide historical documentation of all events, incidents, and projects that members of the organization participated in during a specific time period. They are maintained at the company, district/battalion, and administrative levels of an organization. Each level supplies the next higher level with an accumulation of information until the records become part of the organization's information management section. Activity records are contained in the company/station logbook and on forms provided for each type of activity. Records include information about:

- Emergency and nonemergency responses

- Inspections

- Investigations

- Training

- Communications

Personnel

Personnel records include training, performance, attendance, hazardous materials or biological/medical exposures, and medical **(Figure 6.8)**. Personnel information must be kept current as it may be needed in an emergency or a line-of-duty death (LODD).

Personnel records are confidential with the exception of attendance records (daily personnel roster) and similar documents. Company officers must be careful to protect confidentiality and keep all personnel records secure. Personnel records may be maintained at the company, district, or battalion level, in the administrative office, in the medical or safety officer's office, or in the jurisdiction's human resources office.

Training records are essential components of a successful training program. Accurate records give an organization long-term inventories of its training activities. Insurance Services Office (ISO), International Fire Service Accreditation Congress (IFSAC), National Board on Fire Service Professional Qualifications (Pro Board), and International Association of Fire Chiefs/International City/County Management Association (IAFC/ICMA) accreditation programs may be important and necessary in legal proceedings and management reviews. The company officer must document company level training and should include:

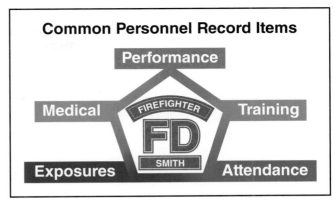

Figure 6.8 Fire and emergency services personnel records should contain, at a minimum, a variety of information relating to each individual's performance, medical conditions, training, exposures, and attendance.

- Topic of training session
- Time designated for training
- Date of training
- Location
- Participants
- Outcomes

Performance is documented and measured through personal job-performance evaluations. These are part of an individual's personnel file, which are maintained by the organization for each employee. The supervisor may also retain a copy for future job-performance evaluations. These records (like medical records) are confidential. Performance evaluations are an important part of an officer's ability to help steer a subordinate's career in a successful direction. Evaluations can help individuals:

- Spot trends and habits in personal performance and behavior.
- Help reinforce good skills and discipline.
- Correct unfavorable behaviors.
- Help individuals improve their knowledge, skills, and abilities.

Attendance records for all personnel are maintained to provide data for payroll and benefit distribution. Depending on an employee's classification, a formal time card may be required as evidence of actual hours on duty. Other attendance records may be included in the company or unit logbook. Overtime, vacation leave, compensatory (comp) time, duty exchanges (exchange of work shifts between members), and sick-leave benefits are based on the information that is included in daily attendance records.

Attendance records that support training requirements are also maintained. These records document that an individual or unit has completed a specified number of hours of training in a specific topic. Volunteer and combination personnel should maintain accurate attendance records for both training and emergency operations. This practice ensures that participants receive credit for their participation in the activities. It can also establish a trend for nonparticipation that may result in changing training or activity schedules or termination from the department if applicable.

Hazardous materials or biological/medical exposure records document significant individual exposures to hazardous materials such as smoke, chemicals, and biological, radiological, and nuclear materials are part of an individual's medical record. Exposure to patients with communicable diseases must also be reported. Because of the delayed effects of some of these hazards and the compounding effect of others, the organization must retain accurate records for 30 years following the end of an individual's employment. Attendance records may also be used to support exposure records when a facility is determined to contain a toxic atmosphere, such as a carbon monoxide leak from a gas-powered water heater.

Medical records are kept on all employees for the duration of their employment plus 30 years. This record includes the individual's pre-employment medical examination, periodic medical evaluations and examinations, post-medical-leave examination, exposure reports, and the postemployment or termination medical examination. Company officers must record:

● All job-related injuries or illnesses that affect personnel assigned to them

● Non job-related illnesses when they result in the use of sick or injury leave

● Trends that might indicate the abuse of sick leave

Electronic Data Storage/Retrieval

Figure 6.9 Computers serve many valuable functions in the modern fire and emergency services.

Many organizations maintain all types of records using some form of electronic data collection, analysis, organization, distribution, and storage/retrieval system. They are also using computer-based word processors for writing reports and completing forms. Company officers must learn to use the computer-based system in their organizations if they are to stay current and function at maximum efficiency.

Computer-Based Systems

The variety of hardware and software available for electronic records management is almost overwhelming. In terms of hardware, company officers must learn to operate the components that are required to make any computer function **(Figure 6.9)**. In terms of software, they must learn to use programs designed for their organization's particular operating system. Countless software programs are available for these systems, and many of them are cross-platformed and able to function on different operating systems.

Company officers must understand the local as well as state/provincial and federal laws regarding the proper use of computer systems, access to the Internet, and various issues that are specific to the use of computers.

Computer-Use Concerns

Company officers must be aware of certain situations that can result from using computers the jurisdiction owns. They must also communicate these concerns to their subordinates to prevent any potential problems. The following list gives computer-specific concerns that company personnel must be aware of when using the organization's computer system:

- *Copyright* — Material found on the Internet may be copyright-protected. If a member wishes to use the material for training purposes or providing information in reports, it is important to gain permission from the original author or the agency that owns the web site.

- *Password Protection* — Members may be assigned a password that allows access to either a computer or the Internet/intranet. Passwords are created to prevent the unauthorized use of a computer or access to records that are not public. Members must not provide their passwords to anyone else.

- *Viruses* — Computer systems are the target of viruses (infection/disruption programs) and spyware (private information access programs). Viruses and spyware disrupt computer systems or access information that is not normally available to the public. Company officers must ensure that the organization's computer security and protection programs (firewalls and antivirus and antispyware programs) are not compromised and must report any evidence that a virus or spyware is present on a computer.

- *Unauthorized use* — Company officers must adhere to all policies that define the appropriate use of an organization's computers and limit access to the Internet. Generally, only software that is licensed to an organization can be installed on its computers. Company officers should track personnel computer usage to ensure that they are not accessing unauthorized sites. There may be restrictions placed on the use of organization-provided equipment for personal use.

- *Public Information* — Any information created on a computer or other electronic device can be the basis of a public information request.

Internet and Intranet

Most organizations provide access to the Internet through their computer systems. Some organizations have intranets (internal networks) that link all the organization's computers together to improve communication and share software and files. The Internet and intranet allow company officers or their personnel the ability to manage information electronically. The Internet is a worldwide network, while the intranet is generally an organizational network. Company officers should be familiar with, understand, and enforce their organization's policies concerning the use of both.

Internet-Specific Concerns

Company officers must be aware of four areas where caution is advised when using the Internet:

- The Internet contains sites that are inappropriate for access from work-related computers. In many jurisdictions, such access is illegal and can result in an employee's termination.

- The accuracy of some of the information found on the Internet is questionable. Always authenticate the information before using it to support or justify a recommendation.

- Data and e-mail messages live forever on computers and in cyberspace. Trained computer personnel can recover an erased document. Never put into writing anything that is inappropriate or illegal.

- There may be agency specific restrictions regarding the use of social media sites.

Privacy Versus Public Access

What people write in e-mails, text messages, and blogs is sometimes viewed as personal and private. However, personnel should not have any expectations of their information remaining private when they use organizational equipment or any personal devices connected to the organization's systems. The company officer must be familiar with local, state/provincial, and federal laws that regulate both privacy and public access to data, reports, and records.

Privacy

Records that must be kept confidential (with limited access) include personnel files, individual training records, and medical files. Training records may also be considered part of an individual's personal, private employment file, requiring an organization to limit access to them. Organizations should develop and adopt policies that limit access to confidential records to only those personnel with a legal right to know.

Public Access

While individual personnel records are confidential, other organizational records are not. Generally, open-meeting laws and open-records acts define the type of records that are available to the public and news media.

Some records, such as incident reports or fire investigations, are available to individuals who own the involved properties or are involved in the incidents unless statute exempted. The state/province defines the exact definition and list of records.

Chapter Summary

As the first level of supervision, the company officer serves as a representative of the organization to the public so the concept of customer service needs to be a dominant principle in daily operations. Proper customer service will help to ensure that department is held in high regard throughout the community.

To provide a high level of customer service, the company officer should have an understanding of the needs of both internal personnel and external groups and being able to win and maintain their goodwill and support.

Internal personnel and the organization's customers influence the creation and implementation of policies and procedures and budget development. The company officer may play a part in these administrative functions and so it is important to become familiar with the policies and procedures and the process used for budget creation.

Tracking activities and being able to ensure that the raw data collected illustrates accurate, complete, and legible records can also be a large part of the company officers' routine operations. An understanding of the information management systems and processes within the organizations helps ensure that the correct data is collected in the proper form. An important thing to remember is that privacy requirements and the public's right to know may determine which of the documents or data collected may become public record. The public can then access them.

Review Questions

1. How does the concept of customer service relate to the fire service? (p. 144)

2. In what ways do company officers interact with policies and procedures? (pp. 147-152)

3. What are the steps in the budget process? (pp. 152-153)

4. How are the different types of confidential records used in the fire service? (p. 157)

Learning Activities

Learning Activity 6-1

Objective 5: Propose a revision to existing departmental procedures.

When given a situation that requires revision to policies and procedures, company officers must be able to clearly communicate a proposal for changes, as well as justification for those changes.

For this activity, you will need access to the follow resources:

- A computer with a word processing program

Create a short proposal in the form of a memo or e-mail (see Chapter 5) addressed to your superior officer that suggests a revision to a specific departmental SOP. You may choose any SOP you wish, or you can use the following scenario:

Scenario:

Weekly washing and cleaning of the department's vehicles is scheduled to be done every Thursday. With the addition of the new apparatus, however, cleaning all the vehicles on the same day has become more challenging. You've noticed that Fridays have traditionally been slow days and some cleaning could easily get done on that day.

Answer Key:

Answers for this activity will vary; however, your document should include the following:

- A clear identification of the SOPs being discussed
- A description of the proposed change in the SOP
- A justification for that change
- A polished, professional appearance to the document, including:
  — Clear purpose and organization
  — A formal and professional tone
  — Proper grammar, and error-free punctuation and spelling

Learning Activity 6-2

Objective 6: Develop a budget request for a specific departmental need.

Using the correct forms and supporting data, company officers must be able to prepare budget request forms accurately and completely.

Complete the following budget request form using the information in the scenario provided below.

Scenario:

The department has just hired two new firefighters, both of whom are very tall. The department is going to need to special order their PPE. Looking through your department's product information, it appears the price will be about $2,000 a person. There is currently $15,000 left in the budget for PPE, and is found in account number 678055. You will need to prepare a purchase request made out to the company, Larson Protective Equipment, Inc. Once the order is placed, delivery is expected in one week.

Expenditure Request Form

Prior to initiating any purchase or expenditure in excess of $1,000 but less than $10,000 the following form shall be completed and approved. Upon approval of the appropriate Administrative Team member, the department may proceed with the purchasing process for the requested item. A copy will be distributed to the City Manager and to the Finance Department. All expenditures of $10,000 or more must be approved in advance by the City Council.

Please complete all sections of the form.

Department: _____

Division: _____

Description of requested item: _____

Explanation of Need/Purpose: _____

Budget Account Number: _____

Amount Approved in Current Budget: _____

Estimated Cost: _____

Expected Date of Delivery of equipment or materials/supplies: _____

Expected payment schedule for service: _____

Projected completion date: _____

Employee making request: _____ Date: _____

Recommended by: _____ Date: _____
                 Department Manager or Designee

Approved by: _____ Date: _____
              Administrative Team

Routing: Please submit the completed form by email to the appropriate Administrative Team member. Approved requests will be returned to the department head or designee, forwarded to the staff accountant in the Finance Department and the City Manager.

Learning Activity 6-3

Objective 6: Maintain a log of routine, unit-level administrative functions.

Company officers must be able to keep clear records and logs so that all pertinent actions are recorded and maintained.

Fill out the log sheet provided by recording the series of events listed in the scenario below.

Scenario:

- At 1:30 p.m., you sent Firefighter Jackson to fill up Rescue 5, reminding him to get a receipt. He came back a half-hour later having put $43 worth of fuel in the tank.

- At 2:17 p.m., Driver/Operator O'Reilly complained of severe stomach pains and went to the doctor. He called two hours later having been told by the doctor to go home and get some rest.

- At 3:49 p.m., Firefighter Ramirez reported finding a flaw in the Rope #14. Rope #14 was removed from service. Rope #72 was placed in service.

- At 6:49 p.m., you responded to an alarm at a commercial building at 654 Center St. Engine 8, Rescue 5, and Chief 2 responded, cleared the building, and found it to be a false alarm.

- By 7:13 p.m., all units returned to station from 654 Center St.

Answer Key:

Answers for this activity will vary; however, the log should include:

- All information given in the scenario
- A time in and time out
- Any remarks necessary that should be communicated to the next shift

Time out	Time in	Activity	Remarks

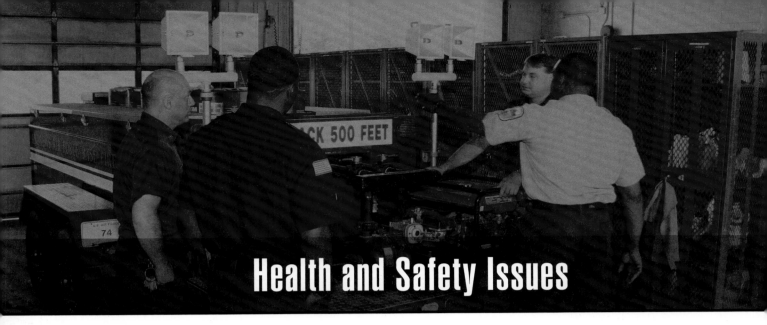

Health and Safety Issues

Chapter Contents

Key Terms

NFPA® Job Performance Requirements

This chapter provides information that addresses the following job performance requirements of NFPA® 1021, *Standard for Fire Officer Professional Qualifications* (2014).

4.6.2

4.7.1

4.7.2

4.7.3

Health and Safety Issues

Learning Objectives

After reading this chapter, students will be able to:

1. Explain organizational risk management. [NFPA® 1021, 4.7.1, 4.7.2, 4.7.3]

2. Describe emergency services casualties. [NFPA® 1021, 4.6.2, 4.7.1, 4.7.2, 4.7.3]

3. Identify basic workplace safety policies and procedures. [NFPA® 1021, 4.6.2, 4.7.1, 4.7.2, 4.7.3]

4. Describe basic workplace safety. [NFPA® 1021, 4.6.2, 4.7.1, 4.7.2, 4.7.3]

5. Identify elements of a health, wellness, and safety program. [NFPA® 1021, 4.6.2, 4.7.1, 4.7.2, 4.7.3]

6. Identify preventative measures for common safety hazards. [NFPA® 1021, 4.7.1, 4.7.3; Learning Activity 7-1]

7. Perform an initial accident investigation at the scene of an incident. [NFPA® 1021, 4.7.2; Learning Activity 7-2]

Chapter 7
Health and Safety Issues

Case History

Charles Johnson is a busy man. His job, his family, and his fire company obligations keep him constantly on the move. Although he knew his fire company had a policy requiring annual physicals for all members, he had been delaying his physical due to his busy schedule. In August 2011, he finally scheduled his annual physical.

Everything with his physical went well, up to the point of completing a stress test. The doctor did not like the results, directed Charles not to respond on any emergency calls, and advised him to consult a cardiologist. Heeding his doctor's advice, Charles went immediately to a cardiologist and found himself two days later in the hospital undergoing a cardiac catheterization. One of his arteries was found with a 95% blockage, and a stent was put in place.

Charles had no prior indication of having a cardiac problem. He was under 45 years of age, a non-smoker, ate sensibly, and had no family history of cardiac problems. Charles reflects back on his experience; "Had this cardiac problem not been caught, had it not been for the county government funded firefighter physical that is mandated and enforced by my department, I am certain that I would have had a life-changing – if not fatal – event."

Charles has since returned to duty without any restrictions and looks forward to many more years with his family as well as serving his community thanks to the mandatory physical program his department implemented. His experience clearly demonstrates the value of health and wellness programs and the benefit to both individual members and the department as a whole.

To protect the lives and property of those they serve, fire and emergency responders must first protect themselves. Injured or incapacitated responders cannot assist a victim and simultaneously divert resources away from the primary objectives of the incident or operation that would otherwise be needed for that victim.

Company officers' responsibilities go beyond their own personal health and safety. They should also create a culture of safety within their command in order to minimize the exposure to risk for their crew. In order to achieve a safety culture within their organizations, company officers must be familiar with their organization's health and safety policies and procedures and must also be aware of the following:

- Common causes of personal injuries and accidents that affect members
- Local safety policies and procedures
- Basic workplace safety
- Components of an exposure control program
- Current trends in fire and emergency services health and safety initiatives

Figure 7.1 A company officer checking on a firefighter injured in the fire station.

While emergency scene safety receives a great deal of attention, nonemergency safety is equally important. Injuries and fatalities can and do occur at the station, training facility, and other facilities while personnel are performing daily nonemergency activities **(Figure 7.1)**. Policies and procedures that identify risks in the facilities, activities, and behaviors will help create and maintain a safe work environment.

Stress, exertion, and other medical-related issues continue to contribute to both firefighter fatalities and injuries. Cardiac arrest continues to be the leading cause of firefighter fatalities. An effective method to reduce cardiac arrest and other medical issues is the implementation of an organizational health and wellness program. The program includes education in and the application of proper nutrition, exercise, and the cessation of tobacco products.

Company officers are responsible for fostering a positive health and safety environment. They should strive to influence their subordinates' perceptions regarding compliance with the organization's health and safety policies and procedures. Company officers must also comply with the health and safety issues of the department to set a good example for their units.

This chapter describes the risk management concept. It also discusses the casualties that can result from unsafe acts and conditions. It contains a review of the most commonly applied fire service safety standards and emergency services safety initiatives. The chapter also describes health, wellness, and safety issues as they relate to the fire and emergency services.

Risk Management

There is inherent risk associated with fire and emergency services. Company officers should understand how to manage the risks associated with this work through a risk management program. **Risk management** is the process of identifying and analyzing the exposure to hazards, selecting appropriate techniques to handle exposures, implementing chosen techniques, and monitoring the results of those techniques. The maximization of health and safety in the fire and emergency services is directly related to policies and procedures designed to reduce risk.

The overall risk management plan should have three distinct sections. First is the community risk assessment. While this section is not a direct function of the company officer, the information from this process will provide the company officer with known risks in the community that responders may be exposed to. Second is the organizational risk management plan. This section evaluates risks and hazards that can affect the organization and provides control measures to reduce the frequency, severity, and probability of a negative event from occurring. Third is the operational risk management process. All three sections of the risk management plan provide the fire and emergency service organization with a foundation to address the inherent risks and hazards that can potentially harm the organization and its members.

Organizational Risk Management Plan

The organizational risk management plan requires a systematic approach and shall include risk identification, risk evaluation, risk prioritization, risk control techniques, and risk monitoring. There are five distinct components of the organizational risk management plan as follows:

- **Risk identification** — risks are identified in the community, within the organization, and within the operational setting at emergency and non-emergency incidents.

- **Risk evaluation** — risks are evaluated on their probability and potential for negative consequences, including the anticipated severity and frequency of occurrence.

- **Establishment of priorities for action** — a ranking of the identified risks will be based on the degree of severity and frequency.

- **Risk control techniques** — control measures will be identified for each significant risk.

- **Risk management monitoring** — monitoring of the risk control measures will be an ongoing process. Recommendations for plan revision will be based on the monitoring process.

Operational Risk Management Process

There is inherent risk associated with fire and emergency services. Company officers should understand how to manage the risks associated with this work through a risk management program. The maximization of health and safety in the fire and emergency services is directly related to policies and procedures designed to reduce risk. One example of operation risk management contains a five-step process that maintains a continuous loop in order to evaluate the most current risks. This five-step process is:

- **Situational awareness** — consider communications plan, weather factors, and previous incident behavior.

- **Hazard assessment** — identify hazard, consider severity and future impact.

- **Hazard control** — contain, isolate, and eliminate.

- **Decision point** — determine if appropriate resources are available, if assignments have been made and understood, and if tactics are appropriate.

- **Evaluate** — determine if the risk management plan is working, what is changing, and if personnel are able to complete assignments.

Emergency Services Casualties

Utilizing a risk management plan can reduce risk, but not all risk can be eliminated. Casualties can occur at emergency incidents, in transit to and from incidents, during training, and during work shifts at the station and other facilities. Knowing the statistics and the causes of casualties helps company officers provide company-level safety training and instruction to reduce and perhaps eliminate these consequences.

Company officers can also use a broad range of initiatives to spread health and safety messages with their personnel. These initiatives will be explained in the Fire and Emergency Services Health and Safety Initiatives section later in this chapter. The result can be the implementation of safety policies and procedures that ensure a safe work environment.

Additional information regarding fire and emergency services health and safety programs can be found in IFSTA's **Fire Department Safety Officer** and **Occupational, Safety, Health, and Wellness** manuals and Fire Protection Publication's **Understanding and Implementing the 16 Firefighter Life Safety Initiatives**.

Emergency Scene Casualties

Fire and EMS personnel frequently incur injuries while providing emergency services. The leading injuries among these responders are sprains and strains. These injuries are the result of the physical demands of emergency responses **(Figure 7.2)**. Other injury types included trauma, cuts and bruises, burns, asphyxiation, and thermal stress. The majority of injuries occurred during fire attack and search and rescue activities.

Emergency responders must be able to recognize unsafe acts and conditions in order to reduce injuries and fatalities. An individual, a member of the crew, or an outside force may contribute to unsafe acts and conditions. Company officers must be able to recognize when crewmembers are performing unsafe acts or not avoiding unsafe conditions and take appropriate action to prevent injuries and fatalities.

Company officers should reference injury and fatality statistical data in order to stay current on trends within the fire and emergency services. The following organizations in the United States and Canada are good sources for current, injury and fatality information:

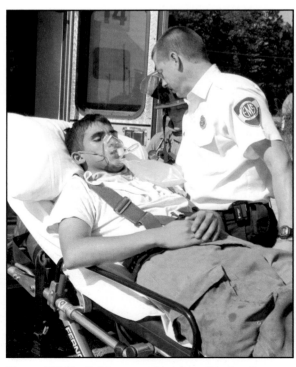

- United States:
  - National Institute for Occupational Safety and Health (NIOSH)
  - Bureau of Labor Statistics (BLS)
  - U.S. Fire Administration (USFA)
  - National Fire Protection Association® (NFPA®)
- Canada:
  - Workplace Health and Safety Compensation Commission (WHSCC)
  - Canadian Centre for Occupational Health and Safety (CCOHS)

Figure 7.2 Firefighters may be injured during fire fighting operations.

Structural Fire Survivability

Results from a variety of studies on civilian and firefighter survival during structural fires have provided the following data:

- During normal fire conditions, the maximum survival time for civilians is 10 minutes
- The majority of firefighter line-of-duty deaths (LODD) occurs within the first 12 minutes after arriving on the scene
- The combination of carbon monoxide (CO) and hydrogen cyanide (HCN) commonly found at structural fires is toxic at 135 ppm (parts per million)
- It takes 16 firefighters approximately 35 minutes to rescue a lost or downed firefighter

Additional information on the results of structural fire and survivability studies can be found in Chapter 11, Emergency Services Delivery I.

Nonemergency Workplace Casualties

Nonemergency casualties include any fatalities or injuries that occurred while performing administrative duties, training, code enforcement and inspections, maintenance, or other non-incident-related situations. The percentage of cardiac arrest training-related fatalities has risen in recent years.

Fire and Emergency Services Health and Safety Initiatives

Health and safety initiatives have become a high priority intended to reduce injuries and fatalities throughout the fire and emergency services. Company officers should be aware of these initiatives and encourage their crews to following these initiatives. Some of these initiatives include:

- **Firefighter Life Safety Initiatives** — a blueprint to reducing firefighter deaths and injuries **(Figure 7.3, p. 174)**.

- **FirefighterCloseCalls.Com** — originally an e-mail group, this website produces an independent newsletter that shares information about "close call" incidents that resulted in firefighter injuries and fatalities.

- **EVENT (EMS Voluntary Event Notification Tool)** — is designed to improve the safety, quality and consistent delivery of Emergency Medical Services (EMS). EVENT collects data from EMS practitioners in order to develop policies, procedures, and training programs to improve the safe delivery of EMS.

- **EMS Safety Foundation** — a not-for-profit think tank, consortium group with a mission to promote an EMS safety innovation, collaboration, research, knowledge transfer, education, and safety information dissemination.

- **Fire/EMS Safety, Health, and Survival Week** — The International Association of Fire Chiefs (IAFC) and the International Association of Fire Fighters (IAFF) sponsor the event. The IAFC Safety, Health and Survival Section and the IAFF Division of Occupational Health, Safety and Medicine, and more than 20 national fire service organizations coordinate the event. During the week, fire departments are encouraged to suspend all non-emergency activity and focus entirely on safety, health, and wellness-related training and education until all personnel and shifts have taken part.

The 16 Firefighter Life Safety Initiatives

The Firefighter Life Safety Summit held in Tampa, Florida, in March 2004, produced 16 major initiatives that will give the fire service a blueprint for making changes.

1. Define and advocate the need for a cultural change within the fire service relating to safety; incorporating leadership, management, supervision, accountability, and personal responsibility.

2. Enhance the personal and organizational accountability for health and safety throughout the fire service.

3. Focus greater attention on the integration of risk management with incident management at all levels, including strategic, tactical, and planning responsibilities.

4. All firefighters must be empowered to stop unsafe practices.

5. Develop and implement national standards for training, qualifications, and certification (including regular recertification) that are equally applicable to all firefighters based on the duties they are expected to perform.

6. Develop and implement national medical and physical fitness standards that are equally applicable to all firefighters, based on the duties they are expected to perform.

7. Create a national research agenda and data collection system that relates to the initiatives.

8. Utilize available technology wherever it can produce higher levels of health and safety.

9. Thoroughly investigate all firefighter fatalities, injuries, and near misses.

10. Grant programs should support the implementation of safe practices and/or mandate safe practices as an eligibilit requirement.

11. National standards for emergency response policies and procedures should be developed and championed.

12. National protocols for response to violent incidents should be developed and championed.

13. Firefighters and their families must have access to counseling and psychological support.

14. Public education must receive more resources and be championed as a critical fire and life safety program.

15. Advocacy must be strengthened for the enforcement of codes and the installation of home fire sprinklers.

16. Safety must be a primary consideration in the design of apparatus and equipment.

National Fallen Firefighters Foundation
www.firehero.org

Figure 7.3 The 16 Firefighter Life Safety Initiatives.

- **International Association of Fire Chiefs' (IAFC) Rules of Engagement for Firefighter Survival** — 11 rules that provide guidance to individual firefighters regarding risk and safety issues when operating on the fireground.

- **IAFC's Incident Commander's Rules of Engagement for Firefighter Safety** — 11 rules that provide guidance to incident commanders regarding risk and safety issues when operating on the fireground.

- **National Firefighter Near-Miss Reporting System** — is a voluntary, confidential, non-punitive and secure reporting system with the goal of improving firefighter safety. This system is a cooperative effort between the IAFC and the IAFF.

- **National Volunteer Fire Council's (NVFC) Rules of Engagement for Firefighter Health** — 10 rules to encourage firefighters to pursue healthier lifestyles.

Safety Policies and Procedures

Company officers must be knowledgeable of all local, state/provincial and federal law relating to firefighter safety and health. In order to promote a safe work environment for its members, each department should establish safety policies and procedures specific to its department's operation. An organization's safety policies and procedures may reference the following safety standards or regulations:

- NFPA® 1500, *Standard on Fire Department Occupational Health and Safety Program*

- NFPA® 1521, *Standard for Fire Department Safety Officer*

- NFPA® 1561, *Standard on Emergency Services Incident Management System*

- NFPA® 1581, *Standard on Fire Department Infection Control Program*

- NFPA® 1582, *Standard on Comprehensive Occupational Medical Program for Fire Departments*

- NFPA® 1584, *Standard on the Rehabilitation Process for Members During Emergency Operations and Training Exercises*

- NFPA® 1852, *Standard on Selection, Care, and Maintenance of Open-Circuit Self-Contained Breathing Apparatus (SCBA)*

- Occupational Safety & Health Standard (OSHA) 29 CFR 1910.134, *Respiratory Protection*

Company officers should be familiar with the local safety policies and procedures and their applications. Training sessions should be held periodically to ensure that unit members are familiar with these policies and procedures. Practical training evolutions and company-level training should include the application of all appropriate safety policies.

Basic to all safety policies and procedures is the establishment of a health and safety program. The health and safety program is comprised of smaller programs or components that focus on specific areas of health and safety. One component is the accident, injury, and illness prevention program that provides hazard information and training. Another is the exposure control program that protects responders. The health and safety program should include a comprehensive physical fitness and wellness program to improve the health of employees and alter behavior patterns that may increase the likelihood of injury or illness.

Basic Workplace Safety

Company officers should address safety issues with their personnel each shift **(Figure 7.4)**. Workplace safety consists of activities that ensure a safe work environment and protect employees from job-related injuries, illnesses, and exposures to hazardous materials. The organization's management holds the ultimate responsibility of providing a safe workplace. This goal is attained through training, policies, procedures, and maintenance of facilities and equipment. It is the responsibility of the company officer to implement policies and procedures and report the need for any maintenance or the replacement of unsafe equipment.

Emergency responders must be able to recognize unsafe acts and conditions in order to reduce injuries and fatalities. Company officers must be able to recognize when crewmembers are performing unsafe acts or not avoiding unsafe conditions and take appropriate action to prevent injuries and fatalities.

For fire and emergency responders, the workplace is not a single location — it is rather multiple locations that routes of transportation connect **(Figure 7.5)**. The organization and company officer have no control over the majority of these locations. Only the organization's facilities, stations, and apparatus can be directly controlled and made as safe as possible. Therefore, the workplace can be generally divided into emergency scene, en route to and from emergency scene, and facilities.

The company officer must also be familiar with the organization's health and safety program. This program should apply to all areas of the workplace and provide information and methods for ensuring that a safe work culture is developed.

Figure 7.4 Roll call can be a perfect opportunity for company officers to provide safety briefings.

Figure 7.5 Examples of common fire and emergency services workplaces.

En Route to and from Scene

Unsafe acts or conditions are responsible for many injuries and fatalities while personnel are en route to and from the incident. Some of these accidents can be controlled through apparatus design and maintenance and driver/operator training and certification. Although accidents occur, there may be some underlying causes that can be avoided. Company officers should recognize and correct unsafe acts and conditions in order to reduce and prevent accidents.

Unsafe Acts During Response

Emergency responders should be trained on safe vehicle operations well before responding to an incident or leaving an emergency scene. Unsafe acts may occur both in organizational vehicles and privately owned vehicles (POVs). In the case of POVs, the company officer should pay special attention to the training and education of those drivers. A company officer must enforce the organizational policies regarding driving POVs as well as organizational vehicles. During times that personnel are traveling to and from a scene, the company officer should address any an unsafe act immediately. Examples of unsafe acts may include but are not limited to:

- Speeding
- Driving too fast for conditions

- Not seat belted
- Driving too close to other vehicles
- Not obeying traffic laws
- Lack of vehicle maintenance

Unsafe Conditions During Response

Unsafe conditions are out of an officer's control. As a result, the company officer must recognize these conditions and ensure that drivers take the appropriate precautions. Examples of unsafe conditions may include but are not limited to:

- Inclement weather **(Figure 7.6)**
- Pedestrians in or near the roadway
- Poor road conditions
- Traffic **(Figure 7.7)**

Figure 7.6 Emergency responses can be inherently dangerous, but responses in inclement weather can be even more so.

Figure 7.7 Fire apparatus may experience different levels of traffic during emergency responses.

Emergency Scene

Emergency scene injuries or fatalities can be prevented or reduced through the application of policies and procedures that regulate emergency scene activities. Doing so helps to ensure a safe work environment. Company officers should comply, enforce, and educate their personnel regarding these policies and procedures as well as maintain accountability of their personnel while on an emergency scene. The company officer must address both unsafe acts and conditions to ensure scene safety. Unsafe acts are internal factors that the company officer or a member of the crew performs, while unsafe conditions are externally controlled and should be recognized and addressed appropriately.

Unsafe Acts at Emergency Scenes

Scene safety should be taught in training programs before company officers or crew members are ever allowed to respond to an emergency. Training is the best way to ensure that responders do not perform unsafe acts during an incident. If an unsafe act occurs during on scene operations, the company officer or the crew member who recognized the act should address the situation immediately. Examples of unsafe acts may include but are not limited to:

- Operating independently of the incident commander's (IC) control (freelancing).
- Not maintaining crew integrity.
- Not having proper communication with the IC or dispatch.
- Not having appropriate PPE.
- Lack of situational awareness.
- Lack of appropriate rehab

Unsafe Conditions at Emergency Scenes

Since unsafe conditions are a product of the emergency scene environment, they are usually out of the company officer's control. As a result, the company officer must recognize these conditions and act appropriately to maintain scene safety. Examples of unsafe conditions may include but are not limited to:

- Zero visibility
- Unsafe structural conditions
- Rapidly moving or uncontrolled fires
- Hostile Crowds
- Unstable vehicles
- Environmental

Facilities

Poorly maintained fire stations, training centers, administrative offices, and maintenance buildings may contribute to an accident, injury, illness, or fatality. Proper maintenance is one of the best methods for providing a safe workplace. Company officers or building managers are responsible for reporting the need for repairs and ensuring that they are completed. They are also responsible for the safe operation and maintenance of their facilities. Annual facility inspections should be conducted in accordance with the organizational policies. Company officers should recognize that there are unsafe acts and conditions in and around facilities.

Unsafe Acts at Facilities

The company officers should be able to recognize and address unsafe acts within facilities. These acts may include but are not limited to:

- Not using warning signs for wet surfaces
- Using power and hand tools improperly
- Climbing stairs improperly
- Improper lifting of heavy objects
- Horseplay

Unsafe Conditions

The company officers should be able to recognize and know how to address unsafe conditions within facilities. These conditions may include but are not limited to:

- Poor lighting
- Wet or oily floors **(Figure 7.8)**
- Slippery or icy sidewalks
- Poor maintenance issues

Health, Wellness, and Safety

The company officer is also responsible for providing subordinates with information on the organization's health and safety program. The organiza-

Figure 7.8 Safety signs can help warn personnel of unsafe conditions, such as wet floors.

tion's health and safety program should include information on emergency and nonemergency safety practices, overall wellness and fitness, inspections, and accident investigations.

Wellness

Cardiac arrests are the most common cause of firefighter fatalities. Wellness programs are intended to lower firefighters' risk of cardiac arrest as well as other health problems. Wellness can be addressed through education, fitness, and nutrition. Company officers should encourage the following to help unit members maintain good health:

- Routine medical screening
- Proper nutrition
- Weight control
- Physical fitness **(Figure 7.9)**

- Participation in tobacco cessation programs
- Participation in drug and alcohol abuse programs
- Participation in employee assistance programs (EAP)

Safety Related Inspections

Safety related inspections are meant to ensure the integrity of equipment, vehicles, facilities, and personnel qualifications. Proper integrity works with risk analysis to ensure safety becomes the end product. Company officers should ensure that proper safety related inspections occur in accordance with organizational policies. Many organizations have established time frames that inspections must occur. Company officers may be asked to conduct safety inspections at any time.

Equipment

Company officers should conduct safety inspections of equipment that includes PPE, tools, and gear. Equipment may include but is not limited to:

- Fire fighting gear **(Figure 7.10)**
- Medical gear
- Rescue gear

Figure 7.9 Physical fitness training should be a part of every firefighter's daily regimen.

Figure 7.10 Company officers may conduct impromptu protective clothing inspections.

Vehicles

Company officers should conduct safety inspections for any vehicles that have been assigned to the facility. Vehicle safety inspections may include but are not limited to:

- Traffic deterrent devices
- Aerial tests
- Pump tests
- Vehicle maintenance

Facilities

Company officers should conduct safety inspections of assigned facilities **(Figure 7.11)**. Facility safety inspections may include but are not limited to:

- Proper lighting
- Trip hazards
- Up-to-date and fit-for-service fire extinguishers
- Compliance with the local electrical code
- Installed systems and equipment

Personnel Qualifications

Company officers should ensure personnel qualifications are appropriate and current for each individual's duty assignment. Examples of personnel qualifications can include but are not limited to:

- Medical certifications
- Vehicle and apparatus operation certifications
- Professional qualifications

Figure 7.11 Company officers should inspect fire and emergency services facilities on a regular basis.

Infection Control

Some occupational illnesses result from exposures to infectious diseases. To control and manage this potential threat to the organization's members, an infection control program should be established. NFPA® 1581, *Standard on Fire Department Infection Control Program,* refers to this as a medical exposure program. Company officers should be knowledgeable of their organizations' infection control programs.

The written infection control plan should clearly explain its intent, benefits, and purposes and include the following components:

- Education and training requirements
- Vaccination requirements for potential threats, such as anthrax or hepatitis B virus, annual flu vaccinations and tuberculosis (TB) inoculations
- Documentation and record-keeping requirements
- Cleaning, decontamination, and disinfection of personnel and equipment
- Infection control and reporting protocols

Rehab

The physical stresses of fire fighting along with the dangers of extreme hot or cold weather conditions can negatively impact the health and safety of emergency responders. Members who are not provided adequate rest and rehydration (**rehabilitation**) during emergency operations or training exercises are at increased risk for illness or injury, and may jeopardize the safety of others on the incident scene (**Figure 7.12**).

Company officers should support and enforce their organizations' policies and procedures for incident scene rehabilitation to reduce the risk of illness or injury to its members when operating at an incident scene or training site. If an organization does not have a rehab procedure, NFPA® 1584, *Standard*

Rehabilitation — Allowing firefighters or rescuers to rest, rehydrate, and recover during an incident; also refers to a station at an incident where personnel can rest, rehydrate, and recover.

Figure 7.12 Rehabilitation is important to relieving the physical stresses of fire fighting operations. *Courtesy of Bob Esposito.*

on the Rehabilitation Process for Members During Emergency Operations and Training Exercises, should be used as a guide when developing a departmental policy and procedures for rehabilitation.

Company officers should also:

- Comply with the rehab policies and procedures
- Monitor and evaluate environmental and work activities of their personnel
- Ensure rehab is established and adequate resources are available
- Ensure medical monitoring and rehydration is provided
- Ensure the appropriate locations and notifications of rehab facilities

Accident Investigation

Company officers must follow their organizations' prescribed procedures and accurately complete the appropriate accident investigation forms. In conducting an investigation, company officers collect basic information about the participants, event, or incident. The investigation should provide the following information:

- **General information:**
  — Date and time of incident
  — Type of incident, illness, injury, or fatality
  — Location and emergency response type
  — Names of witnesses and their accounts of the situation
- **Employee characteristics (participant):**
  — Name and unit assignment (company/shift)
  — Age and gender
  — Rank/function
  — Personal protective clothing or equipment in use
- **Environmental information:**
  — Weather and temperature
  — Day or night conditions
  — Noise and visibility
  — Terrain
- **Apparatus/equipment information:**
  — Type of equipment involved
  — Age and condition
  — Location
  — Maintenance history
  — Distinguishing characteristics

A narrative description of the incident is the final portion of the investigation report. This narrative includes observations from the officer, eye-witness reports, participant interviews, and information from other sources such as law-enforcement reports and dispatch information.

Injuries, Illnesses, and Exposures

When a unit member experiences a job-related injury, illness, or exposure, the first duty of a company officer is to ensure prompt medical treatment for the individual. If the injury, illness, or exposure is serious, the individual must be transported to a medical treatment facility. Once the company officer has ensured the individual is receiving treatment, the investigation should commence.

Investigations of job-related injuries, illnesses, or exposures generally include gathering the same information needed for accident investigations. Some differences may exist based on the nature of the incident. For instance, an investigation into an illness claim that is perceived to be job-related may require more time and the services of a specialty organization (air and water sampling, for example). These investigations may occur at some time after the event. The company officer must focus on the idea that the investigation's data may lead to the discovery of an environmental cause for the illness.

Exposure investigations may occur immediately following the incident or at some future point when symptoms of exposure appear in the individual. Accurate and thorough documentation of all incidents and exposures is basic to any current or future investigation. A long-range investigation might involve the frequent occurrence of cancer in a large number of personnel from a single station in one city. Symptoms may not appear until many years after someone has retired. Attempts to determine the cause of the trend would include water and air sampling, testing for asbestos, and a review of all emergency responses the members had been on.

Chapter Summary

An efficient, effective fire and emergency services organization depends on the health, safety, and wellness of its personnel. Risk management is a key element of safety programs in the fire and emergency services. Company officers are responsible for ensuring a safe working environment through training, education, equipment, policies, procedures, leadership, and supervision. This safe environment is accomplished through the development and implementation of a comprehensive health and safety program that addresses both the obvious and obscure hazards to the health and well-being of the members.

Implementing a holistic physical fitness and wellness program for employees must become an organizational reality. The wellness component should include proper nutrition, back care, heart and lung disease awareness, and stress-reduction counseling. The organization should work to address all areas of health and wellness both through prevention and education. Through these efforts, the organization can reduce injuries, reduce fatalities, reduce health and lost-time costs, and improve the morale of the membership.

Company officers must make health and safety their primary concern for their subordinates. They must set the example for others to follow and ensure that all operations are performed in a way that is consistent with standard operating procedures/standard operating guidelines (SOPs/SOGs) and safe practices.

Review Questions

1. What are the basic principles of organizational risk management? (p. 170)

2. What are emergency services casualties? (pp. 172-175)

3. What is the purpose of having basic workplace safety policies and procedures? (p. 175)

4. How does basic workplace safety affect a fire fighting organization? (p. 176)

5. What are the components of a health, wellness, and safety program? (pp. 180-184)

Learning Activities

Learning Activity 7-1

Objective 6: Identify preventative measures for common safety hazards.

Company officers must be able to apply preventative measures during emergency and nonemergency situations after identifying safety hazards.

Read the following scenarios and identify the safety hazards that are present in each. Describe accident prevention measures that a company officer can take for each of the identified hazards.

Scenario 1:

Engine 5 has responded to a vehicle accident at 1700 hours on a holiday weekend Friday afternoon. One vehicle is located on the side of road, and is fully involved with fire upon arrival of the engine. The second is wrapped around a telephone pole. Flames are blowing across the right lane of the highway with smoke totally obscuring the left (passing) lane. A light rain is falling and conditions are overcast. A number of vehicles have pulled to the right side of the highway, and the occupants are standing by them watching the fire. Some are less than thirty feet from the involved vehicle.

Scenario 2:

Engine 5 has returned to the station after the incident described above. The rain picked up towards the end of the incident, and everyone and everything, including the floor, is wet as the crew dismounts the apparatus inside the station. The unit had to extricate a victim from the second vehicle, and several unit members were working closely with jagged and sharp metal debris. The rookie lifted the extrication power unit off the apparatus, struggling with the weight. He carried the unit to a small, enclosed vehicle bay to refuel it, and then left the fuel can by the side of the apparatus.

Answer Key:

Answers for this activity will vary slightly; however, your outline should address:

Scenario 1:

- Visibility of company members is hindered due to weather conditions. – All members must wear safety vests.

- Traffic that is approaching the incident scene may not see company members. – Travel lanes should be blocked by engine utilizing emergency warning lights.

- Traffic may approach scene at too great a speed. – Cones or other traffic control devices should be deployed.

- Emergency vehicles may contribute to the confusion around the accident scene. – The incident management system should be employed to limit this confusion.

- Too many tasks to be accomplished by too few company members. – Request additional assistance to control the scene and provide emergency services.

- Possibility of civilian injuries. – Cordon off area around crash scene and move unauthorized individuals away.

Scenario 2:

- The floor of the station has gotten wet. – The floor must be mopped to prevent slips and falls.

- Jagged and sharp edges may have punctured or cut PPE. – PPE must be inspected for holes or tears.

- Power unit is heavy and unwieldy. – Another unit member must help lift and carry it.

- Vehicle bay is small and enclosed. – Must be properly ventilated while refueling the unit.

- Fuel can was left at side of apparatus. – Must return container to proper storage.

Learning Activity 7-2

Objective 7: Perform an initial investigation at the scene of an accident.

A company officer must be able to conduct an initial accident investigation and prepare all documentation according to policies and procedures.

Read the following scenario and fill out an employee accident report from your organization following your organization's SOPs, or use the form provided below.

Scenario:

During emergency incident 07-011283 at 1323 hours, 1204 West Market Street, January 29, 2013, Anytown Fire Department, Engine 5, deployed 500 feet (150 m) of 5-inch (125 mm) supply line fire hose.

"Loss stop" was declared by IC Grader (Battalion Chief/Shift Commander) at 1642 hours and demobilization began. The supply line was then drained of water and company members began to reload it into the hosebed of the engine, a 1998 engine. The safety officer on scene was Captain Fortney. While this was being performed, Firefighter Ramirez (B Shift), age 32, slipped then fell from the rear step of the engine and injured his ankle. Firefighter Ramirez was wearing all personal protective equipment except for SCBA.

Firefighter Tipton witnessed the fall and stated, "He was up on the rear step pushing hose to me when he yelled and fell off." The engine was not moving at the time of the accident. Driver/Operator Burke did not see Ramirez fall, but said "All I know is, I heard him yell, and then a thud when he hit the ground. It was clear that he was hurt bad because he was screaming in pain."

Weather at the time of the accident was windy and the temperature was 33°F (0.5°C). Freezing rain was falling, glazing the street and other surfaces. Medics from PA 101 treated Firefighter Ramirez at the scene and transported him to the Mercy Hospital for additional evaluation and care. It was later learned that Ramirez's ankle was fractured and would require surgery. Estimated recovery and rehabilitation time for Ramirez is four months.

Answer Key:

Answers may vary according to local SOPs. If students used the leaning activity's SOPs and form, answers should resemble the following:

Date: **February 1, 2013**	Date of Accident: **January 29,2013** Time of Accident: **1645 hrs. approx.**
Accident Classification: **X** Injury ☐Illness ☐Fatality	Incident/Accident Location: **1204 West Market Street**
Employee Name: **Ramirez**	Incident Number: **07-011283**
Employee Assignment Location: Shift: ☐A **X** B ☐C	Employee Rank/Classification: **Firefighter**
Employee Age: 32 Gender: ☐Female **X** Male	
Weather at Time of Accident: **Windy, freezing rain**	Temperature at Time of Accident: **33°F (0.5 °C)**
Scene Conditions at Time of Accident: **Icy**	
Incident Commander: **Battalion Chief Grader**	Shift Commander: **Same**
Safety Officer: **Captain Fortney**	EMS Unit(s): **PA 101**
Motorized Equipment Involved in Accident: **E-5, 1998 fire apparatus**	
Personal Protective Equipment: **All personal protective equipment except for SCBA was being worn at the time of the accident.**	
Narrative 1. How did the accident occur? **During hose reloading following a fire at 1204 West Market Street, Firefighter Ramirez slipped and fell from the rear step of Engine 5, a 1998 engine. The conditions at the time of the accident were freezing rain with icy conditions.**	
Narrative 2. Why did the accident occur? **The rear step of the fire apparatus was icy as a result of the freezing rain, contributing to poor footing. The slippery conditions resulted in Firefighter Ramirez falling from the rear step to the street.**	
Narrative 3. What could be done to reduce exposure risk for future accidents? **A method to remove ice from the rear step during icy conditions and additional supervision to monitor hazardous conditions that may result in injury.**	
Name of Witnesses: D/O Brian Burke, FF Tipton	
Signature of employee: Date: **02/01/13**	Signature of Employee Supervisor: **Your Signiture** Date: **02/01/13**
Name of person filling out report: **Your Name**	

Anytown Fire Department
Employee Accident Report

Date:	Date of Accident: Time of Accident:
Accident Classification: ☐ Injury ☐ Illness ☐ Fatality	Incident/Accident Location:
Employee Name:	Incident Number:
Employee Assignment Location: Shift: A B C	Employee Rank/Classification
Employee Age: Gender: ☐ Female ☐ Male	
Weather at Time of Accident:	Temperature at Time of Accident:
Scene Conditions at Time of Accident:	
Incident Commander:	Shift Commander:
Safety Officer:	EMS Unit(s)
Motorized Equipment Involved in Accident:	
Personal Protective Equipment:	
Narrative 1. How did the accident occur?	
Narrative 2. Why did the accident occur?	
Narrative 3. What could be done to reduce exposure risk for future accidents?	
Name of Witnesses:	
Signature of employee: Date:	Signature of Employee Supervisor: Date:
Name of person filling out report	

Company-Level Training

Chapter Contents

Key Terms

NFPA® Job Performance Requirements

This chapter provides information that addresses the following job performance requirements of NFPA® 1021, *Standard for Fire Officer Professional Qualifications* (2014).

4.2.3

Company-Level Training

Learning Objectives

After reading this chapter, students will be able to:

1. Identify considerations for determining training needs.

2. Describe the four-step method of instruction. [NFPA® 1021, 4.2.3]

3. Recognize uses of lesson plans in company-level training.

4. Describe methods of company-level training [NFPA® 1021, 4.2.3]

5. Create a plan to direct fire personnel during a training session. [NFPA® 1021, 4.2.3; Learning Activity 8-1]

Chapter 8
Company-Level Training

Case History

Company officers have learned that informal training can contribute to the company's success. For many firefighters, the large classroom setting can be boring. To others, it can be intimidating. Also, the formal hands-on classes offered at the department-level can lead to inattention and inactivity. Informal training offers learning opportunities in less structured settings that appeal to many firefighters.

Company officers like to involve their veteran firefighters in informal training. For example, one officer had an engineer that had been in that position for over twenty-five years. The engineer was relatively quiet and did not accept the officer's invitation to teach a formal class. However, the company officer discovered that the engineer enjoyed teaching new personnel about pump operations. He loved to go over pump operations and maintenance procedures with young firefighters.

The company officer decided to use his engineer to teach pump operations as part of their department's engineer training program. Although shy in front of large groups, the engineer excelled at teaching one or two firefighters at a time. Those firefighters walked away from the lessons much more informed than they would have in a more structured class. The company officer learned how to identify the needs of his subordinates and find creative ways to utilize his veteran personnel.

Training is critical to safe, efficient, and effective fire and emergency services operations. NFPA® 1021, *Standard for Fire Officer Professional Qualifications*, requires that all Fire Officer I candidates complete Instructor I training as defined in NFPA® 1041, *Standard for Fire Service Instructor Professional Qualifications*. Company officers and officer candidates should refer to the IFSTA's **Fire and Emergency Services Instructor** manual for a detailed presentation of formal instructor training. This chapter provides an overview of the topic as it applies to Fire Officer I and is based on information that is contained in that manual.

The goal of company- or unit-level training is to maintain and reinforce knowledge, skills, and abilities that each unit member has upon completion of formal entry-level training. Company-level training should also provide the opportunity to develop mastery of those skills. Company-level training may also be used to integrate new company members into the unit and improve the teamwork of the unit.

Company officers should ensure that the company-level training conducted meets the organization's standards. According to NFPA® 1201, *Standard for Providing Fire and Emergency Services to the Public*, the organization must evaluate the effectiveness of its training programs, including the teaching skills of the company officer. Company officers must also possess good leadership skills and enthusiasm to create a team. When company officers combine leadership, supervision, safety and training, they create a strong foundation for developing an effective company.

Documenting Company-Level Training

Company officers must document company-level training. State and federal requirements often mandate this documentation. Additionally, this documentation may fulfill some requirements of the department's ISO Rating or accreditation. Training documentation should be thorough and accurate since it may serve as evidence during litigation involving the organization.

This chapter includes an overview of the following:

* Methods to determine the company's training needs

* Elements of the four-step instructional method

* Lesson plans and the ways they can be modified

* Training methods such as presentations, demonstrations, and practical training evolutions in the context of company-level drills.

During company-level training, the company officer and members of the unit assume new roles. The company officer assumes the

Figure 8.1 The company officer often serves as an instructor during company-level training evolutions.

role of instructor, and company members become the students **(Figure 8.1)**. In the remainder of this chapter, unit members may be referred to as students to emphasize this role in the relationship.

Training Needs Determination

The organization will establish most company-level training needs. Company officers must determine their personnel's training needs to meet the organization's requirements. This determination is based on a number of considerations, including the following:

* Legally mandated training

* Performance during emergency operations

* Annual refresher or recertification requirements

- **Post-incident analysis** reports
- Personnel evaluation reports
- Changes in operational procedures
- Compliance with the individual's personal development plan
- Implementation of new equipment
- Changes in the types of services that the organization delivers
- Job task analysis

Four-Step Method of Instruction

Although numerous teaching models exist, one of the most effective is the four-step method of instruction. This model is used to develop lesson plans and for teaching lessons and courses. Company officers can use the process for company-level training. The model consists of:

Step 1: *Preparation* — Introduces the topic, gains the students' attention, states the learning objectives, and identifies how the students will be evaluated. Also includes the self-preparation that the instructor or company officer takes before beginning the lesson or class. Instructor preparation includes:

- Reviewing the lesson plan, if provided
- Gathering any additional information that may be required
- Assembling the audiovisual training aids and props
- Practicing the skills that will be taught

Step 2: *Presentation* — Presents the information to be taught using an orderly, sequential outline. Identifies the teaching method that is appropriate to the learning styles of the students and the topic being taught. Presentation can be combined with the next and most important step, application. Generally, the presentation choices available are:

- Lecture
- Illustrated lecture
- Discussion
- Demonstration
- Learning activities, such as role-playing, when the topic benefit from these approaches

Step 3: *Application* — Provides opportunities for learning through activities, exercises, discussions, work groups, skill practices, practical training evolutions, and similar learning activities. The purpose is to reinforce the student's learning. Most learning takes place during the application step, making this step critically important.

Step 4: *Evaluation* — Measures how much students have learned through a written, oral, or practical examination or test. Determines how well students have performed skills or evolutions and provides them with feedback to assist them in improving those skills. The purpose is to determine whether or not students achieved the lesson objectives or course outcomes. Instructors or company officers can base most evaluations on observation of individual skills and practical training evolutions unless they administer an examination that the training division has provided.

The format of most lesson plans will follow the four-step method of instruction. Company officers should be prepared to alter the lesson plan to meet the organizational specific conditions without altering the four-step method of instruction.

Lesson Plans

The **lesson plan** is basic to all teaching. It is essentially a road map that guides the instructor, teacher, or company officer through the topic. It is what the company officer will use to deliver the required training regardless of whether it is simply a lecture presentation on a new policy, a demonstration of a piece of equipment, or a practical training evolution intended to improve company teamwork.

All company officers must be familiar with the basic lesson plan components in order to use and modify them when necessary **(Figure 8.2)**. Company officers should review the lesson plan and clarify any points that they do not understand with the appropriate authority.

Planning the topic and how much to teach is a prelude to instruction. Planning a lesson helps company officers carefully think about what to teach and strategies for teaching. Company officers should never begin a training session without a plan, which, at a minimum, describes what they are trying to teach and how they will teach it.

Company officers may need to adapt a lesson plan. Adaptation may be necessary for the following reasons:

- Time may not be available to present the lesson completely. Adaptation may include dividing the topic into smaller components and creating a brief review for each of the topics.

- Audiovisual aids that are required in the lesson plan may not be available. An alternate teaching method or approach may need to be created.

- A lesson plan may be outdated and not accurately represent the current process or policy. The company officer may need to adapt the lesson plan, with administrative approval, to meet the current situation.

- Members of the audience may not respond to the teaching methods listed in the lesson plan. The company officer may need to substitute a different teaching method that will provide a better learning experience for students.

- Environmental conditions may prevent the presentation of the lesson plan as originally intended. Inclement weather may force the company officer to adapt the practical training evolutions for use in an apparatus room or other enclosed space.

Lesson Plan — Teaching outline or plan for teaching that is a step-by-step guide for presenting a lesson or presentation. It contains information and instructions on what will be taught and the teaching procedures to be followed. It covers lessons that may vary in length from a few minutes to several hours.

Firefighter I   Student Lesson 9

1. Preparation

Topic:	Ground Ladders
Time:	1 hour
Level of Instruction:	Application
Learning Objective:	Inspect a ladder as part of a maintenance schedule.
Resources Needed:	Ladder to be inspected — ladder should be old enough to show some wear and tear
	Stick of chalk for marking defects
	Two sawhorses
	Important: Set up ladder on sawhorses in demonstration area before class begins.
Prerequisites:	Completion of ladder lifts and carries, as tested in Skill Sheets 9-2 through 9-8
References:	NFPA® 1001, Fireground Operations 5.3.6
	Essentials of Fire Fighting, Chapter 9
Summary:	Regular and proper cleaning of ladders is more than a matter of appearance: Dirt or debris from a fire may collect and harden, making the ladder sections inoperable. Ladders should be cleaned and inspected after each use. They should also be inspected on a regular monthly basis.
Assignment:	Additional practice, if needed
Comments:	If time permits, consider showing the video *Ground Ladders*.

2. Lesson Outline

A. Maintenance

   1. Keep ground ladders free of moisture.
   2. Do not store or rest ladders in a position where they are subjected to exhaust or engine heat.
   3. Do not store ladders in any area where they are exposed to the elements.
   4. Do not paint ladders except for the top and bottom 12 inches (300 mm) of the beams for purposes of identification or visibility.

B. Cleaning ladders

   1. Clean ladders after every use and before inspecting.
   2. Use a soft-bristle brush and running water for cleaning.
   3. Wipe the ladder dry, checking for defects.

C. General maintenance, inspection, and repair

   1. Maintenance means keeping ladders in a state of usefulness or readiness
   2. Repair means either restoring or replacing that which has become inoperable.
   3. Ladders meeting NFPA® 1931 are marked by the manufacturer with a certification label on the ladder beam.
   4. All firefighters should be capable of performing routine ladder maintenance.
   5. Only trained ladder repair technicians should perform ladder repairs.

Page 1 of 2

Figure 8.2 The basic components of a lesson plan.

Methods of Training

Presentations, discussions, demonstrations, and practical training evolutions comprise most company-level training, but this section will focus on the latter two. The company officer should review all of the training material that has been provided for the topic, practice the required method, and request any assistance necessary before starting the lesson.

Demonstrations

A *demonstration* is the act of showing how to do something or how something operates and is a basic means for teaching manipulative (psychomotor) skills, physical principles, and mechanical functions. Demonstrations can be used effectively to show the operation of tools, equipment, apparatus, or materials and show the results of their use.

To use the demonstration method effectively, company officers should follow a few guidelines. **Table 8.1** shows the guidelines for the two critical areas: preparing and demonstrating.

Company officers may ask company members who are trained in specialized skills to give demonstrations. For example, following a lesson plan, a certified EMT could give refresher training in cardiopulmonary resuscitation (CPR) **(Figure 8.3)**. A hazardous materials team member could provide Awareness-Level hazardous materials training. Thus, the company officer can involve subordinates in the teaching process, providing them with additional teaching skills and experience.

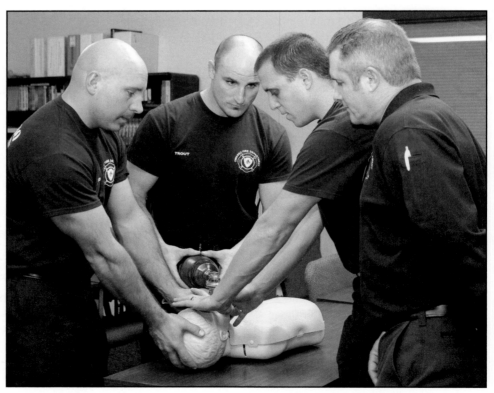

Figure 8.3 A company officer watches as an EMT guides his crewmates through emergency medical refresher training.

Table 8.1
Demonstration Method

Prepare	Demonstrate Skill
1. Know clearly what is to be demonstrated and its learning objective.	1. Begin the demonstration by linking new information with the students' current knowledge.
2. Be proficient in every step of the demonstration by practicing in advance with other company officers or personnel who will be involved in the teaching.	2. Explain what the demonstration will show the group how to do. 3. Explain why the skill is important.
3. Acquire all equipment and accessories, ensure that they work, and arrange them for use.	4. Demonstrate the skill once at normal speed. 5. Repeat the demonstration step by step while explaining each step slowly.
4. Arrange the room or demonstration area so that all participants can see and hear the demonstration.	6. Repeat the demonstration again while a class member or the group explains each step. 7. Consider using a video camera and large-screen monitor when the group is large in order to allow students to see the process up close or observe small details.
	8. Allow students the opportunity to ask questions and clarify any misunderstandings.
	9. Ask for a student volunteer to demonstrate the skill while explaining the steps. Give reassurance by coaching and guiding the student through the process. Offer suggestions or corrections during the demonstration.
	10. Provide the opportunity for students to practice, and allow them to supervise and correct each other as they become skilled. Again, closely monitor student activities when students practice potentially dangerous skills for the first time.
	11. Reassemble the group and demonstrate the skill one more time at normal speed and/or one more time slowly as the group explains the steps as a summary. Relate the skill to the learning objective and performance on the job.

Practical Training Evolutions

In order to minimize the possibility of injuries and liability, practical training should be conducted in accordance with applicable federal/state/provincial/local requirements, NFPA® standards, and other professional association directives. Company-level **practical training evolutions** reinforce the skills learned during formal training sessions and help company personnel to learn to work together.

Practical training evolutions are also opportunities for personnel and units from various agencies, organizations, and jurisdictions to train together for potential joint operations. Multicompany evolutions should include all units within the assigned response area. Instructors, safety officers, and chief officers should monitor evolutions. Company officers can and should develop multicompany evolutions that involve small numbers of units.

Practical Training Examples

Examples of practical training evolutions can include:

- An engine company officer arranging training with a truck company to familiarize the unit with ladder, ventilation, and salvage tasks
- An engine company officer arranging a relay drill with an adjoining engine company
- A truck company officer arranging a rescue exercise with a private or 3rd - agency ambulance

Training locations should be selected to enhance the student's learning experience and reflect actual locations and emergency conditions in which the unit may operate. To ensure realism while maintaining personnel safety, the company officer must plan the training evolutions based on established criteria. The officer must maintain control of the training evolution at all times.

CAUTION
Safety is the primary concern during any and all practical training evolutions.

The company officer must also be creative in selecting the resources needed to develop a realistic learning experience. Examples of a wide variety of company-level training evolutions can be found in Fire Protection Publications' **The Sourcebook for Fire Company Training Evolutions**.

Simple Evolutions

Simple training evolutions involve small groups performing a single task that requires only a few skills. Some examples include:

- Lifting and setting ground ladders
- Performing search and rescue techniques

- Taking and recording patients' vital signs
- Deploying and advancing attack hoselines **(Figure 8.4)**
- Driving and parking fire apparatus

    To begin each evolution, the company officer

- Explains the learning objectives
- Demonstrates the evolution
- Relates the evolution to the classroom presentation
- Emphasizes the safety requirements for the evolution

NOTE: If the evolution involves more than one participant, the demonstration may require the use of an experienced group of responders to perform.

While monitoring the actual evolution, the company officer should immediately stop and correct any performance weaknesses or errors if it is a new skill. The sooner corrections are made, the more likely students are to recognize problems and adjust their behaviors. If it is an existing skill, the students may be allowed to continue to problem-solve to self-correct their performance. Safety infractions must always be corrected immediately.

CAUTION

Company officers should immediately stop the exercise if an injury occurs or seems imminent. In the case of weak or erroneous performance, the company officer should evaluate the impact of interrupting the exercise prior to completion.

Figure 8.4 Advancing hoselines is a common company-level training evolution.

A simple training evolution should be performed as though it is a real emergency incident. The appropriate personal protective equipment (PPE) should be worn during the evolution. All policies and procedures that affect personnel at a real incident are applied during the training evolution, including the National Incident Management System-Incident Command System (NIMS-ICS). Practical training evolutions should also be practiced with both the minimum and maximum staffing level requirements.

For instance, if an engine company is staffed by one person who may arrive at the incident ahead of the rest of the crew, that scenario should be part of the training. If a company is normally staffed by four people but has a minimum level of three, both scenarios should be practiced. This approach assists students in practicing and learning skills they will use on duty.

Complex Evolutions

Complex training evolutions may involve multiple units, agencies, or jurisdictions in scenarios that require high levels of cooperation and coordination. Company officers may be involved in planning and participating in these evolutions. Complex scenarios may include:

- Structure fires
- Urban search and rescue incidents
- Hazardous materials incidents
- Mass casualty scenarios

All training evolutions and exercises should include NIMS-ICS. The use of NIMS-ICS during practical training evolutions has two benefits:

1. It helps ensure the safety and accountability of participants.
2. It acquaints participants with the system's operation. Participants can take this training experience and apply what they have learned at the actual emergency scene.

Locations

A wide variety of sites may be used for practical training evolutions. The most obvious place to perform evolutions is at the station in the apparatus room, in a large indoor classroom (dormitory or living room), or on the parking lot/driveway. These spaces are ideal for training with fire hose, portable fire extinguishers, ground ladders, or other equipment. Caution should be utilized to prevent damage to the station or inconvenience to the public. Company officers must also monitor weather conditions to ensure that adverse weather, limited visibility, icing, and temperature extremes do not increase risks to participants, citizens, or exposures.

Remote training sites may include a wide variety of locations and types. The company officer or the training division may have a list of available remote sites that include the following information:

- Location
- Name of owner/representative
- Availability (access and time)
- Water supply source
- Possible types of training evolutions that the site could support

The company officer must coordinate the training with the training division and property owner. The fire department should have written permission when using private property. Potential remote training sites and their possible training uses include the following:

- Parking lots — Driver/operator training, supply and attack hose deployment, and vehicle extrication operations

- Subdivisions under construction — Driver/operator and building construction training

- Abandoned/condemned structures — Ventilation and forcible-entry training

- Industrial sites — Confined-space rescue, technical and rope rescue, hazardous materials, fire-suppression training, and joint-training evolutions with the local industrial fire brigade

- Structures under demolition — Building collapse, ventilation or forcible entry, and rapid intervention team training

- Vehicle salvage yards — Vehicle extrication operations **(Figure 8.5)**

- Parking garages — Standpipe operations and high-angle rescue training

WARNING!

Company officers must not attempt a live-burn training exercise without approval from the administration and the training division. They must adhere to the requirements of NFPA® 1500, *Standard on Fire Department Occupational Safety and Health Program*, and NFPA® 1403, *Standard on Live Fire Training Evolutions*, regarding safety during live-burn training exercises.

Figure 8.5 Vehicle salvage yards provide an ideal location for vehicle extrication training.

Planning Factors

When planning practical training evolutions, company officers must consider many factors that contribute to a safe and effective learning experience. These factors include:

- **Safety** — Realism in the training evolution must be balanced with the risk to the students' safety and health. In all cases, safety must take precedence over realism. Safety means not only using proper PPE, but planning the evolution with safety as a key component. The safety factor cannot be over-emphasized in planning training. It is never acceptable to sustain injuries during training evolutions.

- **Learning objectives** — Practical training evolutions must result in students meeting the lesson's learning objectives. If it does not meet these criteria, time and effort are wasted. A lesson plan must be created to help define the learning objectives.

- **Justifications** — The training must meet learning objectives, cost/benefit, legal requirements, positive community perception, allotment of resources, and other criteria.

- **Supervision** — Company officers and/or personnel with appropriate training and experience must supervise and monitor every training evolution. The larger the evolution, the more supervisors are required for supervision. NFPA® 1403 requirements recommend an instructor-to-student ratio of one -to-five **(Figure 8.6)**.

- **Resources/logistics** — The plan must provide for all the resources necessary to perform the tasks and complete the evolution, which is especially critical for evolutions that occur at remote sites. Requirements:

  - Water supply quantities must be calculated based on NFPA® 1142, *Standard on Water Supplies for Suburban and Rural Fire Fighting* requirements.

  - Apparatus, tools, extinguishing agents, and personnel must be available at the site.

  - Rest and rehabilitation resources and emergency medical resources must be planned for and brought to the site, including food and water.

  - Sufficient time must be provided to complete the evolution.

- **Weather** — Schedule evolutions when the weather will not be a distraction or create a safety hazard. Be prepared to alter plans when the weather becomes inclement.

- **Legal requirements** — Considerations include those laws, regulations, or standards that require the training and those that limit, constrain, or prohibit training evolutions. Legal requirements that place limitations on training evolutions include environmental laws, zoning, building and fire codes, and ownership.

- **National Incident Management System-Incident Command System (NIMS-ICS)** — Training evolutions must adhere to the same type of command structure used at emergency incidents. NIMS-ICS must be established and followed at all single company, multiple companies, or multiple agencies and jurisdictions training evolutions.

Figure 8.6 Company officers should strive to meet the recommended instructor-to-student ratio of one-to-five.

- **Exposures** — Exposures at remote training locations must be considered when planning a practical training evolution that involves the release of smoke, embers, water, or other residue. Exposure protection must be provided during all live-fire evolutions. Other considerations:
  - Smoke and fire embers moving on wind currents may affect area residents.
  - Water runoff could contaminate drinking water supplies or create a skidding hazard.
- **Evaluations/critiques** — Lesson plans should include an opportunity for company officers and participants to evaluate evolutions and their performances in the following ways:
  - Assist students with attaining proficiency and addressing weaknesses.
  - Assist the training division in determining the effectiveness of the particular evolution.
  - Assist company officers in determining their own effectiveness in teaching and supervising a practical training evolution.
  - Provide critique processing models for all participants when they are involved in emergency incident critiques.

The company officer should apply the following guidelines when planning a practical evolution and establishing the desired learning objectives for experienced personnel during company drills:

- Give each participant the opportunity to have input and influence the final learning outcome based on the established learning objectives. Participants must know their roles and the desired learning objectives.
- Do not assign too many participants to specific tasks. Keep all participants busy, and eliminate or greatly reduce stand-around time.
- Provide a safe staging area for students and an observation area for non-participants.

Figure 8.7 All company-level training must be documented.

- Maintain a suitable instructor-to-participant ratio. The exact ratio varies with the type of evolution. The one-to-five ratio given earlier may be used as a gauge.

- Ensure that training participants have the necessary skill levels and knowledge needed for a particular training evolution.

- Design the practical evolution so that a positive outcome is possible. Assigning a task that is very difficult or impossible to accomplish provides a limited learning experience.

- Provide a summary of what has been learned and what can be carried into the operational environment and actual emergency setting. Discuss the training scenario and its results.

- Videotape the evolution if possible to assist with the critique and for future use as a visual training aid.

- Document all company-level training accurately, including times, topics, participants, and results **(Figure 8.7)**.

Chapter Summary

Company officers are essential to the training process if training goals are to be met. Company-level training builds teamwork and ensures the company will operate safely and effectively during emergency situations.

Training drills allow officers to evaluate the skills of unit personnel. Through observation, the officer can spot trends, strengths, weaknesses, and habits that can be altered, reinforced, or supported to benefit the unit. Company officers are responsible for instilling teamwork, leadership, resourcefulness, and pride so that the unit can operate safely and efficiently during training and actual emergencies.

Review Questions

1. What are the considerations for determining training needs? (pp. 194-195)
2. What are some elements of each of the steps in the Four-Step Method? (pp. 195-196)
3. Why might a company officer need to adapt a lesson plan? (p. 196)
4. What is the difference between the methods of training? (pp. 198-206)

Learning Activity

Learning Activity 8-1

Objective 5: Create a plan to direct fire personnel during a training session.

A company officer must direct training evolutions that are safe, efficient, and clearly stated.

For this activity, you will need access to the following resources:

- Training policies and procedures – You may obtain one from your own department OR by using an Internet search engine

By using the scenario below or by providing your own scenario, create an informal written document that outlines a plan for completing a training evolution and follows all training policies and procedures.

Scenario:
- Your department has recently replaced some of the vehicle extrication power tools kept on the apparatus, and the chief has decided that now is a good time to review and update the company's training on both new and existing vehicle extrication tools.

Answer Key:
Answers for this activity will vary; however, answers should include the following:

- Selection of a suitable site or location, including a justification for choosing this location

- All tools and equipment necessary to complete the evolution safely and effectively

- A list of expectations and hazards that may be encountered

- A pre-training briefing that communicates details the directions and hazards that personnel need to know about

- Methods of evaluation for the training

- Examples of possible feedback to students using appropriate coaching techniques

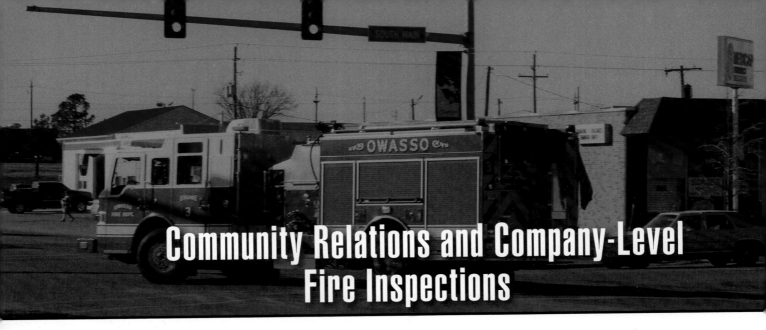

Community Relations and Company-Level Fire Inspections

Chapter Contents

Key Terms

NFPA® Job Performance Requirements

This chapter provides information that addresses the following job performance requirements of NFPA® 1021, *Standard for Fire Officer Professional Qualifications* (2014).

4.3.1

4.3.2

4.3.3

4.5.1

4.5.2

Community Relations and Company-Level Inspections

Learning Objectives

After reading this chapter, students will be able to:

1. Describe community relations. [NFPA® 1021, 4.3.1, 4.3.2, 4.3.3]

2. Explain the process of company-level fire inspections. [NFPA® 1021, 4.5.1, 4.5.2]

3. Identify inspection and testing procedures for fire protection systems. [NFPA® 1021, 4.5.1, 4.5.2]

4. Implement a course of action that addresses a community need. [Learning Activity 9-1; NFPA® 1021, 4.3.1]

5. Address the concern of a citizen in your jurisdiction. [Learning Activity 9-2; NFPA® 1021, 4.3.2]

Chapter 9
Community Relations and Company-Level Inspections

Case History

In a high-rise building for elderly, low-income residents, one resident kept burning food on a stove, causing frequent fire alarms and near-miss fires. Company officers from all three battalions that responded to these alarms realized that the resident's behavior was putting everyone in the building at risk. These officers notified the fire department's Fire Prevention Division. The Fire Prevention personnel worked to educate the resident and recommended installing a safety element on his stove. These were not installed because the apartment owner and the resident could not agree who should pay for the element. In the end, the resident was forced to remove the stove.

As a company officer, you should always consider the safety of your customers. Your job is not to just respond to these automatic alarms, ventilate the smoke, and then reset the alarm. Your job to save lives and reduce property loss can and should be done at the company level utilizing fire prevention techniques. Look at the broader picture and determine what can be done to ensure the safety of all occupants. Look for outside help from the prevention department, building management, and community organizations.

Community relations and company-level fire inspections can help build relationships with the community served. Customer service concepts should be applied to these topics with the intent of strengthening the bonds between the emergency services organization and its customers. Company officers and crew members are the first, and sometimes only, contacts that citizens have with the fire and emergency services organization.

Fire and life safety inspections are key components of any fire and emergency services organization. If conducted properly, they can serve two purposes:

1. Identify and correct potential fire and life safety hazards.

2. Demonstrate the organization's concerns for citizen safety and well-being.

This chapter covers community demographics and **diversity**, interacting with the community, and public relations. This chapter also addresses community risk analysis and the fire and life safety inspection programs.

Diversity — The inclusion of people of different races or cultures in a group or organization.

Community Relations

To establish a positive relationship with the community, the company officer must first know who the external customers are as well as the environment where they live and work. The company officer must recognize and understand the demographics of the service area. Next, officers must be able to use the appropriate method for dealing with customer concerns and complaints. The goodwill of the organization and the credibility of the officer depend on the resolution of citizen concerns. The public information officer (PIO), a senior staff, or the fire chief may need to handle complex citizen complaints or concerns.

Community Demographics

Company officers must know the community's statistical characteristics and demographics in order to understand its composition. Populations are categorized into groups based on physical, social, or economic characteristics such as **(Figure 9.1)**:

- Age
- Education
- Occupation
- Geographic location
- Sex
- Marital status
- Family size

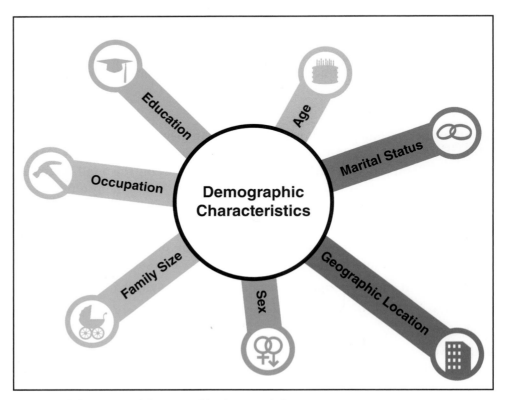

Figure 9.1 Examples of demographic characteristics.

Demographics are used in public service to determine the specific groups within the service area in order to properly serve their needs. Generic public safety education programs can be more effective when diversity and cultural beliefs are considered and accepted, giving these programs more credibility.

Sources for demographic data on the national, state, and local levels in the U.S. are as follows:

- U.S. Census Bureau
- U.S. Department of Labor
- U.S. Department of Health and Human Services
- State, regional, and local government agencies
- Local school board

In Canada, sources include the Canadian Census Bureau and provincial, regional, and local government agencies. The most recent data were compiled following the 2010 U.S. census and the 2011 Canadian census. Information is also available in almanacs that are privately published and accessible through public library systems, on the Internet, or at retail outlets.

Appropriate Terminology

The terms *sex* and *gender* are sometimes confused. *Sex* is a biological fact and, in the case of humans, is defined as male and female. *Gender* refers to males' and females' culturally and socially defined roles and responsibilities based on characteristics that are attributed to each group. These roles and responsibilities may be self-perceptions that the individual holds or society enforces.

Demographics vary regionally and between urban, suburban, and rural areas. It is necessary to research the community that the emergency response organization serves to determine the population's exact composition.

Community Diversity

The fire and emergency services organization's customers may be as diverse as the total population of the world. Classifications that are used to define diversity include (**Figure 9.2**):

- Age
- Religion
- Gender
- Politics
- Sexual orientation
- Socioeconomic level
- Ethnicity
- Education
- Race

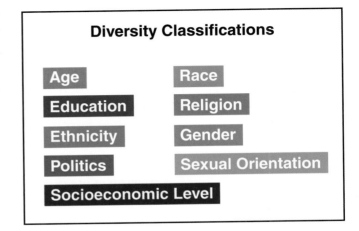

Figure 9.2 Examples of diversity classifications.

Company officers and fire and emergency services personnel must be aware of the various groups that comprise their community. For company officers, the community is not just their immediate response area. The community includes the composition of the organization's area of responsibility. With a mobile and shifting population, the area of responsibility includes individuals who commute into the area, live in the area and work elsewhere, or are only in the response area temporarily, such as university students, tourists, or migrant workers.

The diversity of language, cultural customs, and cultural values should be viewed as assets. Listening to others, constantly being open to new ideas, and respecting differences strengthen an organization and its members and increase the bonds between the various community elements.

Diversity can also create challenges between service providers and customers. A lack of understanding creates an *us-them* mentality that separates people. The language people use or their attitudes and perceived priorities are often used to classify them. The inability to speak or understand a population's language makes it extremely difficult to resolve issues or provide services. People who speak the dominant language can be classified by their accents and stereotyped by generic perceptions.

Interacting with the Community

As the jurisdiction's visible representatives, company officers and crew members will receive citizen concerns, complaints, and inquiries. How company officers resolve these issues determines the organization's public image. When dealing with the public, the company officer must always keep good customer service in mind.

Customer Service Element

Resolving citizen concerns or complaints is an important customer service element. How these concerns or complaints are resolved often determines how the public views its fire and emergency services organization. Fire and emergency organizations are committed to providing the highest level of service, and the relationship between customer service and the organization's public image is valuable. All such issues must be resolved or referred as reasonably and quickly as possible in accordance with the organization's policies and procedures.

Concerns/Complaints/Inquiries

The term *citizen concerns* often translates into *citizen complaints*; that is, a citizen has a concern/complaint based on something the organization, service-area provider, or municipality has done or not done. Issues may involve something directly under the control of the fire and emergency services organization, such as burning regulations, inspections, or weed abatement. Questions on these issues are appropriate for the company officer to answer.

But the issue may also involve something over which the fire and emergency services organization has no jurisdiction — parking regulations, for example. Regardless, company officers must be prepared to deal with the concern or complaint in a friendly, courteous, and professional manner. However, if citizens become verbally abusive or threaten physical violence, officers should call for law-enforcement assistance.

One of the first skills company officers need when dealing with irate citizens is effective listening **(Figure 9.3)**. Company officers must develop the ability to hear or interpret what citizens mean, even if they are unable to articulate the concern clearly. This ability may require an extraordinary degree of familiarity with the different idioms people use, which can be developed through community awareness or the ability to read nonverbal language — or both. Often, just allowing citizens to voice a complaint helps calm them and enables them to look at an issue more rationally. The essential point is that company officers must try to understand the complaint's true nature in order to address.

Once the real issue has been identified, the company officer can either resolve it or refer the citizen to the appropriate person or office. Resolving all concerns, complaints, and inquiries, including those involving personnel acts or omissions, is a duty of all members of the organization. Quality customer service should be modeled for the entire company to follow.

Figure 9.3 Company officers must learn to listen effectively in order to understand the concerns of irate citizens.

Resolutions

Complaint resolution may require that the company officer speak on the citizen's behalf with whoever is empowered to deal with the issue. The citizen's concern must remain a priority until it is resolved. In some cases, the best solution is to let the citizen speak directly to the appropriate person **(Figure 9.4)**.

If a concern or complaint is voiced during an emergency operation, it should not interfere with emergency operations. This situation requires tact because the company officer must explain, without insulting the citizen, that the emergency is more important at the moment than the complaint. The company officer will need to wait until the emergency incident is terminated to resolve the concern or complaint.

Figure 9.4 The company officer may direct a citizen to meet with a higher ranking officer to help resolve the citizen's concern.

In some cases, a citizen will approach a chief officer with a complaint or problem. The chief officer may assign a company officer to investigate the concern. In this case, the company officer should use the necessary organizational resources to research and address the concern.

To refer a citizen to the appropriate authority, a company officer must be thoroughly familiar with the organizational and jurisdictional rules and regulations that apply. The company officer must also know the full range of services that are available to citizens from the fire and emergency services organization and other governmental agencies.

The company officer's duty is to use every legal and ethical means to satisfy a citizen's concern. The company officer must also document the complaint and its disposition. Such documentation may prove to be invaluable should the issue progress to litigation.

Employee Acts or Omissions

One class of citizen complaints involves a member's acts or omissions. These cases must be handled with extreme care because of the sensitivity of these issues in terms of the organization's image, the concern for the rights of all involved, and possible litigation.

The company officer receiving the complaint must know and follow the organization's policy to the letter. Policy usually requires documenting the incident. The officer needs to gather as much pertinent information as possible from the concerned customer regarding the alleged incident. Some organizations use a standardized form for this purpose.

Once the information is gathered, the officer reassures the citizen that the complaint will be fully investigated and the citizen will be informed of the results. The complaint form is then forwarded through channels to the appropriate individual or office.

The company officer who received the original complaint may or may not be involved in the incident's investigation. If the company officer receiving the original complaint is assigned the task of contacting the complainant, care must be taken to not divulge any privileged or confidential information. Before contacting the complainant, the company officer needs to consult with the appropriate organization office to clarify what information can and cannot be made public. The jurisdiction's legal department may also be able to provide guidance.

Public Inquiries

While often similar to handling citizen concerns, resolving public inquiries is usually less challenging and confrontational. Citizen concerns or complaints often begin with a seemingly straightforward inquiry. It is only when a citizen gets the anticipated response that the true nature of the inquiry is revealed. In most cases, citizen inquiries are just genuine requests for information or clarification. Just like resolving concerns and complaints, company officers must develop the ability to hear what citizens mean as well as what they ask. The company officer should be able to refer the citizen to the appropriate authority that can best meet their needs.

Public Relations

A public relations program markets the organization to the community. Its purpose is to build a relationship with the community that is based on trust and commitment. This should be in line with the organization's mission and vision.

The company officer's role is to create and maintain a positive public image. To accomplish this, company officers should be familiar with the process, participate in community activities, and may assume the duties of a public information officer (PIO), if required **(Figure 9.5)**. All statements made to the public must be factual and truthful, which is both ethical and one that wins the greatest support from the customer base.

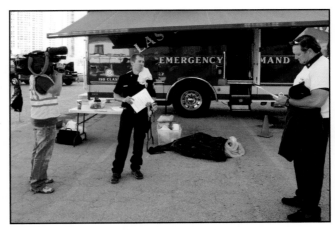

Figure 9.5 A company officer acting as a public information officer (PIO) during a high-rise exercise.

Speaking Engagements and Presentations

The company officer who functions as PIO or represents the organization at speaking engagements or presentations must have good communication skills. Additional information on public information and education can be found in the IFSTA **Fire and Life Safety Educator**, **Public Information Officer**, and **Fire and Emergency Services Instructor** manuals.

Company-Level Inspections

Company officers may be responsible for conducting company-level fire and life safety inspections within their area. Fire and life safety inspections have a two-fold purpose:

1. Ensuring that fire and life safety code requirements are adhered to within public facilities

2. Providing the owner/occupant with safety education materials and information

Ensuring that fire and life safety code requirements are adhered to within public facilities is a proactive loss-control approach intended to reduce the potential for and severity of fires and other incidents. Reducing losses that hazardous conditions cause requires both a proactive and reactive approach. For many years, the reactive approach took precedence. In recent years, the proactive approach has gained more attention and, consequently, more resources. Fire prevention has expanded to include life-safety topics; public education has added information targeted at specific at-risk groups of people, and investigations have increased the use of advanced technology and subject profiling. As a basis for the proactive approach, the fire and emergency services organization must know what hazards the community might be exposed to and the risks that those hazards create.

The second purpose of fire and life safety inspections is to provide the owner/occupant with safety education materials and information. The information can simply explain why an act or condition is unsafe, like the storage of ignitable liquids near an open-flame water heater, or information regarding the type and size of first aid kit that is appropriate for the occupancy. Either way, the inspection is an opportunity to provide a service to the public.

According to NFPA® 1021, Level I Fire Officers are responsible for conducting fire and life safety inspections. To perform this function, company officers must recognize the authority and the limits of the authority permitting them to make inspections. They must also be familiar with the ordinances, codes, and standards that the building owner/occupant is required to meet. The officer must know the steps to take in preparing for and conducting the inspection, how to conduct exit drills, and how to inspect and test private fire protection and signaling systems.

Authority

In general, unless an emergency is in progress on the property, fire and emergency responders cannot enter private property without obtaining permission from the owner or occupant. Under common law and most statutory law, the existence of an emergency constitutes implied permission to enter. There are two exceptions to this fundamental rule of law:

1. Military emergency responders on a military base

2. Members of industrial fire brigades on company property

In these cases, all property is under the ownership or control of the parent organization, and that organization has granted permission for its emergency responders to enter that property.

Exigent Circumstances

Exigent circumstances are conditions that allow emergency responders and law enforcement officers to enter a structure without a warrant. For exigent circumstance to apply, one of these three conditions must be present:

● People may be in imminent danger

● Evidence may face imminent destruction

● A suspect may escape

According to the California Supreme Court case People v. Ramsey, 545 P.2d 1333,1341 (Cal. 1976), an exigent circumstance is: An emergency situation requiring swift action to prevent imminent danger to life or serious damage to property or to forestall the imminent escape of a suspect or destruction of evidence. There is no ready litmus test for determining whether such circumstances exist, and in each case the extraordinary situation must be measured by the facts known by officials.

When no life-threatening emergency condition exists, the owner/occupant or local ordinance must grant the right to enter private property. This applies specifically to fire and life safety inspections that the inspectors or fire and emergency service companies perform. The local governing body (city or borough council, county board of supervisors) must adopt an ordinance that authorizes the fire chief and designated representatives to enter private property within the jurisdiction, at any reasonable hour, to conduct fire and life safety inspections. This ordinance should contain a section that specifically authorizes inspection personnel to enter and provides for the issuance of an inspection warrant if the occupant refuses to allow inspection personnel to enter.

Ordinances, Codes, and Standards

Local jurisdictions often adopt one or more ordinances delegating authority to the fire chief for protecting the public from fires and other life safety hazards. Through these ordinances, the local jurisdiction adopts national model building and fire codes and standards by reference. For example, rather than write its own fire code, the governing body may choose to adopt the current edition of the International Code Council's International Fire Code (IFC) or NFPA® 1, *Uniform Fire Code*™. When adopting a particular model code's edition, the governing body may also amend it to make it more applicable to local conditions. The ordinance would adopt that specific edition of the code, as amended, as the law within the jurisdiction. This edition of the code continues to be applicable within the jurisdiction, even after a new edition is published, unless the governing body chooses to adopt the newer edition in the same way it adopted the first one.

Company officers should refer to their fire prevention division when inspecting buildings and facilities when they have questions regarding potential code infractions. Local fire prevention officers should be notified if significant life safety issues are found during inspections.

Communities have shifted much of the responsibility for fire and life safety to the owners and occupants of structures. Stronger fire and life safety codes have required improvements in the passive and active fire protection elements of building construction and process control. Suppression systems have been required in new buildings of a given size or occupancy type, hazardous processes have been eliminated from certain construction types, and building ventilation systems have been designed with controls to permit their use in moving contaminated atmospheres out of the structure.

Model Building Codes

Model building codes provide municipalities and jurisdictions with the ability to control structures' construction and use and ensure life safety for these building's occupants. There are primarily two major organizations that develop model building codes, which include structural, electrical, plumbing, and safety requirements:

1. National Fire Protection Association (NFPA®)

2. International Code Council (ICC)

Local jurisdictions adopt the model codes, sometimes with alterations, and assign enforcement responsibilities to the building, electrical, plumbing, and/ or fire inspections departments. The ICC and NFPA® publish individual code books for building construction, electrical installation, plumbing installation, and many other building components.

Building Construction Types

Each model building code classifies building construction in different terms. Basically, construction classifications are based upon materials used in construction and upon hourly fire-resistance ratings of structural components.

The jurisdiction's adopted building code determines the types of buildings constructed in an area. In many instances (old areas in particular), existing structures may not be required to meet the current building code unless significant renovations are performed. If this is the case, the inspection bureau, building and safety department, or other agencies should be notified.

It is necessary to conduct individual building inspections to determine the type of construction, the current occupancy use, what alterations have been made, and potential hazards that the structure may present to occupants and emergency responders. Most building codes have the same five construction classifications, but may use different terms to describe each classification.

This section will address the building construction classifications identified in NFPA® 220 and the International Building Code **(Table 9.1)**. Company officers should understand the building code that their jurisdiction adopts.

NFPA® 220, *Standard on Types of Building Construction*, and the International Building Code® (IBC®) both use classifications that are consistent with those used in the National Fire Incident Reporting System (NFIRS). NFPA® 220 uses Roman numerals to designate the five major classifications (Types I through V). Each classification is further divided into subtypes using a three-digit Arabic number code or several letters. IBC® designates five construction types (Types I through V) with two subcategories (A and B) for each type except for Type IV. In both classification systems, structures are composed of the following building elements:

- Structural frame
- Load-bearing walls, both interior and exterior
- Exterior nonbearing walls and partitions
- Interior nonbearing walls and partitions
- Floor assemblies
- Roof assemblies

NFPA® 220 Classifications

NFPA® 220 classifications designate five major building construction classifications that are then divided into subtypes that are based on the fire-resistance rating of the various structural components. The classifications range from Type I (most fire-resistive) through Type V (least fire-resistive). The NFPA® 220 construction classifications include:

**Table 9.1
NFPA© 220 Construction Types
Compared to IBC Construction Types**

NFPA© 220	IBC
I (443)	—
I (332)	I A
II (222)	I B
II (111)	II A
II (000)	II B
III (211)	III A
III (200)	III B
IV (2HH)	IV HT
V (111)	V A
V (000)	V B

- **Type I construction** — Also called fire-resistive construction in some codes. Structural members, including walls, columns, beams, floors, and roofs, are made of noncombustible or limited combustible materials **(Figure 9.6, p. 222)**. Buildings of this type were originally designed to confine any fire and its resulting products of combustion to a given location. Characteristics:
  — The primary **fuel load** (total fuel available) is composed of the structure's contents because of the limited combustibility of the construction materials.
  — Openings made in partitions and improperly designed heating, ventilating, and air-conditioning (HVAC) systems can compromise fire containment to a certain area.

- **Type II construction** — Also called noncombustible or noncombustible/limited combustible construction. Structural members are similar to Type I except that the degree of fire resistance is lower. Materials with no fire-resistance rating (such as untreated wood) may be used **(Figure 9.7, p. 222)**. The heat buildup from a fire in the building can cause structural supports to fail. Another potential problem is the type of roof. Characteristics:
  — Contents of the structure compose the primary fuel load.
  — Roofs are often flat, built-up types that may contain combustible felt (tar paper) and roofing tar. Fire extension to the roof can eventually cause the entire roof to become involved and fail.

- **Type III construction** — Commonly referred to as ordinary construction. Exterior walls and structural members that are portions of exterior walls are made of noncombustible or limited combustible materials. Interior structural members, including walls, columns, beams, floors, and roofs, may be completely or partially constructed of wood **(Figure 9.8, p. 222)**. The wood used in these members has smaller dimensions than that required for heavy timber construction (Type IV). Fire hazards can be reduced if fire-stops (solid materials) are placed inside concealed spaces to limit the spread of combustion by-products. Fire concerns:
  — Fire and smoke spreading through concealed spaces between walls, floors, and ceilings
  — Heat conduction to concealed spaces through finish materials (drywall or plaster) or holes in finish materials, causing heat, smoke, and gases to spread to other parts of the structure
  — Fire actually burning within concealed spaces and feeding on combustible construction materials in the space

- **Type IV construction** — Also called heavy timber construction. Exterior and interior walls and their associated structural members are of noncombustible or limited combustible materials. Other interior structural members, including beams, columns, arches, floors, and roofs, are made of solid or laminated wood with no concealed spaces **(Figure 9.9, p. 222)**. Characteristics:
  — Wooden members must have large enough dimensions to be considered heavy timber.
  — Dimensions that qualify as heavy timber vary (depending on the particular code being used) but are usually defined as being at least 8 inches (203 mm) in its smallest dimension.

Fuel Load — Amount of fuel present, expressed quantitatively in terms of weight of fuel per unit area. This may be available fuel (consumable fuel) or total fuel and is usually dry weight. *Also known as* Fuel Loading.

Figure 9.6 An example of Type I construction.

Figure 9.7 A Type II structure under construction.

Figure 9.8 A common Type III structure.

Figure 9.9 Heavy timbers found in Type IV construction.

Figure 9.10 An example of a Type V construction structure.

- **Type V construction** — Exterior walls, bearing walls, columns, beams, girders, trusses, arches, floors, and roofs are made entirely or partially of wood or other approved combustible material. Buildings are typically wood-frame structures used for various mercantile occupancies, most single-family and multifamily residences, and other free-standing structures up to about six stories in height **(Figure 9.10)**. Just as in Type III construction, Type V construction differs from Type IV mainly in the smaller dimensions of the structural members.

International Building Code® Classifications

The IBC® designates five construction types with two subcategories for each type with the exception of Type IV. Each construction type defines the materials and fire performance of the building element of the structure. IBC® construction types are similar to the NFPA® categories and range from Type I, which is most fire-resistive, to Type V, which is least fire-resistive. IBC® construction classifications are described in the following list:

- **Type I construction** — Consists of noncombustible materials that use steel, iron, concrete, or masonry structural elements. Subcategories:
  - *Type IA*: Requires a 3-hour fire-resistance rating of the structural frame and load-bearing walls; floors must have a 2-hour fire-resistance rating; and roofs must have a 1½-hour fire-resistance rating (most stringent classification)
  - *Type IB:* Requires a 2-hour fire-resistance rating for the structural frame and load-bearing walls; floors must have a 2-hour fire-resistance rating; and roofs must have a 1-hour fire-resistance rating

- **Type II construction** — Consists of noncombustible materials but with a reduced fire-resistance rating when compared with Type I construction. This type is often referred to, although not entirely accurately, as a 1-hour building with bearing walls and floors have a 1-hour fire-resistance rating. Subcategories:
  - *Type IIA:* Requires noncombustible fire-resistive materials similar to Type I buildings with the structural elements made of steel, concrete, or masonry
  - *Type IIB:* Requires approved noncombustible materials that may have no assigned fire-resistance ratings

- **Type III construction** — Consists of structural elements made of any materials that the code permits. Exterior bearing walls must have a 2-hour fire-resistance rating. Subcategories:
  - *Type IIIA:* Requires materials that will provide a 1-hour fire-resistance construction throughout the structure
  - *Type IIIB:* Lacks the 1-hour fire-resistance construction requirement

- **Type IV construction** — Consists of structural elements of any type permitted by the code with exterior walls being constructed of noncombustible materials while interior building elements are constructed of solid or laminated wood having no concealed spaces (also known as heavy timber or HT). Buildings must have permanent partitions, and members of the structural frame must have a minimum fire-resistance rating of at least 1 hour. Characteristics:

— *Exterior walls:* May have fire-retardant-treated wood framing with a 2-hour fire-resistance rating or less

— *Wooden columns:* Requires a minimum 8 inch (203 mm) dimensioned lumber (not less than 6 inches [152 mm] nominal in width) when supporting a floor or not less than 8 inches (203 mm) nominal depth when supporting roof or ceiling loads only

— *Floor framing (including wood beams and girders):* Requires sawn or glued-laminated timber of at least 6 inches (152 mm) nominal width and not less than 10 inches (254 mm) depth

— *Roof framing:* Requires wood-frame or glued-laminated arches for roof construction that rises from the floor with a minimum of 6 inches (152 mm) nominal width and 8 inches (203 mm) nominal depth for the first half of its length and then no less than 6 inches (152 mm) nominal dimension for the top half of its length

— *Roofs:* Must be constructed without concealed spaces

- **Type V construction** — Consists of structural elements and exterior and interior walls constructed of any materials that the code permits (also known as wood-frame construction) Subcategories:

— *Type VA:* Requires a 1-hour fire-resistance rating for all structural elements except for nonbearing interior walls and partitions

— *Type VB:* May have non-fire-rated structural elements

Inspection Responsibilities

If a company officer's primary duty is managing/supervising an emergency response unit, the inspection function is secondary to emergency response duties. All unit members must understand that the inspection may be interrupted by an emergency.

While private citizens may ignore hazardous conditions, on-duty company officers must not. All emergency responders have a legal and moral duty to act when they confront a hazardous condition. When the local jurisdiction adopts a national model code, the fire and emergency services organization's responsibility to inspect all buildings and facilities (other than private residences) within the jurisdiction is clearly identified in the code. Each of these model codes specifies that the fire chief is responsible for ensuring that these buildings and facilities are inspected. The fire chief delegates this responsibility to the fire marshal who usually delegates the actual inspections to fire prevention officers or personnel at the unit level **(Figure 9.11)**.

Most fire codes require each building or facility to be inspected at least once each year. Certain high hazard occupancies, such as places of public assembly, may require more frequent inspections.

When conducting fire and life safety inspections, company officers must identify those hazardous conditions that might cause a fire or contribute to its spread. They must also identify conditions that might impede the occupants' **egress** from the structure in an emergency **(Figure 9.12)**. Any of these

Egress — Escape or evacuation.

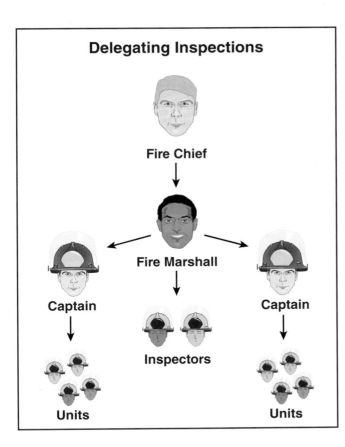

Delegating Inspections

Fire Chief

Fire Marshall

Captain

Inspectors

Captain

Units

Units

Figure 9.11 The responsibility of conducting fire and life safety inspections can be delegated from the fire chief to company officers and their personnel.

Figure 9.12 A blocked exit can restrict occupant evacuation during a fire or emergency and must be brought to the occupant's attention.

conditions is a violation of one or more sections of the applicable code. It is the company officer's responsibility, in accordance with organizational SOPs, to identify the specific code section that applies and to see that the owner/occupant takes appropriate, timely action to correct the hazardous condition and comply with the code.

The time allowed to correct any particular violation varies depending upon the violation and organizational policies. Some violations, such as an obstructed or locked exit door, must be corrected immediately before the inspector leaves the premises. The occupant can eliminate these hazards immediately. Other violations may require more time to correct, such as when a fire extinguisher's inspection tag is outdated, and the occupant must be given a reasonable amount of time to comply. Some violations may be of less immediate concern and the occupant may be incapable of complying with the code immediately. For example, if one or more of the building's fire extinguishers appear to be functional but are due for annual service, the inspector should allow the occupant a reasonable amount of time to arrange for them to be serviced.

When a violation has been reported to the occupant and the required corrective action explained, a written notice is issued including the date and time of the follow-up or reinspection. The company officer must ensure that the follow-up inspection is made on the specified date.

If the follow-up inspection reveals that the hazard has been eliminated, the code enforcement inspection process has served its purpose. All that remains is to thank the occupant and to complete the necessary paperwork.

However, if the violation has not been corrected or if a halfhearted attempt was made and the hazard still exists, then the inspector must follow the organization's guideline regarding how to gain code compliance. Several possible avenues are available. These range from making another attempt to convince the occupant to comply and scheduling a second follow-up inspection to issuing the responsible party a citation. In some cases, the inspector may be empowered to force the business to cease operation or vacate the occupancy until code compliance is achieved. The action taken depends on the situation and organization's policy. It is the company officer's responsibility to know local code enforcement policy and apply it appropriately.

NOTE: The inspector must not attempt to apply code requirements that the jurisdiction has not adopted. Also, the company officer should not attempt to apply current code requirements to existing structures unless the code states that it covers all or all new and existing structures.

Preparing for Inspections

A major factor in a successful life safety inspection is preparation. All inspections have certain characteristics in common. However, each occupancy class has characteristics that make it different from all other classes, and within each class there are differences among individual occupancies. The extent to which the company officer prepares to inspect a particular occupancy often determines the quality of the results of the inspection.

The purpose of any fire and life safety inspection is to leave the occupancy safer than before the inspection and the occupants more knowledgeable about protecting themselves and their property from fires. When a company officer is assigned to inspect a particular occupancy, the first step in preparing for the inspection is gathering information. The information may come from a variety of sources and varies with the type of occupancy and the officer's level of expertise.

Except for information about completely new occupancies, one of the best information sources about a particular occupancy is the record of previous inspections made there. This record provides background information about the building or facility's ownership, occupancy, telephone numbers, and emergency contacts. The record also shows the types of activities that are conducted within the facility, as well as any previous code violations and their nature.

Information about previous inspections may reveal compliance patterns or noncompliance that can indicate the owner's level of commitment to fire and life safety **(Figure 9.13)**. For example, if there are fewer and less serious violations found each time the building is inspected, it indicates that management is making a conscientious attempt to comply with the code. On the other hand, a record showing the same number and types of violations during each previous inspection may indicate that the ownership/management do not take safety issues very seriously. At the very least, the record indicates a need for more public education with the building's owner/occupant.

The most specific and authoritative information sources about any particular occupancy class or type are the model building and fire codes that the jurisdiction adopted. Model codes describe general fire and life safety requirements that apply to all occupancies and detail exactly what is required for various processes in many different occupancy types. Company officers should consult the locally adopted building and fire codes and other sources needed to become familiar with the requirements for the type of occupancy they have been assigned to inspect. Further information is provided in IFSTA's **Fire Inspection and Code Enforcement** manual.

Figure 9.13 Company officers should examine data from previous inspections prior to conducting an inspection.

Figure 9.14 The company officer should contact the facility manager and set up an inspection appointment.

Once the preparation is complete, the inspection is ready to be scheduled. Contact each business in advance to make an appointment for the inspection **(Figure 9.14)**. Contacting each business allows the owner/occupant to prepare for the inspection and reduces the possibility of disrupting personnel work schedules. Some organizations require a systematic scheduling of inspections based on geographical areas to ensure the public that the inspection process is consistent and not selective. Other organizations inspect similar types of occupancies at the same time. Company officers must know the inspection policy and follow it.

During an inspection, the company officer and unit personnel must dress and act in a completely professional manner. All unit members should be briefed on their responsibilities during the inspection, present a well-groomed appearance, and wear clean uniforms. Their behavior and appearance will reflect on the jurisdiction, the organization, and the officer. Coveralls and protective clothing are often used to protect the uniform. Badges and official identification are mandatory for all inspection personnel. A large part of the success of the inspection depends on how the business owner and employees perceive the personnel conducting the inspection.

Conducting Inspections

The inspection begins as the unit approaches the building or facility. The unit should be driven around the facility, or the block on which it is located, to observe the surrounding area. Personnel should note or photograph hydrants, potential exposures, overhead obstructions, business name and address as displayed on the front of the building, and anything else that might impede or improve locating and gaining access to the building or facility **(Figure 9.15)**.

The apparatus should be parked so that it does not interfere with employees or customers and allows the unit to respond quickly if an emergency arises. Most organizations require one unit member to remain with the apparatus during the inspection. This allows the apparatus to be moved if necessary and provides security for the apparatus and its tools and equipment.

The company officer should enter the business through the main entrance and go directly to the main office or reception desk. The officer should contact the person responsible for the safety and security of the building or facility. In small businesses, this may mean dealing directly with the business owner; in larger firms, it may be a manager or maintenance supervisor. Company officers should introduce themselves and unit members. The company officer states the reason for the visit, explains the purposes of the inspection, how it is conducted, and the possible outcomes.

Before starting the inspection tour, ask the representative to review the background data listed in the inspection record (address, building ownership building, business ownership, both business and emergency phone numbers) to ensure the information is still current **(Figure 9.16)**. For a new business, this data should be compiled at this time.

Figure 9.15 Identifying the location of key boxes is part of inspecting the exterior.

Figure 9.16 The facility manager should discuss the facility's background information with the company officer.

The representative should be asked to either accompany the company officer throughout the tour or designate someone to do so. Having a representative of the business with the company officer is very important to the inspection's success. The representative can answer questions, open locked doors, and explain processes or activities in the facility.

Life safety is the inspection's primary concern. It should be made clear to the representative that the company officer is interested in more than just fire extinguishers. The company officer must be able to visually inspect every room, space, or compartment. If the company personnel must don special clothing to avoid contaminating clean rooms or other environmentally controlled areas, then they should do so. If there is concern about trade secrets being compromised during the inspection, some reasonable accommodation must be made that allows the company personnel to inspect the sensitive room or area. For example, the company personnel may sign confidentiality agreements. Some private firms working under contract with the federal government require inspecting personnel to complete a personal data form before being allowed to enter the premises.

There is no set pattern for conducting fire inspections. However, whatever pattern is chosen must be systematic and thorough. Some businesses are so small that inspecting their premises is relatively simple and takes only a few minutes. Others are quite large and complex, often occupying more than one building and covering large land areas, and they take several hours to inspect. The officer may choose to start the formal inspection from the outside. This allows the inspector to measure the building, make notes or take pictures of important features, such as fire department connections (FDC) or security gates or window coverings **(Figure 9.17)**. If the occupancy has a sprinkler system, the inspectors may want to check the post indicator valve (PIV) to ensure it is in the open position. If the PIV is closed, the company officer can address this with the building supervisor.

Figure 9.17 The company officer should examine a facility's fire department connections (FDCs) during a fire and life safety inspection.

Once inside the building, company personnel may start at the lowest level and systematically work their way to the roof, or vice versa. Some inspectors feel that starting from the roof allows them to see the entire facility from a different vantage point and can expose features that were missed from grade level. The most important consideration is to ensure that the inspection is done in a way that results in each and every compartment within the building or facility being inspected. The building representative should be asked to open any doors that are found to be locked. The floor plan should be checked against the previous one to see whether any major remodeling has been done or additions have been made. If no floor plan exists, one should be drawn during the inspection tour.

General Inspection Categories

In all occupancies, there are certain general fire and life safety items that must be inspected. Many fire and emergency services organizations list these common violations on their inspection form so that the inspector only needs to check the appropriate box to indicate a code section violation. These items fall into the following categories:

- Means of egress
- Housekeeping
- Processes
- Storage
- Waste management
- Fire protection

Means of Egress

The means of egress from the building is the single most important life safety item to be inspected. The means of egress consists of three parts:

- Access to the exit
- The exit itself
- The exit discharge

The exit may discharge into a public way or lead to a point of safety or area of refuge. According to NFPA® 101®, *Life Safety Code*®; NFPA® 1, *Uniform Fire Code*; and ICC/ANSI A117.1, all means of egress must be usable by a person with a severe mobility impairment.

The inspector should look for obstructions, markings, lighting, door swing, hardware, and stairwells:

- *Obstructions* — Any permanent or moveable object that will reduce the width of the original exit passageway. Obstructions may include furniture, plants, or storage of materials, which block or partially block the pathway. These obstructions must be removed immediately. Walls or other construction features that have been added that reduce or alter the passageway would also be considered obstructions. These violations, if severe, may result in the temporary closing of the facility until corrections are made.

- *Markings* — Exit doors and the passageways to them must be marked with signs that are visible in the dark. Signs are usually electrified and have auxiliary power in the event of a power failure. Some fire codes permit reflective, self-luminous signs. Signs are traditionally over the door, although additional alternate signs may be at floor level to permit people who are crawling under smoke to see them. In occupancies that require them, exit path maps must be displayed at various locations.

- *Lighting* — Auxiliary emergency lighting systems that operate during power failures should also be checked for operation. Rechargeable hand lights may also be required for medical facilities staff.

- *Door swing* — Depending on the occupancy type, exit doors usually swing in the direction of travel. On a door's exit discharge side, the door opening should not extend into the passageway and reduce the exit passage width.

- *Door hardware* — Exit doors must remain unlocked from the inside whenever the building is occupied and must be capable of being opened from the inside with a single motion without a key or any special knowledge. Depending upon the occupancy type and occupant load served (maximum number of people), exit doors may be required to swing open in the direction of exit travel and be equipped with panic hardware.

- *Stairwells* — The condition of exit stairs should be inspected. Stair treads and handrails must be secure to prevent tripping and falling **(Figure 9.18)**. Interior locks should not prevent reentry onto all floors, if required. Reentry permits sheltering in place on selected floors. Lights and signs must be in place and operational.

Figure 9.18 Company-level fire and life safety inspections should include inspecting stairs to prevent trips and falls.

Housekeeping

Workplace trash and litter accumulation in the workplace can be hazardous in several ways. Trash and litter can obscure or block access to the means of egress. Even though trash and litter rarely start a fire (except in the case of spontaneous combustion), they can provide additional fuel to any fire that does start. They can also create trip and fall hazards and conceal other hazards, such as leaking pipes or exposed wiring. Housekeeping is also an indication of how owners/employees feel about a safe work environment.

Processes

Industrial processes can create a variety of hazards. They can start fires, contribute to fire spread, or contaminate the environment. Process requirements for each occupancy class are included in the various codes. The specific hazards for each of the major **occupancy classifications** are discussed later in this chapter. Company officers must thoroughly research the applicable occupancy code requirements before inspecting them.

Storage

Storage areas come in all sizes and may contain various items, some hazardous. Small storage rooms may contain janitorial supplies, office supplies, or miscellaneous materials. Larger store rooms may contain retail merchandise, such as toys, clothing, maintenance parts, or ignitable liquids. Storage buildings may contain the raw materials used to produce finished products, boxes containing the finished products, or both. Flammable materials, such as cardboard boxes, packing materials, or ignitable liquids, must be kept separate from sources of ignition. This may include prohibiting smoking and/or welding and cutting operations in storage areas. Storage must not interfere with automatic sprinklers or other built-in fire protection devices or systems. High-stack storage may require in-rack automatic sprinkler systems. Exit passageways must be marked and unobstructed.

Waste Management

Accumulations of flammable or combustible waste, such as wastepaper or oily rags, can be a significant fire and life safety hazard. These materials must be kept separate from ignition sources. This often means proper containment, such as putting oily rags into approved, self-closing containers or putting flammable trash in metal containers in sprinklered enclosures.

Fire Protection

This item is based on the assumption that other fire prevention strategies may not always be successful in preventing fires. Fire protection includes many components such as:

- Employees' ability to recognize and report a fire
- Employees' ability to correctly use portable fire extinguishers
- Built-in fire detection and alarm systems
- Automatic sprinklers and other built-in fire suppression systems

Company-level personnel must possess sufficient knowledge and skill to be able to:

- Answer employee questions related to fire prevention and protection
- Assist plant safety and security personnel in these areas when asked
- Inspect and, if required, test built-in fire detection and suppression systems

Company-level pre-inspection research is critical for all inspections. Such preparation is even more important if the company is assigned to inspect highly complex and very specialized occupancies. The inspection criteria unique to the most common of these occupancies are discussed in the following section.

Model Code Families

The majority of model codes relating to buildings and fire safety currently used in North America are based on the occupancy type or use of the building or structure. All model codes classify buildings in this manner. The primary fire and life safety codes in use are those that the National Fire Protection Association® (NFPA®), International Code Council (ICC), and National Building and Fire Codes of Canada (NBFCC) developed. The occupancy classifications for each of these are provided in **Table 9.2**.

Hazard of Contents

NFPA® 5000 and NFPA® 1 further classify each individual occupancy according to the relative fire hazard of its contents. These classifications are based on a subjective evaluation of the relative danger of the start and spread of fire, the danger of smoke or gases generated, and the danger of explosion or other occurrence potentially endangering the lives and safety of occupants of the building or structure. There are three contents-hazard classifications:

- *Low hazard* is the classification for contents of such low combustibility that a self-propagating fire cannot occur in them. Such materials might include fiberglass insulation or minerals that do not contain hydrocarbons.

- *Ordinary hazard* is the classification for contents that are likely to burn with moderate rapidity or give off a considerable volume of smoke. These materials might include paper, cardboard, textiles, and some plastics.

- *High hazard* is the classification for contents that are likely to burn with extreme rapidity or from which explosions are likely. Examples of these materials might include flammable liquids or highly reactive substances.

NOTE: The preceding hazard levels are incorporated within the ICC and Canadian codes under each occupancy classification.

Hazardous Materials Markings

Company-level personnel must be familiar with the marking systems that are used to identify hazardous materials and processes. In addition to Department of Transportation (DOT) placards, labels, and markings, a number of other markings, marking systems, labels, labeling systems, colors, color codes, and signs may indicate the presence of hazardous materials at fixed facilities, on piping systems, and on containers. These other markings may be as simple as the word *chlorine* stenciled on a fixed-facility tank exterior or as complicated as a site-specific hazard communication system using a unique combination of labels, placards, emergency contact information, and color codes. Some fixed-facility containers may have identification numbers that correspond to site or emergency plans that provide details on the product, quantity, and other pertinent information.

Company-level personnel conducting inspections need to be familiar with the more widely used specialized hazardous materials marking systems. This section highlights the most common specialized systems in North America, including NFPA® 704, common hazardous communication labels, piping systems, and color codes. Additional information can be found in IFSTA's **Hazardous Materials for First Responders** manual.

NFPA® 704. NFPA® 704 provides a widely recognized method for indicating the presence of hazardous materials at commercial, manufacturing, institutional, and other fixed-storage facilities. Local building and fire codes commonly require this system for all occupancies that contain hazardous

Table 9.2
Occupancy Classifications
This table is a general comparative overview of the occupancy categories for three major model code systems. Readers must consult the locally adopted code and amendments for complete information regarding each of these occupancies.

Occupancy	ICC	NFPA	NBFCC
Assembly	**A-1** - occupancies with fixed seating that are intended for the production and viewing of performing arts or motion picture films. **A-2** - those that include the serving of food and beverages; occupancies have nonfixed seating. Nonfixed seating is not attached to the structure and can be rearranged as needed. **A-3** - occupancies used for worship, recreation, or amusement, such as churches, art galleries, bowling alleys, amusement arcades, as well as those that are not classified elsewhere in this section. **A-4** - occupancies used for viewing of indoor sporting events and other activities that have spectator seating. **A-5** - outdoor viewing areas; these are typically open air venues but may also contain covered canopy areas as well as interior concourses that provide locations for vendors and other commercial kiosks.	**Assembly Occupancy** - An occupancy (1) used for a gathering of 50 or more persons for deliberation, worship, entertainment, eating, drinking, amusement, awaiting transportation, or similar uses; or (2) used as a special amusement building, regardless of occupant load.	**Group A Division 1** - Occupancies intended for the production and viewing of the performing arts. **Group A Division 2** - Occupancies not classified elsewhere in Group A. **Group A Division 3** - Occupancies of the arena type. **Group A Division 4** - Occupancies in which occupants are gathered in open air.
Business	*Business Group B* - Buildings used as offices to deliver service-type or professional transactions, including the storage of records and accounts. Characterized by office configurations to include: desks, conference rooms, cubicles, laboratory benches, computer/data terminals, filing cabinets, and educational occupancies above the 12th grade.	*Business* - Occupancy used for the transaction of business other than mercantile.	**Group D** - Business and personal services occupancies

Table 9.2
Continued

Occupancy	ICC	NFPA	NBFCC
Educational	***Educational Group E*** - Buildings providing facilities for six or more persons at one time for educational purposes in grades kindergarten through twelfth grade. Religious educational rooms and auditoriums that are part of a place of worship, which have occupant loads of less than 100 persons, retain a classification of Group A-3.	**Educational Occupancy -** Occupancy used for educational purposes through the twelfth grade by six or more persons for 4 or more hours per day or more than 12 hours per week.	Covered under Group A
Factory Industrial	***Factory Industrial Group F*** - Occupancies used for assembling, disassembling, fabrication, finishing, manufacturing, packaging, repair, or processing operations. - ***Factory Industrial F-1 Moderate Hazard*** (examples include but not limited to: aircraft, furniture, metals, and millwork) - ***Factory Industrial F-2 Low Hazard*** (examples include but not limited to: brick and masonry, foundries, glass products, and gypsum) ***High Hazard Group H*** - Buildings used in manufacturing or storage of materials that constitute a physical or health hazard. - ***High-hazard Group H-1*** - detonation hazard - ***High-hazard Group H-2*** - deflagration or accelerated burning hazard - ***High-hazard Group H-3*** - materials that readily support combustion or pose a physical hazard - ***High-hazard Group H-4*** - health hazards - ***High-hazard Group H-5*** - hazardous production	**Industrial Occupancy -** Occupancy in which products are manufactured or in which processing, assembling, mixing, packaging, finishing, decorating, or repair operations are conducted.	**Group F Division 1 -** High-hazard industrial occupancies **Group F Division 2 -** Medium-hazard occupancies **Group F Division 3 -** Low-hazard industrial occupancies

Table 9.2
Continued

Occupancy	ICC	NFPA	NBFCC
Occupancy Institutional (Care and Detention)	**Institutional Group I** **Group I-1** - Assisted living facilities holding more than 16 persons on a 24 hour basis. These persons are capable of self rescue. **Group I-2** - Medical, surgical, psychiatric, or nursing care facilities for more than 5 people who are not capable of self-preservation or need assistance to evacuate. **Group I-3** - Prisons and detention facilities for more than 5 people under restraint. **Group I-4** - Child and adult day care facilities.	**Ambulatory Health Care** - Building (or portion thereof) used to provide outpatient services or treatment simultaneously to four or more patients that renders the patients incapable of taking action for self-preservation under emergency conditions without the assistance of others. **Health Care** - An occupancy used for purposes of medical or other treatment or care of four or more persons where such occupants are mostly incapable of self-preservation due to age, physical or mental disability, or because of security measures not under the occupants' control. **Residential Board and Care** - Building or portion thereof that is used for lodging and boarding of four or more residents, not related by blood or marriage to the owners or operators, for the purpose of providing personal care services. **Detention and Correctional** - An occupancy used to house one or more persons under varied degrees of restraint or security where such occupants are mostly incapable of self-preservation because of security measures not under the occupants' control.	**Group B Division 1** - Care or detention occupancies in which persons are under restraint or are incapable of self-preservation because of security measures not under their control. **Group B Division 2** - Care or detention occupancies in which persons having cognitive or physical limitations require special care or treatment.
Mercantile	**Mercantile Group M.** - Occupancies open to the public that are used to store, display, and sell merchandise with incidental inventory storage.	**Mercantile** - An occupancy used for the display and sale of merchandise.	**Group E** - Mercantile occupancies
Residential	**Residential Group R** **R-1** - Residential occupancies containing sleeping units where the occupants are primarily transient in nature (boarding houses, hotels, and motels) **R-2** - Residential occupancies containing sleeping units or more than 2 dwelling units where the occupants are primarily permanent in nature (apartments, convents, non-transient hotels, etc...)	**Residential Occupancy** - Provides sleeping accommodations for purposes other than health care or detention and correctional. **One- and Two-Family Dwelling Unit** - Building that contains not more than two dwelling units with independent cooking and bathroom facilities.	**Group C** - Residential occupancies

Table 9.2
Continued

Occupancy	ICC	NFPA	NBFCC
Residential (continued)	**R-3 -** Residential occupancies where the occupants are primarily permanent in nature and not classified as Group R-1, R-2, R-4, or I **R-4 -** Residential occupancies shall include occupancies buildings arranged for occupancy as residential care/assisted living facilities for more than 5 but less than 16 occupants (excluding staff)	**Lodging or Rooming House -** Building (or portion thereof) that does not qualify as a one- or two-family dwelling, that provides sleeping accommodations for a total of 16 or fewer people on a transient or permanent basis, without personal care services, with or without meals, but without separate cooking facilities for individual occupants. **Hotel -** Building or groups of buildings under the same management in which there are sleeping accommodations for more than 16 persons and primarily used by transients for lodging with or without meals. **Dormitory -** A building or a space in a building in which group sleeping accommodations are provided for more than 16 persons who are not members of the same family in one room, or a series of closely associated rooms, under joint occupancy and single management, with or without meals, but without individual cooking facilities. **Apartment Building -** Building (or portion thereof) containing three or more dwelling units with independent cooking and bathroom facilities.	**Group C -** Residential occupancies
Storage	***Storage Group S –*** Structures or portions of structures that are used for storage and are not classified as hazardous occupancies. - ***Moderate-hazard storage, Group S-1*** (examples include but not limited to: bags, books, linoleum, and lumber) - ***Low-hazard storage, Group S-2*** (examples include but not limited to: asbestos, bagged cement, electric motors, glass, and metal parts)	**Storage Occupancy -** An occupancy used primarily for the storage or sheltering of goods, merchandise, products, vehicles, or animals.	Covered under Group F
Utility/ Miscellaneous	***Utility/Miscellaneous Group U*** - These are accessory buildings and other miscellaneous structures that are not classified in any specific occupancy. (agricultural facilities such as barns, sheds, and fences over 6ft [2m])	—	—

Figure 9.19 Company officers should ensure hazardous materials found during a fire and life safety inspection are properly labeled and annotated as being in the facility.

materials. It is designed to alert fire and emergency services responders to health, flammability, instability, and related hazards (specifically, oxidizers and water-reactive materials) that may be present **(Figure 9.19)**.

Be Aware!

NFPA® 704 markings provide very useful information, but the system does have its limitations. An NFPA® diamond doesn't state exactly what chemical or chemicals may be present in specific quantities. Nor does it tell exactly where they may be located when the sign is used for a building, structure, or area (such as a storage yard) rather than an individual container. Positive identification must be made through other means, such as container markings, employee information, company records, and preincident surveys.

Hazard Communications Labels and Markings

The OSHA *Hazard Communication Standard* (HCS) (Subpart Z, Toxic and Hazardous Substances, 29 *CFR* 1910.1200) requires employers to identify hazards in the workplace and train employees how to recognize those hazards. Employers are required to ensure that all hazardous material containers are labeled, tagged, or marked with the substance's identity, along with appropriate hazard warnings. The standard does not specify what identification system (or systems) employers must use. Company-level personnel may encounter many unique labeling and marking systems in their jurisdictions. Preincident surveys can assist responders in identifying and understanding these systems.

Company officers performing inspections should be aware that many employers have devised their own hybrid labeling systems that often look very similar but may have significant differences in interpretation. It is important that emergency responders use preincident surveys and inspections to become familiar with the systems used at facilities in their jurisdictions.

Canadian Workplace Hazardous Materials Information System

The Canadian Workplace Hazardous Materials Information System (WHMIS) requires that hazardous products be appropriately labeled and marked. A WHMIS label can be a mark, sign, stamp, sticker, seal, ticket, tag, or wrapper. It can be attached, imprinted, stenciled, or embossed on the controlled product or its container. There are two different types that are used most often:

1. Supplier label

2. Workplace label

Supplier labels. A supplier label must appear on all controlled products received at workplaces in Canada and contain the following information:

- Product identifier (name of product)
- Supplier identifier (name of company that sold it)
- Statement that a safety data sheet (SDS) is available
- Hazard symbols (pictures of the classifications)
- Risk phrases (words that describe the main hazards of the product)
- Precautionary measures (how to work with the product safely)
- First aid measures (what to do in an emergency)
- All text in English and French
- HMIS hatched border

If the product is always used in the container with the supplier label, no other label is required (unless the supplier label is lost or becomes unreadable). If the material is moved into another container for workplace use, this new container must have a workplace WHMIS label.

Workplace labels. These labels must appear on all controlled products that the employer produced in a workplace or transferred to other containers. The labels must provide the following information:

- Product identifier (product name)
- Information for the safe handling of the product
- Statement that the SDS is available

The employer may wish (but are not **legally** required) to put more information on the labels such as the WHMIS hazard symbols or other pictograms. Workplace labels may appear in placard form on controlled products received in bulk from a supplier.

U.S. and Canadian Safety Color Codes

Colors codes can provide clues to the nature of hazardous materials in buildings and facilities. For example, the company officer can determine that an oxidizer may be inside a container if the placard background color is yellow. If the placard color is red, the material may be flammable. Most flammable liquid storage cabinets are painted yellow as well as many portable containers of corrosive or unstable materials. Flammable liquid safety cans and portable containers are often red.

ANSI Z535.1 establishes a color code system that is recommended for use in the U.S. and Canada:

- **Red** — Means Danger or Stop; is used on containers of flammable liquids, emergency stop bars, stop buttons, and fire-protection equipment
- **Orange** — Means Warning; is used on hazardous machinery with parts that can crush, cut, or injure a worker
- **Yellow** — Means Caution; solid yellow, yellow and black stripes, or yellow and black checkers may be used to indicate physical hazards such as tripping hazards; also used on containers of corrosive or unstable materials
- **Green** — Marks safety equipment, such as first-aid stations, safety showers, and exit routes
- **Blue** — Marks safety information signage, such as labels or markings indicating the type of required personal protective equipment (PPE)

Closing Interview

When the inspection has been completed, the inspection findings should be discussed with the business owner or designated representative during a closing interview **(Figure 9.20)**. If no violations were found, the company officer should congratulate the owner/occupant and thank the individual for assisting with the inspection. If any violations were found, the company officer should review and discuss them. Immediate threats to life safety, such as locked or obstructed exits, must be corrected before the company officer leaves the premises. Less critical violations should be identified to the representative and the necessary corrective measures explained. A reasonable amount of

Figure 9.20 The company officer should brief the facility manager on the findings of the inspection.

time should be allowed for the corrections to be made. The amount of time allowed varies depending upon the nature of the violations and the difficulty involved in their correction.

During the closing interview, the company officer should establish a date and time for a follow-up inspection, if needed. The company officer and the representative should develop a correction plan if correcting the violations will take some time (for example, installing a fire detection and alarm system). The plan should include reinspections at specified intervals to ensure that reasonable progress is made and that full compliance is eventually obtained.

Documentation

As with other fire and emergency services organization activities, documenting fire and life safety inspections is extremely important. The documentation must be as complete, accurate, and readable as possible. This documentation creates an inspection history for every occupancy that the organization inspects. This documentation may be needed to force reluctant property owners to comply with code requirements, or it may be needed as evidence should there be a fire in a particular occupancy. This data may also be needed for statistical purposes at the state/provincial level.

Reports can also be provided to the operational units that respond to the building or facility. Changes in the floor plan, use or processes, access, and occupancy status are all important to emergency responders. This information can be used to update the preincident plans or generate a preincident survey.

Conducting Exit Drills

Inspectors or company-level personnel may be required to conduct exit drills in some occupancies. Exit drills are particularly important in schools and similar occupancies where many people are gathered. These drills are used to familiarize the occupants with the exit procedures and routes. Emergency response units can also be involved in the drill to familiarize them with the locations of exit discharges, exterior safe havens, and interior areas of refuge. Learning the possible access routes the emergency response units will take to approach the facility also benefits the occupants. The company officer must be aware of situations that will prevent conducting exit drills in educational occupancies. Coordination and communication with school officials are essential to ensure that all life safety and educational requirements are met.

Only the hospital and nursing home staff should participate in exit drills. Plans must be in place for evacuating the patients or moving them to an area of refuge. Because these facilities typically operate 24-hours a day, drills should be conducted with all shifts.

Inspection personnel also may be involved in helping certain occupancies develop their emergency exit plans. Even if these plans are well-written, they should be tested periodically through realistic exercises. From time to time, it may be appropriate to conduct these drills without prior notification.

Inspecting/Testing Fire Protection Systems

Inspecting and testing fire protection systems is a very technical process. Company officers may be required to witness or assist in these inspections and tests under the supervision of the contracted firm. Company officers should be capable of performing inspection and fire protection system tests at the level that their organization requires.

Fire Detection/Signaling Systems

Different types of fire detection and signaling systems are installed in various types of occupancies. Regardless of the type of system or the activation means, each must meet the requirements of NFPA® 72, *National Fire Alarm Code®*. Inspectors and company-level personnel must be familiar with how these systems operate and how to test them. The most common types of systems are:

- Local
- Auxiliary
- Remote station
- Proprietary
- Central station
- Emergency voice/alarm communications.

Additional information can be found in IFSTA's **Fire Detection and Suppression Systems** manual.

Local alarm systems. Local alarm systems may be activated manually. Sensors that detect heat, smoke, or flame can also activate them. They share one common feature: they initiate an alarm signal only on the premises where they are installed. They do not transmit a signal to the fire and emergency services organization or to any other location. Their primary purpose is to alert building occupants to a fire so that they will leave the building. Their secondary purpose is to alert passersby to a fire in the building so that they will report it.

Auxiliary alarm systems. These systems are used only in communities that have municipal alarm box systems. Auxiliary alarm systems are installed within a building and connected directly to a municipal alarm box located on the street adjacent to the building. When a fire activates the system, the system transmits a signal to the fire and emergency services organization.

Remote station systems. These systems are also are connected directly to the fire and emergency services organization communications/dispatch center. However, remote station systems transmit an alarm, usually over a leased telephone line, rather than the municipal fire alarm box circuits. A radio signal on a dedicated fire and emergency services organization frequency may be used instead. Commonly used in communities that are not served by a central station system, remote station systems may be coded or non-coded. A non-coded system may be used where the system covers only one building. A coded system is necessary in occupancies consisting of buildings at different locations. One remote station system may cover up to five buildings, and it may or may not have local alarm capability.

Proprietary systems. A proprietary system is used to protect large commercial and industrial buildings, high-rise buildings, and groups of commonly owned buildings in a single location, such as a college campus or an industrial complex. Each building in the complex is protected by a separate system connected to a common receiving point somewhere on the premises. The receiving point must be in a separate structure or in a part of a structure that is remote from any hazardous operations. An employee who is trained in system operation and the protocols for handling system alarms should constantly staff the receiving point. Some proprietary systems are also used to monitor facility security systems.

Central station systems. A central station system differs from a proprietary system in two ways: First, the receiving point is not on the protected premises, and second, the owner of the protected premises does not employ the person receiving the alarm. The operator works in a receiving location called a central station and is an employee of the alarm service company contracted to protect the premises. When the central station receives an alarm, the operator notifies the fire and emergency services organization and a representative of the property owner/occupant.

The central station may be located in another state so it is critically important that the operator provides the fire and emergency services organization with the correct address of the property and identify what area of the protected property is involved. Some fire and emergency services organizations require that the central station provider be listed by Underwriters Laboratories (UL).

Emergency voice/alarm communications systems. These are supplementary systems installed in properties in addition to one of the other types of systems previously listed. Their purpose is to increase the capability of providing detailed information to occupants and/or emergency responders who are on the premises. These systems may be separate from or integrated into the facility's main fire detection/signaling system. They may be one-way communication systems in which information can be announced to, but not received from, the occupants; they may be two-way systems in which communications also can be received from the occupants.

Water Supplies

Inspectors or company-level personnel may inspect occupancies that have their own private water supply to operate required sprinklers and/or standpipes. In the absence of a municipal water system, or if the municipal system's water pressure is too low to properly supply the fire protection system, the owner/occupant may have an elevated water tank on the building's roof or a freestanding water tank on the property **(Figure 9.21)**. The inspector or company-level personnel will not determine the system's adequacy, but only how well it is maintained. Company personnel should look for signs of rust or corrosion around valves and fittings and should check the pressure readings of any gauges. The owner/occupant should have flow data available; however, the company officer may have to conduct flow tests to verify these figures. For more information on inspecting water supplies, see the IFSTA **Fire Inspection and Code Enforcement** manual.

Stationary Fire Pumps

Stationary fire pumps may be installed in occupancies where it is impractical or impossible to maintain water storage for fire protection. These installations must conform to NFPA® 20, *Standard for the Installation of Stationary Fire Pumps for Fire Protection*. The pumps are used to increase the pressure in the fire protection system when needed. They are almost always electrically-

Figure 9.21 Company-level personnel should be familiar with private water supplies found in their company's assigned area.

driven centrifugal pumps with a discharge capacity from 500 to 4,500 gpm (2 000 L/min to 18 000 L/min). Inspection personnel usually are not required to test these pumps, but they may be present when the tests are performed or make a visual inspection of the pumps during regular visits. Company officers should be familiar with the pump types installed in the response area. When inspecting these installations, they should check the owner/occupant's pump maintenance and test records. NFPA® 20 requires these pumps to be run for at least thirty minutes per week. The company officer should also look for signs of water or oil leaks, rust, corrosion, or damage to the pumps or associated piping. For more information see IFSTA's **Fire Detection and Suppression Systems** manual.

Public Fire Alarm Systems

The fire and emergency service's municipality or other entity usually owns and maintains public fire alarm systems. They may include dedicated fire alarm circuits connected to street fire alarm boxes or street boxes that are individual radio transmitters on a dedicated fire alarm frequency. These systems are classified as either Type A (manual retransmission) or Type B (automatic retransmission). In Type A systems, the alarm operator must manually retransmit alarms received from the street boxes to the designated fire stations. Type A systems are necessary in jurisdictions with a large call volume to prevent stations from being inundated with fire calls for which they are not part of the assigned initial response. In Type B systems, alarms received from the street boxes are automatically retransmitted to all fire stations within the jurisdiction.

Technical personnel usually perform routine maintenance and testing of these systems, but not always. In some cities, line personnel are assigned these duties. For more information on the installation, maintenance, and testing of these systems see NFPA® 1221, *Standard for the Installation, Maintenance, and Use of Emergency Services Communications Systems.*

Standpipe and Hose Systems

Standpipe and hose systems are required in single-story buildings, in large area buildings, on each floor of structures that are greater than four stories, and in industrial facilities. These systems provide a quick and convenient source of water for the manual application of water for firefighting. These systems must be installed according to NFPA® 14, *Standard for the Installation of Standpipe and Hose Systems*, and must be supplied with water in sufficient volume and at adequate pressure. NFPA® 14 classifies standpipe systems as Class I, II, or III according to their intended use **(Figure 9.22)**:

- Class I systems are intended for fire fighting personnel who are trained in handling large handlines (2½-inch [65 mm] hose). They usually consist of strategically located valve-controlled 2½-inch (65 mm) outlets attached to the standpipe riser. Class I systems do not have permanently attached hoses or nozzles.

- Class II systems are intended for building occupants who have no specialized fire training. These systems allow occupants to control fire spread until the fire department or fire brigade arrives. They are usually equipped with a rack or reel of 1½-inch (38 mm) fire hose (with nozzle) connected to a valve-controlled outlet. These systems are not intended for emergency responder use and are not a substitute for the organization's nozzles and hoses.

- Class III systems combine the features of both of the other classes and are intended for firefighters, brigade members, and untrained occupants. The system must permit the 2½-inch (65 mm) outlet and the 1½-inch (38 mm) house line to be used simultaneously. This combination allows the occupants to apply water to a fire until firefighters or brigade members arrive, and it allows the trained firefighters to attack the fire with heavy hose streams.

When inspecting any of these systems, the company officer should perform the following duties:

- Check the hose cabinets to see that they are free of trash and debris.

- Check the hose for signs of deterioration (water stains, cuts, or abrasions on its surface).

- Feel the hose between the connection and the first fold to see whether water has accumulated in the hose, which is an indication that the valve is partially open or is leaking.

- Disconnect the hose on 1½-inch (38 mm) hose connections and test the valve by opening it to allow water to flow into a bucket held close to the outlet.

- Check the condition of the hose threads and gasket while the hose is disconnected.

- Remove the hose nozzle and check its operation and gasket.

- Remove the cap and check the threads on 2½-inch (65 mm) hose connections, and connect a pressure gauge to the outlet so that the valve can be opened to test it.

- Check the system's fire department connection (FDC) to ensure that the threads are undamaged and the inlets are free of debris.

NOTE: For more information on inspecting standpipe systems, see the IFSTA **Fire Inspection and Code Enforcement** manual.

Figure 9.22 Examples of Class I, II, and III standpipe systems.

Fire Extinguishing Systems

Inspectors and company-level personnel may have to inspect and test a variety of fire extinguishing systems and equipment. The most common of these are automatic sprinkler systems, special-agent fixed fire extinguishing systems, and portable fire extinguishers.

Automatic sprinkler systems. An automatic sprinkler system consists of a water source, distribution piping, and one or more individual sprinklers **(Figure 9.23, p. 248)**. Depending on the particular situation, either a wet system or a dry system may be installed.

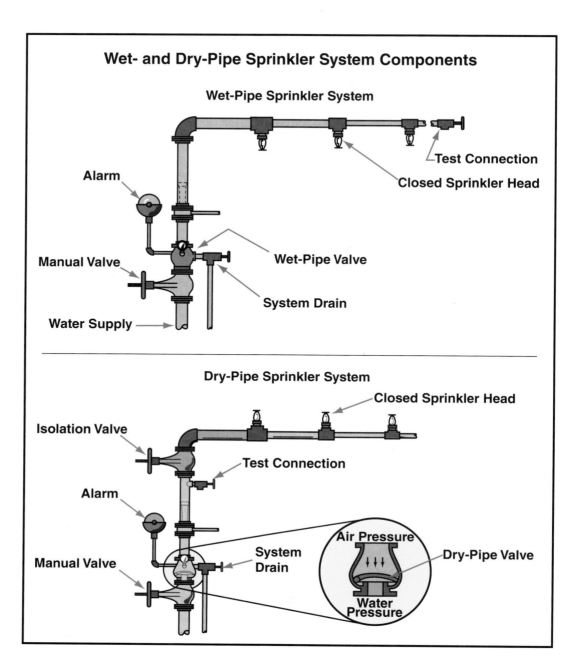

Figure 9.23 Common components of wet- and dry-pipe sprinkler systems.

In wet-pipe systems, the piping is constantly full of water under pressure **(Figure 9.24)**. Heat from a fire causes one or more sprinkler heads to activate (sometimes referred to as fused or opened) at a specified temperature allowing water to be discharged directly onto the fire. Wet-pipe systems can apply water onto a fire faster than dry systems, but the water in the piping is subject to freezing. Frozen distribution piping can burst and the linkage in individual sprinklers can be broken. When frozen piping thaws, water flows through the open sprinklers and piping, causing water damage. In cold-storage units and occupancies in cold climates, dry sprinkler systems are required.

In dry-pipe systems, the distribution piping is filled with air. This allows the system to remain functional during freezing temperatures, but it delays the application of water onto a fire. There are three types of dry sprinkler systems:

- **Dry-pipe systems** — Fire-suppression system that consists of closed sprinklers attached to a piping system that contains air under pressure. When a sprinkler activates, air is released, activating the water or foam control valve and filling the piping with extinguishing agent. Dry systems are often installed in areas subject to freezing.

- **Preaction systems** — Fire-suppression system that consists of closed sprinkler heads attached to a piping system that contains air under pressure and a secondary detection system; both must operate before the extinguishing agent is released into the system. Similar to a dry-pipe sprinkler system.

- **Deluge systems** — Fire-suppression system that consists of piping and open sprinklers. A fire detection system is used to activate the water or foam control valve. When the system activates, the extinguishing agent expels from all sprinkler heads in the designated area.

Figure 9.24 A company officer and crewmember examining a wet-pipe sprinkler riser.

Dry chemical systems. Dry chemical systems must conform to NFPA® 17, *Standard for Dry Chemical Extinguishing Systems.* They are used in areas where a rapid extinguishment of the fire is required but reignition is unlikely. These systems are either engineered or pre-engineered. Engineered systems are specifically calculated and constructed for a particular occupancy; pre-engineered systems are designed to protect a given amount of area in any occupancy type.

Fixed dry chemical systems use the same fire extinguishing agents as portable dry chemical fire extinguishers. These agents are nontoxic and non-conducting, but leave a very fine powdery residue that is extremely difficult to clean up. In some systems, the agent and expellant gas are stored in the same tank; in others, they are stored in separate tanks. There are two main types of dry chemical systems:

1. Local application

2. Total flooding

Local application is the most common type of dry chemical system. These systems discharge agent directly onto a relatively small area, such as the cooking surfaces in a commercial kitchen. If installed over a deep fryer or commercial range, these systems are designed to shut off the flow of gas to the unit when the extinguishing system actuates. Inspectors or company personnel inspecting these systems should perform the following:

- Check the discharge nozzles to see that they are not so heavily coated with grease or other material that they would not function as designed.

- Check the manual controls to see that the safety seals have not been broken.

- Check the fusible link(s) to see that they are clean and intact.

- Check the pressure gauge on the agent tank(s) to see that it is within the operating range, and check the service tag to see that the system has been serviced within the preceding year.

Total flooding dry chemical systems are installed in areas, such as paint spray booths, where a heavy cloud of agent is needed to fill the entire space when discharged. Total flooding systems may be actuated manually or automatically. Automatic actuation is by means of a fusible link holding a spring-loaded cable to the system controls.

The same items that were listed for local application systems should be inspected on total flooding systems. The company officers should also ensure that the manual activation (pull station) devices are unobstructed, that seals and tamper indicators are intact, and that the occupants are familiar with the operation of the system. Multiple manual activation devices may be required at various exits from the compartment or area.

Wet chemical systems. These systems are designed to be installed in commercial range hoods, plenums, and ducts. They must conform to the requirements of NFPA® 17A, *Standard for Wet Chemical Extinguishing Systems*. Wet chemical systems use an agent that is typically a mixture of water and either potassium carbonate or potassium acetate that is delivered in spray form. Wet chemical systems are especially well-suited for cooking oil-related applications. The agent forms a noncombustible soap on the surface of animal and vegetable oils and separates the fuel from oxygen, extinguishing the fire. The components of a wet chemical system are essentially the same as dry chemical systems, as are the items to be inspected. Portable fire extinguishers in the immediate area must be compatible with the wet chemical agent (K-rated).

Carbon dioxide systems. These systems must conform to NFPA® 12, *Standard on Carbon Dioxide Extinguishing Systems*. Like dry chemical systems, carbon dioxide (CO_2) systems are designed as either local application or total flooding systems; the type of system used in a particular area depends upon the situation.

Because CO_2 extinguishes fire by excluding oxygen (smothering), total flooding systems can be hazardous to anyone in a flooded compartment. Total flooding CO_2 systems must have a pre-discharge alarm to warn room occupants of an impending discharge so they can immediately leave the compartment. Both the automatic and manual operation activate the pre-discharge alarm before discharging the agent. Total flooding systems also have emergency manual activation devices that discharge (dump) the agent into the room immediately and without warning. In the automatic mode, these systems are actuated by heat, rate-of-rise, smoke, or flame detectors.

Local application CO_2 systems are usually supplied from one or more small cylinders located near the protected area. Much larger tanks or a bank of cylinders often supply total flooding systems. The agent is discharged through a piping system from the supply to the discharge point. The inspection items are basically the same as for fixed extinguishing systems.

Halogenated agent systems. Halons and the halogenated extinguishing agents contain atoms from one of the halogen series of chemical elements: fluorine, chlorine, bromine, and iodine. The halogenated agents are principally effective on Class B and Class C fires. Halon was originally developed and used because it was considered a clean agent that leaves no residue. International restrictions have been placed on Halon production because it has been proven to be harmful to humans and to the earth's ozone layer. The Montreal Protocol of 1987 provided for a phase-out of Halons and banned the manufacture of new Halon agents after January 1, 1994; limited production continues because there are some exceptions to the phase-out plan.

Use of Halons

Locations where Halon agent use is deemed to be essential may be granted an exemption from the phase-out. The criteria for this exemption are as follows:

- Halon agent use is necessary for human health and safety or critical for the functioning of society. One such use is in aircraft engine fire suppression systems.
- There are no technically or economically feasible alternatives.
- All feasible actions must be taken to minimize emissions from use.
- The supply of substitute Halon agents from existing banks or recycled stocks is not sufficient to accommodate the need.

Halon systems installed prior to the Montreal Protocol may remain in use until such time as they are discharged on a fire or the gas "leaks off."

In portable fire extinguishers, two Halons are still in use:

- **Halon 1211 (bromochlorodifluoromethane — CF_2BrCl)** — Is the one most commonly found in portable fire extinguishers.

- **Halon 1301 (bromotrifluoromethane — CF_3Br)** — Is used in some portable fire extinguishers, but it is more commonly found in fixed system applications.

Halon systems may be engineered or pre-engineered. Except for some local application systems, most Halon systems are engineered for the particular occupancy in which they are installed. Regardless of the design or installation, all Halon systems have the same component parts: agent tanks and associated piping, valve actuators, nozzles, detectors, manual releases, and control panels. Halon systems are equipped with an abort switch to cancel an inadvertent system actuation so that these very expensive agents are not wasted accidentally.

Company officers should check the agent storage tanks for loss of agent. Some systems have a gauge to indicate the amount of agent in the tank. Company officers should ensure that the detectors and discharge nozzles are not obstructed. The service tags should be checked to ensure that a licensed service firm has serviced the system within the time interval specified in the code.

Halon replacement agents. There has been considerable research and development on new clean agents that extinguish fires in the same manner as Halon agents but cause no significant atmospheric damage. NFPA® 2001, *Standard on Clean Agent Fire Extinguishing Systems* defines a clean agent as an electrically non-conducting, volatile, or gaseous fire extinguishing agent that does not leave a residue upon evaporation **(Table 9.3, p. 252)**. Consult NFPA®2001 for more information.

Halon replacement agent examples include:

- **Halotron®** — a "clean agent" hydrochlorofluorocarbon
- **FM-200** — a hydrofluorocarbon considered to be an alternative to Halon 1301
- **Inergen** — a blend of three naturally occurring gases: nitrogen, argon, and carbon dioxide

Table 9.3
Clean Agents

FC-3-1-10	Perfluorobutane	C_4F_{10}
FK-5-1-12	Dodecaflouro-2	$CF_2CF_2C(O)CF(CF_3)_2$
	Methylpentan-3-one	
HCFC Blend	Dichlorotrifluoroethane	$CHCl_2CF_3$
A	HCFC-123 (4.75%)	
	Chlorodifluoromethane	$CHClF_2$
	HCFC-22 (82%)	
	Chlorotetrafluoroethane	$CHClFCF_3$
	HCFC-124 (9.5%)	
	Isopropenyl-1-	
	Methylcyclohexene (3.75%)	
HCFC-124	Chlorotetrafluorethane	$CHClFCF_3$
HFC-125	Pentafluoroethane	CHF_2CF_3
HFC-227ea	Heptafluoropropane	CF_3CHFCF_3
HFC-23	Trifluoromethane	CHF_3
HFC-236fa	Hexafluoropropane	$CF_3CH_2\,CF_3$
FIC-13l1	Trifluoroiodide	CF_3I
IG-01	Argon	Ar
IG-100	Nitrogen	N_2
IG-541	Nitrogen (40%)	N_2
	Argon (40%)	Ar
	Carbon Dioxide (8%)	CO_2
IG-55	Nitrogen (50%)	N_2
	Argon (50%)	Ar

Notes:

1. Other agents could become available at later dates. They could be added via the NFPA® process in future additions or amendments of the standard.

2. Compositton of inert gas agents are given in percent by volume. Composition of HCFC Blend A is given in percent by weight.

3. The full analogous ASHRAE nomenclature for FK-5-1-12 is FK-5-1-12mmy2.

Systems inspections should conform to the manufacturer's recommendation. These systems have the same components and actuation devices found in the older Halon systems.

NOTE: State and local codes vary with respect to conversion to Halon replacement agents. Often, these agents cannot be put directly into existing Halon extinguishing systems or portable extinguishers without certain precautions. For more information, see NFPA® 2001.

Foam systems. Foam systems are used in locations where the application of water alone may not be effective in extinguishing a fire. Such locations include facilities for the processing or storage of flammable or combustible liquids, aircraft hangars, and facilities in which rolled paper or textiles are stored. Foam systems may be designed to produce protein, fluoroprotein, film forming fluoroprotein (FFFP), or aqueous film forming foam (AFFF) in low-, medium-, or high-expansion ratios; depending on the hazards present in the particular occupancy. Systems designed to produce low-, medium-, and high-expansion foam must conform to NFPA® 11, *Standard for Low-, Medium-, and High-Expansion Foam.* Some systems are designed to produce ATC (alcohol-type concentrate) foams for polar solvents and other flammable liquids that are miscible with water. These various types and ratios of foam may be delivered through deluge nozzles or through special foam sprinklers. For additional information on foam systems, see IFSTA's **Principles of Foam Fire Fighting** and **Fire Detection and Suppression Systems**.

Portable fire extinguishers. Inspecting any occupancy involves checking the portable fire extinguishers on the premises **(Figure 9.25)**. All portable fire extinguishers must be installed and maintained according to NFPA® 10, *Standard for Portable Fire Extinguishers.* Depending upon the types of flammable or combustible materials in the particular occupancy, a variety of types and sizes of portable fire extinguishers may be present.

Figure 9.25 Portable fire extinguishers should also be inspected during a fire and life safety inspection.

Portable fire extinguishers use different methods to expel the extinguishing agent and can be broadly classified according to the method used. These include the following:

- Stored-pressure
- Cartridge-operated
- Pump-operated

Extinguishers must be properly distributed throughout the occupancy to ensure that they are readily available during an emergency. Extinguishers should be located near where they may be needed and an adequate number of extinguishers must be provided for the hazard involved.

Several factors influence proper extinguisher selection and distribution, including extinguisher size and the hazard protected. Requirements for extinguisher distribution are contained in NFPA® 10. These requirements are separated into Class A, Class B, Class C, Class D, and Class K hazards. Because local codes and ordinances can be more restrictive, they should be reviewed along with the requirements contained in NFPA® 10. The following elements are important in the selection and distribution of fire extinguishers:

- Chemical and physical characteristics of the combustibles that might be ignited
- Potential severity (size, intensity, and rate of advancement) of any resulting fire
- Location of the extinguisher
- Effectiveness of the extinguisher for the hazard in question
- Personnel available to operate the extinguisher, including their physical abilities, emotional characteristics, and extinguisher training they have received
- Environmental conditions that may affect the use of the extinguisher (temperature, winds, presence of toxic gases or fumes)
- Anticipated adverse chemical reactions between the extinguishing agent and burning material
- Any health and occupational safety concerns such as exposure of the extinguisher operator to heat and products of combustion during firefighting efforts
- Inspection and service required to maintain the extinguishers

Effective extinguisher use requires that they be readily visible and accessible. Proper extinguisher placement is an essential, but often overlooked aspect of fire protection. Extinguishers should be mounted properly to avoid injury to building occupants and to avoid damage to the extinguisher. Improper mounting includes mounting an extinguisher where it protrudes into a travel path or setting it on a surface such as a workbench with no mount at all. Extinguishers are frequently placed in cabinets or wall recesses to protect both the extinguisher and people who might walk into them. If an extinguisher cabinet is placed in a rated wall, then the cabinet must have the same fire rating as the wall assembly. Proper placement of extinguishers should follow these guidelines:

- Extinguishers should be visible and well signed.

- Extinguishers should not be blocked or obstructed

- Extinguishers should be near points of egress or ingress.

- Extinguishers should be near normal paths of travel.

Extinguishers must be placed so that all personnel can access them. Extinguishers should not be placed too high above the floor for safe lifting. The standard mounting heights specified for extinguishers are as follows:

- Extinguishers with a gross weight not exceeding 40 pounds (18 kg) should be installed so that the top of the extinguisher is not more than 5 feet (1.5 m) above the floor.

- Extinguishers with a gross weight greater than 40 pounds (18 kg), except wheeled types, should be installed so that the top of the extinguisher is not more than 3½ feet (1 m) above the floor.

- The clearance between the bottom of the extinguisher and the floor should never be less than 4 inches (100 mm).

Extinguishers are used so infrequently that there is a natural tendency to ignore them until a fire occurs. Regular inspections of extinguishers are very important to ensure their readiness. Unless inspected regularly, some situations can impair extinguisher readiness:

- An extinguisher can be stolen or misplaced.

- A vehicle, such as a forklift, can strike an extinguisher, damaging it.

- Mechanical issues can cause an extinguisher to lose its pressure.

- An extinguisher may have been used on a fire and then replaced on its mount without anyone notifying the proper authorities or the unit being properly serviced or recharged.

During an inspection, the inspector or company-level personnel should perform the following:

- Check that the extinguisher is in its proper location.

- Ensure that objects do not obstruct access to the extinguisher.

- Check the inspection tag to determine if maintenance is due.

- Examine the nozzle or horn for obstructions.

- Check lock safety pins or tamper seals to make sure that they are intact.

- Check for signs of physical damage.

- Check that the extinguisher is full of agent.

- Check that the pressure gauge indicates proper operating pressure.

- Check collar tag for current information and/or damage.

- Check that required signage is in place.

- Check to see if the operating instructions on the extinguisher nameplate are legible.

- Check that the extinguisher is suitable for the hazard protected.

Chapter Summary

Company officers are usually the first line of contact with citizens in their community or response area. To effectively deal with the wants and needs of their customers, company officers must be familiar with the diverse composition of their community based on demographic evidence. Knowledge of the cultural backgrounds of the people living in the unit's response area will assist the company officer in providing public fire and life safety programs, providing public relations information and events, and focusing on the customer service process.

The company officer must be responsive to citizen concerns, complaints, and inquiries. Resolving these will require sensitivity to the citizen and diplomacy on the part of the company officer. Especially challenging will be resolving issues related to employee acts or omissions that involve customers and personnel. The company officer will have to use interpersonal skills, tact, and ethics in order to balance the interests of the customer and organization.

One of the most effective ways of preventing fires and other emergencies is through the adoption and enforcement of appropriate building fire codes and standards. Code enforcement helps ensure that structures and facilities are maintained in a fire-safe condition and owners/occupants follow prescribed behaviors that maintain a safe environment. Enforcement of these regulations may be done by an inspector or by company-level personnel through a conscientiously applied and managed fire prevention and life safety inspection program. Company officers must be able to develop a fire risk analysis for the community or response area, perform fire and life safety inspections, enforce applicable codes and standards, and supervise company-level personnel in inspections. The result will be a proactive approach to fire and life safety that should result in a reduction in life and property loss due to fires and other emergencies.

Review Questions

1. What are some ways that a jurisdiction's demographics can affect how company officers interact with their community? (pp. 212-213)

2. What are a company officer's responsibilities in company-level inspections? (pp. 224-226)

3. What types of fire detection and suppression systems might a company officer encounter during inspection duties? (pp. 243-244)

Learning Activities

Learning Activity 9-1

Objective 4: Implement a course of action that addresses a community need.

A company officer should be able to implement a fire and life safety education program in order to better serve and to maintain a positive relationship with the community being served.

Use the following scenario to:

1. Create a short, written list of the major community fire and life safety problems presented in the scenario.

2. Develop a program the meets the needs of the community as described in the scenario. Explain the elements of each step and how you would apply them. You may wish to use the five-step planning process outlined in Chapter 4.

Scenario:

Anytown is located in an area adjacent to a large wildland area. Current development and expected future growth is expanding the city into portions of this timber- and brush-covered area. Large slash piles have been created by the construction of new roads and are located throughout the development. Due to the quantity of debris, removal has been extremely slow. As the company officer for Fire Station 7, you are concerned that the residents of the new developments are not preparing their property to defend against wildland/interface fires. City code enforcement officials have also expressed concern about these conditions but have not been able to get the developers to remove the piles. To add to the danger, while attempting to keep the rustic outdoor appearance to their homes, many of the new owners have allowed tree canopies to grow over the top of their roofs. Additionally, light-fuels, grasses, weeds and small brush vegetation is being allowed to grow up to the sides of the houses. The development is also served by the city water system that has been extended from adjacent portions of the city. Water pressure is low because planned new storage reservoirs have not been constructed.

The fire department has purchased a brush fire response vehicle and assigned it to Fire Station 7. The unit is cross staffed by Engine 7 personnel and responds as a paired unit for brush or forest fires. Station 7 is the closest station to the new developments, but as development proceeds and population increases in the wildland area an additional station and staffing will be necessary. The new station is planned for construction in three years.

Answer Key:

Answers for this activity will vary; however, answers should include the following:

1. Fire and life safety problems
   - Wildland interface issues
   - Rapid development and growth of the community
   - Homeowner/resident lack of understanding fire safe practices
   - Water supply system shortfalls

2. Program to meet the needs of the community

    1. Identify problem — Wildland interface most critical

    2. Select appropriate response — Most cost effective and timely solution would be community awareness programs

    3. Design steps to meet goal — Create a program that communicates the problems to the community and the hazards facing the community and the fire department. Should also include recommendations to the community improve fire and life-safety practices.

    4. Implement plan — Carry out program to variety of audiences within community.

    5. Evaluation — Determine if program is effective and reaching the desire audience. Identify any improvements that could be made.

Learning Activity 9-2

Objective 5: Address the concern of a citizen in your jurisdiction.

Company officers must be able to resolve concerns and complaints of citizens in their jurisdiction while providing the highest level of customer service.

For this activity, you will need access to the following resources:

- Your department's policies and procedures regarding handling citizen complaints and good neighbor activities

Using the following scenario, create a written document that outlines:

1. What the problem is?

2. Why the neighbor is upset?

3. What would be the neighbor's desired solution?

4. How you could resolve the problem?

5. What the strategy is for addressing the concern? Try to create a win-win situation.

6. How do you plan to follow up with the neighbor?

Scenario:

You are the company officer at Station 5. Your neighborhood is a quiet area with mostly retired residents. Last Sunday evening, you invited several off-duty firefighters and their families to the station to celebrate the retirement of your driver/operator. You grilled steaks, and everyone played basketball. One of your firefighters set up a CD player on the patio and played music during dinner and volleyball. The get-together lasted from 1700 to 2100. All cooking and recreational equipment was cleaned and put away by 2115 hours. At 2133 hours, Engine 5 was dispatched to a vehicle fire, and returned at 2230 hours. On Wednesday morning, a citizen who lives behind the station comes to you angry about the activities at the station on Sunday evening. He states that there was loud noise and music until midnight and that he and the other neighbors couldn't sleep. He insists that you take care of the problem or he is going straight to the chief.

Answer Key:

Answers may vary slightly, but they should include the following:

1. A retired neighbor of the fires station is complaining about the noise and music coming from the station the previous Sunday evening until midnight.

2. Noise kept him awake after he went to bed.

3. Admit that it was too loud and promise that it won't happen again.

4. By treating him like a neighbor and a customer with respect, kindness, patience, and consideration

5. The positive resolution of a customer inquiry or concern of this nature must always be initiated by the company officer usually by approaching the individual and employing effective listening skills to understand what the complaint truly is. Above all, the neighbor must always be treated in a respectful manner and with patience.

   In this instance, it would be appropriate to invite the neighbor into the fire station and offer him a chance to see what the station is like. Explain to him that you were present during the cookout the previous Sunday and that though you or the company didn't intend to disturb him, you were sorry that it did that night. Describe the rules that fire department has implemented (in the form of SOP 750.16 or your department's SOPs) and discuss it with him. Additionally, inform him that Engine 5 had been dispatched to a call at 9:30 at night and that you did not return to the fire station for approximately one hour. Also explain that you were going to try to determine if any individuals came to the fire station after the engine left for the fire and if they could have been playing loud music.

6. By telephone conversation or visit following any investigation or research regarding his complaint.

Preincident Surveys

Chapter Contents

chapter 10

Key Terms

NFPA® Job Performance Requirements

This chapter provides information that addresses the following job performance requirements of NFPA® 1021, *Standard for Fire Officer Professional Qualifications* (2014).

4.5.1

4.5.2

4.6.1

Preincident Surveys

Learning Objectives

After reading this chapter, students will be able to:

1. Differentiate between preincident surveys and fire and life safety code enforcement inspections. [NFPA® 1021, 4.5.1, 4.5.2]

2. Describe various elements of building construction that should be identified during preincident surveys. [NFPA® 1021, 4.5.2]

3. Identify considerations for preparing for preincident surveys. [NFPA® 1021, 4.5.2]

4. Explain the process of conducting preincident surveys. [NFPA® 1021, 4.5.2]

5. Recognize different approaches to developing and managing preincident plans. [NFPA® 1021, 4.5.2, 4.6.1]

6. Develop a preincident plan for a specific occupancy. [NFPA® 1021, 4.5.1, 4.5.2; Learning Activity 10-1]

Chapter 10
Preincident Surveys

Case History

An engine company was assigned to conduct a preincident survey of an older building within the company's response area. Because of the building's age, size, complex interior layout, frequent renovations, and variety of occupancies, the fire department considered it a target hazard. The building was of Type I (fire resistive) construction with a steel frame, poured concrete floors, interior brick walls, and a brick façade. The structure covered more than 450,000 square feet over 3 floors. Initially constructed as an office building, it had undergone numerous occupancy changes and renovations since its construction. At the time of the survey, the structure contained offices, classrooms, laboratories, and mercantile occupancies.

The engine company found that the current floor plan did not match the floor plan from a previous survey. New wood and sheetrock walls had been constructed in some occupancies to make new rooms. Some of these walls blocked old doorways and changed the flow of personnel traffic within the building. Four hallways had been narrowed to increase the size of adjacent rooms. Three interior brick walls and their structural beams had been removed to create larger, open spaces. Two sets of exit doorways were bricked over on the exterior and covered with sheetrock on the interior. Dry-pipe standpipe systems had been retrofitted into stairwells in the four corners of the building.

The engine company's survey report was forwarded to the city's building department and the fire department's prevention bureau for additional investigation. The changes in door locations, narrowing of hallways, and loss of two exit doorways altered personnel evacuation from the structure. The expansion of some rooms and the creation of new rooms with new walls added to the complexity of the building's interior. The removal of some wall beams raised concerns about structural integrity during fire fighting operations. The addition of the four standpipes improved the fire fighting capabilities within the building.

Company officers should be trained and knowledgeable in preincident planning and how it affects emergency services delivery. The company responsible for the response area often collects information during preincident surveys. This information is vital to the preincident planning process and, in turn, influences the size-up and incident management activities of emergency services delivery. The information gathered during preincident surveys can alert fire and emergency personnel to the hazards found in an occupancy.

Preincident planning is the process of gathering and evaluating information, developing initial actions based on that information, and ensuring that the information remains current. To obtain this information, company officers and unit personnel may be assigned to conduct preincident surveys of high value and high-risk (target) hazards within their response areas **(Figure 10.1, p. 264)**.

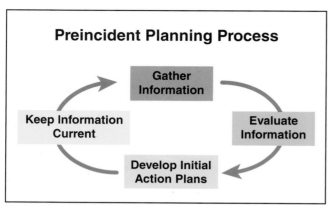

Preincident Planning Process

Gather Information → Evaluate Information → Develop Initial Action Plans → Keep Information Current → (back to Gather Information)

Figure 10.1 Illustrating the preincident planning process concept.

Preincident planning is a multistep process that may include:

- Developing positive relationships with building owners/occupants
- Conducting the preincident survey
- Developing preincident plans
- Managing, storing, and distributing preincident data and plans

This chapter focuses on the preincident planning process. It describes understanding the differences between surveys and inspections, basic building construction, preparing for preincident surveys, developing positive public relations, and conducting preincident surveys. Finally, this chapter addresses managing preincident data and developing preincident plans.

Understanding Surveys and Inspections

Company officers and their department administrations need to understand the difference between preincident surveys and fire and life safety code enforcement inspections. Although similar, preincident surveys are not intended to locate code violations. If violations are discovered during a survey, the company officer may request/require that the owner/occupant correct the violation or report the problem to the inspection division.

Some departments require the same personnel to conduct both preincident surveys and code enforcement inspections during a single visit. However, preincident surveys and code enforcement inspections are conducted for entirely different purposes and, ideally, should not be combined. Preincident surveys are conducted to assist fire fighting operations should there ever be an incident at the building or facility. Code enforcement inspections are performed to ensure that buildings are up to code and therefore less likely to be at risk for fires or other hazards. Because preincident surveys require close cooperation with owners/occupants, they should not be conducted alongside inspections since property management may not be as cooperative during inspections.

Company officers should be familiar with their organization's process for conducting preincident plans and the required forms and formats that the organization uses. NFPA® 1620, *Standard for Pre-Incident Planning*, would be a helpful reference.

Understanding a Building's Construction

Company officers and unit personnel must understand building construction and the building codes that regulate construction in the jurisdiction. Building codes define the type of construction that is used to build structures to be used for specific purposes. These specific purposes determine the type of occupancy classification that will be assigned to the completed structure. Company officers develop preincident plans based on the completed structure and its use.

Company officers should survey buildings while they are under construction. These surveys provide opportunities to view and discuss various construction techniques and building components that will be hidden once those structures are complete **(Figure 10.2)**. The company officer should always obtain permission from the project manager or job superintendent before entering a construction site. The company officer should also speak with the appropriate governmental officials, such as the fire marshal or building officials, to learn about any special issues or considerations applicable to the site. Head, eye, and hearing protection may be required, and all safety regulations must be followed during the survey.

Because each type of building construction behaves differently under fire conditions, company officers must be able to identify the various types during the surveys. The types of building construction were discussed in Chapter 9, Community Relations and Company-Level Inspections. Knowing how stable different materials and assemblies are under fire conditions allows appropriate plans and procedures to be developed that will allow firefighters to operate with greater safety and efficiency. The sections that follow provide a brief overview of the primary structural building assemblies, lightweight construction, and other building components.

Figure 10.2 Preincident planning buildings under construction can help company personnel understand the level of hazard posed by a structure's construction.

Roof Types and Hazards

A number of danger factors must be considered for roof operations. These factors can be tied directly to the construction of the roof, loads placed on roofs, and other hazards.

Roof types include the following:

- Flat
- Pitched
- Arched

Flat

Flat roofs are commonly found on commercial, industrial, and apartment buildings and may have a slight slope to facilitate water drainage. Chimneys, vent pipes, shafts, scuttles, and skylights often penetrate flat roofs. Parapets may surround and/or divide these roofs. Roofs may also support water tanks, air-conditioning equipment, antennas, and other objects that add to a building's dead load (permanent building components). The structural part of a flat roof consists of wooden, concrete, or metal joists covered with sheathing. The sheathing is often covered with a layer of insulating material that is always covered by a finish layer of some weather-resistant material **(Figure 10.3)**.

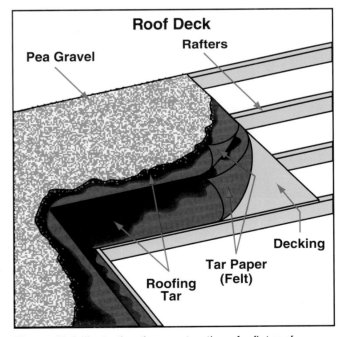

Figure 10.3 Illustrating the construction of a flat roof.

Pitched

Pitched roofs have a peak along one edge or in the center and a deck that slopes downward from the peak. Pitched roofs consist of timber rafters or metal trusses that run from the ridge to a wall plate on top of the outer wall. Sheathing boards or panels are usually applied directly onto the rafters. Pitched roofs usually have a covering of roofing paper (felt) applied before final weather coverings are laid. The final roof covering may be made of wood, metal, composition, asbestos, slate, rubber, concrete, or tile **(Figure 10.4)**.

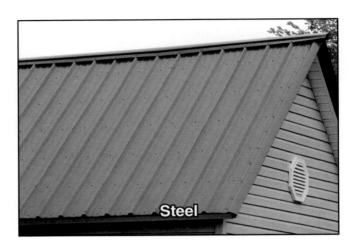

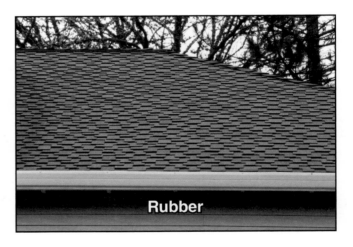

Figure 10.4 Examples of different roof coverings.

Arched

One form of arched roof construction uses **bowstring** (bow-shaped) **trusses** as the main supporting members. The lower chord (bottom longitudinal member) of the truss may be covered with a ceiling to form an enclosed cockloft or roof space. Trussless arched roofs (sometimes called lamella roofs) are composed of relatively short timbers of uniform length. These timbers are beveled and bored at the ends, where they are bolted together at an angle to form an interlocking network of structural timbers. This network forms an arch of mutually braced and stiffened timbers in which the roof exerts a horizontal reaction in addition to the vertical reaction on supporting structural components **(Figure 10.5)**.

Bowstring Truss — Lightweight truss design noted by the bow shape, or curve, of the top chord.

Figure 10.5 A trussless arched (lamella) roof as seen from the interior to illustrate its construction.

Roof Hazards

The primary concern for firefighter safety is a roof's susceptibility to sudden and unexpected collapse because fire has weakened its supporting structure. The combustibility of the surface of a roof is a basic concern to the fire safety of an entire community. Flaming embers have frequently caused major fires. Access into the roof may be limited due to factors such as tongue and groove construction and roofs that are built over the top of an existing roof.

Photovoltaic (Solar) Panels

It has become more common to find photovoltaic (solar) panels on roofs **(Figure 10.6, p. 268)**. These panels are designed to convert solar energy into electricity for use within a structure or structures. These panels and the other components within photovoltaic systems (wiring harnesses, inverters, batteries, and disconnect switches) can become involved in structural emergencies and create additional hazards to emergency responders. When dealing with photovoltaic systems, company officers and firefighters should:

- Never walk on these panels as they will not support the weight of personnel walking on them.

- Always wear full protective clothing and SCBA because these systems give off toxic vapors when on fire.
- Never wear jewelry that will conduct electricity.
- Consider these systems to be charged or "hot" during daylight hours.
- Shut off and Lock Out/Tag Out system disconnects.
- Use insulated tools around photovoltaic system components.
- Photovoltaic system components may remain energized after regular power service has been shut off.

Figure 10.6 An example of a roof-mounted photovoltaic (solar) panel.

Purlin — Horizontal member between trusses that support the roof.

Lightweight Construction

In this type of construction, plywood panels (called panelized roofing) are supported by **purlins** between laminated wooden beams or gusseted wooden trusses that span from outside wall to outside wall. Open web (diagonal member) trusses or wooden I beams have replaced conventional subfloor construction **(Figure 10.7)**. These lightweight components can fail rapidly when exposed to fire and/or run-off from fire streams. Similar conditions can develop from excessive or accumulated rain or snowfall. Roof or floor systems that open web trusses support are prone to sudden and unexpected collapse if the unsupported bottom chord is subjected to downward force. For example, when firefighters inadvertently pull on them while pulling ceiling panels with pike poles. Extreme care should be taken when working above or below this type of construction.

Figure 10.7 Wooden I-beams being used as floor joists in an apartment building under construction.

Building Components

Structures also include electrical systems; plumbing systems; **heating, ventilation, and air conditioning (HVAC) systems**; and fire protection systems **(Figure 10.8)**. The company officer should have a working knowledge of HVAC and fire protection systems. This knowledge is best obtained during preincident surveys.

During a pre-incident survey, the company officer and crew should examine these systems for the following reasons:

- **Electrical systems** — to identify system shut-off locations

- **Plumbing systems** — to identify shut-off locations for both water and sewer systems

- **HVAC systems** — to determine if the system can assist in removing smoke from a structure, to train personnel in the use of HVAC system controls for smoke removal operations, and to determine if roof-mounted HVAC units present a hazard

- **Fire protection systems** — to identify the locations of system controls and fire department connections (FDCs) as well as train personnel to support such systems during emergencies

Preparing for Preincident Surveys

Building the relationship between the company officer and the business owner/occupant is the first step to completing a successful preincident survey. Respect for the owner/occupants should be maintained throughout the survey. When owner/occupants are shown respect, it is much more likely that accurate information will be obtained during the survey.

Good preparation ensures that preincident survey results will be valuable and the process will not inconvenience the facility owners/occupants. Company officers should inform unit members in advance, discuss the survey process, list factors that should be considered during the survey, and assign duties if required. If one member of the unit must remain with the apparatus during the survey, communication between the company officer and the apparatus should be ensured in the event of an emergency dispatch. The company officer should also ensure the necessary survey documents, tools, and equipment are immediately available.

If possible, the company officer should obtain a copy of the facility **plot plan** from the owners/occupants or the building code department. Copies of the last code enforcement inspection and preincident survey should be consulted, when possible, to provide a basis for identifying any changes or discrepancies during the survey **(Figure 10.9, p. 270)**. The company officer must contact the owners/occupants to explain the reason for the visit and establish a mutually acceptable time.

Rooftop HVAC Systems

Figure 10.8 Examples of HVAC or installed fire protection systems that may be part of a structure.

Heating, Ventilating, and Air Conditioning (HVAC) System — Mechanical system used to provide environmental control within a structure and the equipment necessary to make it function; usually a single, integrated unit with a complex system of ducts throughout the building. *Also known as Air-Handling System.*

Plot Plan — Architectural drawing showing the overall project layout of building areas, driveways, fences, fire hydrants, and landscape features for a given plot of land; view is from directly above.

Figure 10.9 The company officer and personnel should review information from the prior preincident survey before conducting the next one.

Emergency Response Considerations

Preincident surveys provide emergency response personnel with vital occupancy information that they will need to handle a fire or other emergency on the premises. During a survey, personnel should concentrate on answering questions about what fire fighting and rescue tactics could be successful in the occupancy such as:

- Where and how will fires or other emergencies most likely occur?
- How are those emergencies likely to develop?
- What are the primary evacuation routes for the occupants?
- What is the layout of the work area?
- Are any of the occupants going to need assistance evacuating during an emergency?
- What will likely happen as a result of a fire or emergency?
- What will be needed in order to mitigate contingencies?
- How can building features, such as fire walls and ventilation systems, be used to confine a fire to one section of the building?
- What potential hazards to firefighter safety exist on the premises, including but not limited to:
  — Hazardous materials or processes
  — High-voltage equipment
  — Unprotected openings
  — Metal-clad doors
  — Overhead power lines
  — Extreme elevation differences
- What will firefighters need to know about this occupancy in order to function safely under obscured vision conditions?

In some jurisdictions, the sheer number of commercial, multifamily residential, and industrial occupancies in each response area makes it virtually impossible for responsible companies to conduct preincident surveys in all of them. Therefore, companies must prioritize the occupancies to be surveyed.

The priorities are normally based on life-safety risk (including the risk to firefighters), property values at risk, and potential frequency and severity of fires or other emergencies occurring. Once these target hazards (occupancies with the highest priority) have been identified, the responsible companies can focus their efforts on those occupancies.

Facility Survey Equipment

The equipment needed for a preincident survey may vary depending upon the organization's guidelines and the nature of the occupancy to be surveyed. Most preincident survey kits include the following supplies:

- Writing equipment
- Drawing equipment
- Flashlight
- Water-pressure gauge
- Camera
- Key box (such as Knox or Lock Box) or master keys
- Measuring tape or rangefinder
- Global positioning system (GPS) locator, if available, to identify the locations of hydrants, fire department connections, and key boxes
- Appropriate personal protection, such as helmets, eye protection, gloves, and hearing protection **(Figure 10.10)**

Figure 10.10 Common firefighter protective equipment that can be used during a preincident survey.

Survey Schedules

Some company officers are required to schedule their own preincident survey visits, while in other organizations, the battalion/district chief or a member of the administrative staff do the scheduling and the company officer is merely informed of the arrangements. The former allows the company officer more control over the company's schedule, and the latter allows for an organization-wide coordination of effort.

The visits should be scheduled at times that are convenient for the building owners/occupants. For example, it would be counterproductive to schedule a preincident survey at a large retail store during the holiday shopping season. If the visit does not unduly inconvenience the owner/occupants, they are more likely to cooperate with the survey team and react positively to the effort. However, visits should be scheduled at times that allow the survey team to obtain a realistic picture of activities that normally take place in the building.

It would be unwise to schedule a preincident survey visit to any building that has had a recent code enforcement inspection — especially if the same personnel perform both functions. Owners/occupants may perceive the survey visit to be another inspection. This misperception can make owners/occupants feel as though they are being harassed, so it is important to avoid this situation. The company officer should carefully explain to owners/occupants the reasons for the preincident survey, the planning process, and how owners/occupants will benefit.

Conducting Preincident Surveys

The company preincident survey process varies between organizations and jurisdictions. Some organizations require that upon arrival at the survey location company members remain at the apparatus, while the company officer contacts the owners/occupants, confirms the appointment, and reviews the survey procedure. The officer, working with the occupancy's chain of command, should consider inviting neighboring fire companies/agencies if they could be included on the first alarm or multiple alarm assignments for larger facilities. The officer should inform the owners/occupants of how many company members will be involved in the facility survey and request any assistance the team may need. The company officer should also explain that, while the facility survey is not a code enforcement inspection, any serious fire or life-safety hazards found will have to be corrected. When serious hazards are found, the best approach is to attempt to obtain an immediate correction.

Preincident surveys should be conducted using a systematic and logical approach, divided between the exterior and interior of the structure. At a large facility such as a chemical plant, the survey may start with the exterior of the main plant building, proceed to the building's interior, and then extend to other surrounding structures on the site.

During the survey, the inspectors should note building components as they encounter them and remain focused on the consideration factors listed earlier. They should look at ventilation systems, fire protection systems, and water supplies. While making the survey, firefighter safety hazards, structural conditions, fuel loading, and property conservation should also be considered.

Survey Information Records

Survey information may be recorded on a form that collects specific information, improving the chance that essential information is gathered. Field sketches should be made of the structure or facility showing its size, location, and components. Photographs or videos may be made of the structure or facility. Owners/occupants may consider some processes and areas proprietary or private, and photography or videography may not be permitted in those locations. In the collection and storage of data/graphics, it should be remembered that this information must be accessed rapidly and under less than ideal conditions. Survey information may be gathered in a variety of methods, including checklists, written essay-style or voice-recorded commentaries, sketches, photographs, or videos.

NOTE: Taking photographs and videos must be with the express permission of the owners/occupants.

Common Survey Form Data

Survey forms are used to record a variety of information identified during the course of a survey. Common information recorded on survey forms may include:

- Occupancy information
- Access
- Water supply to include estimated fire flow
- Location of utility shutoffs
- Hazards
- Ventilation
- Roof construction
- Building factors - internal and exterior
- Stairwell features
- Command post sites
- Evacuation sites
- Triage sites
- Suggested street closures
- Elevator operations information
- High value areas (records, computer system data storage)
- Secondary extinguishing systems

Multistory and large buildings have unique information that should be recorded on survey forms. This information may include:

- Base and staging locations
- Interior command sites
- Lobby control
- System controls
- Traffic and access plan
- Number of stories
- System inspection current on date of preplan
- Building communications system
- Occupant egress plan

Field Sketches

A field sketch is a rough drawing of a building that is prepared during the facility survey. This drawing should show general information about building dimensions and other related outside information, such as the locations of fire hydrants, streets, water tanks, and distances to nearby exposures. All of the basic information for survey drawings that accompany the survey report should be shown on field sketches, but not all of the details need to be included. Making field sketches on graph paper makes it easier to draw them to scale. Drawing to scale is not absolutely necessary, but it helps to keep the drawing proportional. This procedure will make it easier to transfer the information onto the survey drawings.

Photography, Videography, and Global Positioning

Photography can supplement the information contained in sketches. Digital cameras can be used to create, edit, store, and reproduce photographs quickly and economically. Graphic symbols can be added to the photographs, and images can be inserted into the preincident plan.

Videos can show relationships between buildings, manufacturing processes, and how the facility might appear as someone moves through it. Videos and photographs can be used as training aids for personnel who may respond to an emergency at the facility.

GPS can be used to identify locations of key items of interest. They can also assist with mapping of a building and its surroundings to enhance preplanning.

Building Exterior

After contacting the owners/occupants, company members can begin the exterior survey of the facility or building. The exterior facility survey focuses on obtaining information to create a plot plan or compare observations to an existing plot plan. Buildings should be measured, and their dimensions recorded, including distances from each building to exposures. Note on the plot plan the locations of the following items:

- Fire hydrants and valves
- Sprinkler and standpipe connections
- Utility controls (shutoffs)
- Fences and landscaping
- Power lines
- Obstructions to property or structure access or egress
- Underground storage tanks
- Doors, windows, and fire escapes
- Ornamental facings, awnings, or marquees
- Types of roof coverings
- Heavy objects on roofs that are visible from the exterior
- Locations of gathering points for evacuating occupants
- Fire fighting run-off patterns

NOTE: A building's exterior does not provide a good vantage point for gathering building construction information since many buildings are covered with brick, stone, or aluminum siding.

Site access should be noted on the survey plot plan, including the following:

- Access to parking lots, driveways, bridges, and gates
- The proximity of access routes to possible exposures
- Private roadways and bridges that do not meet the weight requirements for emergency apparatus
- Fire lanes on solid-surface roads
- Fire lanes constructed with concrete modules that are covered by grass and indistinguishable from regular turf
- Narrow alleyways or other access routes
- Overhead obstructions in access routes that can create barriers to emergency apparatus

Building Interior

After surveying the facility's exterior, company personnel may move to either the building's top floor (or roof if it is accessible) or lowest floor (basement, subbasement, or ground floor) to begin the interior survey. Unless the organizational policy dictates otherwise, the starting point for the interior survey is a matter of personal preference, but most people prefer to start on the top floor or roof.

Personnel then conduct the interior survey, systematically working either upward or downward. They draw floor plans of each floor to show the locations of permanent walls, partitions, fixtures, and heavy machinery. Furniture and similar items should not be included on floor plans because their locations are not fixed.

The locations of any of the following items should be noted on the floor plan drawings:

- Vertical shafts and horizontal openings
- Fire protection equipment such as standpipe or sprinkler control valves
- Fire control centers
- Safe haven areas where occupants may be sheltered in place
- Open pits and other process hazards

Life Safety Information

Life safety information is collected in two basic topic areas: protection and evacuation of occupants and protection of firefighters. Occupant protection information to be gathered and recorded during the interior survey includes:

- Locations and number of exits
- Locations of escalators and elevators
- Locations of windows and other openings suitable for rescue access
- Special evacuation considerations for disabled occupants, very old or very young occupants, and large numbers of occupants
- Locations of areas of safe refuge
- Flammable and toxic interior finishes or processes

Survey personnel should also gather information about conditions within the building that may threaten firefighter safety. Some of the potential hazards to firefighters that should be noted include (**Figure 10.11a and b, p. 276**):

- Flammable and combustible liquids
- Toxic chemicals
- Biological hazards
- Explosives
- Reactive metals
- Radioactive materials
- Manufacturing processes that are inherently dangerous

Company personnel should also note building conditions that may present or contribute to hazardous situations. The company officer should also record the materials and items that are not part of the structure but that contribute to the structure's fuel load.

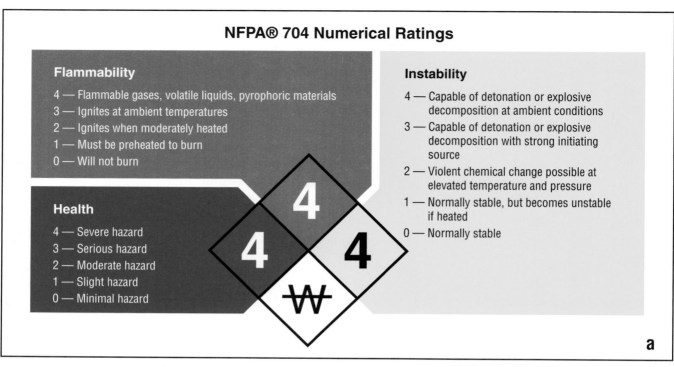

NFPA® 704 Numerical Ratings

Flammability
4 — Flammable gases, volatile liquids, pyrophoric materials
3 — Ignites at ambient temperatures
2 — Ignites when moderately heated
1 — Must be preheated to burn
0 — Will not burn

Health
4 — Severe hazard
3 — Serious hazard
2 — Moderate hazard
1 — Slight hazard
0 — Minimal hazard

Instability
4 — Capable of detonation or explosive decomposition at ambient conditions
3 — Capable of detonation or explosive decomposition with strong initiating source
2 — Violent chemical change possible at elevated temperature and pressure
1 — Normally stable, but becomes unstable if heated
0 — Normally stable

a

b

Hazard Communications Symbols*

Symbol	Description
	Biological Hazard
	Chemical Hazard
	Nuclear/ Radiological Hazard
	Carcinogen/ Cancer Hazard

* These symbols may be presented in a variety of colors and/or formats. For example, they will not always be seen in the center of a circle or rectangle.

Figure 10.11a and b Company officers should be familiar with hazard signage that they may encounter during preincident surveys. Examples: (a) NFPA® 704 numerical ratings and (b) hazard communications symbols.

Building Conditions

The physical condition of the structure should also be noted. Conditions that may be hazardous to emergency responders during a fire include but are not limited to:

• Structural components that may fail during a fire or during high wind conditions

• Construction materials that can lose their strength when exposed to fire

• Lightweight wood construction features

• Unsupported partitions or walls

• Roof construction that could fail quickly when exposed to fire or heavy loads

• Stacked or high-piled storage

• Heavy objects on roofs or suspended from interior roof structures that can cause roof collapse

• Heavy equipment that may fall through floors or cause floors to collapse

• Transformers and high-voltage electrical equipment vaults

• Large open areas

• Building features that may confuse or trap firefighters during a fire, such as:

— Dead-end corridors or hallways

— Open vats, pits, or shafts

— Openings into underground utility shafts or tunnels

— Multilevel floor arrangements

— Mazelike room divisions or partitions

— Alterations that disguise the original construction

Fuel Loads

The term fuel load represents the bulk of fuel available to burn and generally refers to a building's contents. The materials used in the construction of most modern commercial and mercantile buildings contribute relatively little fuel to a fire. The major fuel sources are furnishings and other building contents.

When company officers observe and record the fuel load of buildings during preincident surveys, they are primarily addressing the fire-control considerations of preincident planning. Subsequently, they devise plans for dealing with fires that may feed on this load. See Appendix B for methods of calculating fire-flow.

Ventilation Systems

Most structures have some form of climate control or HVAC system. These systems range from small window-mounted units to huge commercial units. While the potential hazards associated with large commercial units are widely recognized, even the small window-mounted units can be hazardous to firefighters under certain conditions.

Some HVAC systems can be used during emergency operations to remove contaminated atmospheres from a structure if the system itself and natural ventilation is not helping **(Figure 10.12)**. Company officers must have a thorough knowledge of buildings that incorporate these types of HVAC systems. Company officers should consult with building engineers to ensure the system's emergency operations are not overridden.

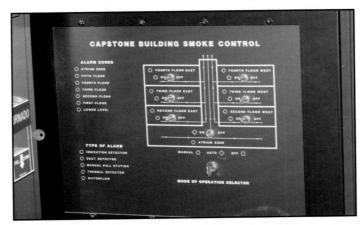

Figure 10.12 An example of a HVAC/smoke evacuation control panel.

The survey should also identify any built-in ventilation devices that can be used to control a fire or remove hazardous atmospheres from the structure. The company officer should be aware of any underflow air distribution systems that may be present.

Built-In Ventilation Devices

Some structures are equipped with built-in ventilation devices that are designed to limit the spread of fire, release heated fire gases, or control smoke and contaminated atmospheres. NFPA® 204, *Standard for Smoke and Heat Venting*, provides guidelines for the design and installation of smoke and heat venting equipment and recommends using automatic heat-activated roof vents and **draft curtains** (curtain boards). Roof and wall vents and curtain boards are most common in large buildings having wide, unbroken expanses of floor space. These built-in ventilation devices may, in some cases, adversely affect the travel of heat and smoke to portions of compartments or attics not immediately involved in a fire.

Draft Curtains — Noncombustible barriers or dividers hung from the ceiling in large open areas that are designed to minimize the mushrooming effect of heat and smoke and impede the flow of heat.

The presence of these devices should be noted in the preincident survey. Company officers need to become familiar with the specific types in use in their areas. The various types of vents and curtain boards include:

- **Automatic roof and wall vents** — Release heat and smoke to the outside through vents that work automatically and are placed at the highest point of a roof or wall to limit the spread of fire within a building **(Figure 10.13)**. Smoke detectors may activate some automatic roof vents, however, most operate through the use of fusible links connected to spring-loaded or counterweighted cover assemblies. Operating sprinklers may slow or prevent the activation of automatic roof vents. If they do not open automatically, firefighters will have to open them manually with manual-release mechanisms.

Figure 10.13 Examples of automatic roof and wall vents.

- **Atrium vents** — Release heat and smoke from atriums (large, vertical openings in the center of structures) to the outside. Building codes in most areas require that atriums be equipped with automatic vents.

- **Monitors** — Release heat and smoke to the outside from square or rectangular structures that penetrate a building's roof. They may have metal, glass, wired glass, or louvered sides. Monitors with solid walls should have at least two opposite sides hinged at the bottom and held closed at the top with a fusible link that allows gravity to open them in case of a fire **(Figure 10.14)**. Those with glass sides rely upon the glass breaking to provide ventilation in case of a fire. If a fire does not break the glass, firefighters will have to remove it.

- **Skylights** — Skylights with thermoplastic panels or ordinary window glass act as automatic vents when a fire's heat melts the plastic or breaks the glass. Skylights without thermoplastic panels or automatic venting will have to be removed or glass panes will have to be broken. In skylights equipped with wired glass, the panes have to be removed from their frames or cut with saws.

- **Curtain boards** — Fire-resistive half-walls (also known as draft curtains) extend down from the underside of a roof to limit the horizontal spread of heat and smoke, which confines them to a relatively small area directly over their sources **(Figure 10.15)**. Curtain boards also concentrate heat and

Figure 10.14 An example of a roof monitor.

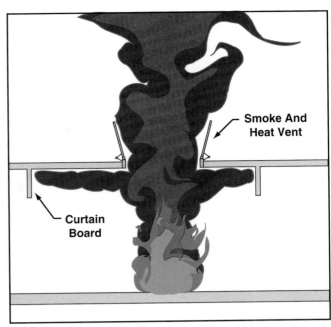

Figure 10.15 Curtain boards can limit the horizontal spread of heat and smoke.

smoke directly under automatic roof vents to accelerate the vents' activation. They may also accelerate the activation of automatic sprinklers in the area.

Underfloor Air Distribution Systems

Underfloor air distribution (UFAD) systems, a recent advance in HVAC system design, introduce thermostatically controlled air into the space through openings in the floor. The absence of overhead ducts or return air plenums allows an increase in ceiling heights. Return air passes through sidewall vents located adjacent to the HVAC system mechanical room.

Concerns have been raised that UFADs pose a life safety risk for two reasons. First, if smoke develops under a floor, it will be distributed into the space at floor level. Second, water may enter the underfloor area and result in a short circuit that could cause a fire in the UFAD's electrical system. As a deterrent, model building codes require smoke detectors in each space as well as in the mechanical rooms. Smoke detectors are not currently required in the UFAD distribution system. In addition, design and installation must meet all existing code requirements to reduce electrical hazards in the system.

Fire Protection Systems

Any built-in fire protection equipment or system should be checked during the preincident survey. It is normally recommended that fire companies not test this equipment, but rather merely note its presence and condition and evaluate its usefulness during a fire on the premises. If the team observes some condition that would reduce the effectiveness of such equipment, it should be reported to the owners/occupants with suggestions for corrective actions. During the survey, personnel should identify the need for specialized hose adapters or possible obstructions that may require greater lengths of fire hose.

During a preincident survey, the survey team should pay particular attention to the absence or locations and conditions of the following systems:

- *Fixed fire-extinguishing systems* — Automatic sprinklers, carbon dioxide, dry chemical, halon-substitute flooding systems, which may reduce the need for interior attack hoselines, but may increase the need for system support.

- *Standpipe systems* — All classes of wet- and dry-pipe systems that permit the use of hoselines on upper floors and in remote areas of large-area structures; may allow firefighters to carry hose packs into a building rather than lay long attack hoselines from outside.

- *Fire detection and alarm systems* — All types of automatic detection systems for smoke, carbon monoxide, low oxygen content, and other situations that result in a toxic atmosphere and all types of systems used to alert occupants to the need to evacuate a structure or area.

- *Smoke, heat, or alarm activated doors* — Alarm initiation or fusible link operation closes the doors to prevent the spread of smoke and heat (**Figure 10.16**). The activation of these assemblies may potentially restrict movement throughout a structure, and door activation may compromise attack lines. Interior operating crews should consider alternate routes whenever possible.

Figure 10.16 These hospital fire doors automatically close when the building's fire or smoke detectors are activated.

Water Supplies

For facilities protected with sprinkler or standpipe systems, the required water supply should have been determined during the design and installation of the systems. Changes in water demand, such as the construction of additional buildings using the same supply line, can reduce the actual water supply available.

Determining the availability and reliability of water supplies is critical to the development of any preincident plan. The preincident survey of any given occupancy should gather the following information:

- Locations of all water supplies
  - Auxiliary water supplies
  - Private water supply systems, such as impounded bodies of water or wells
- Locations of water-system interconnections
  - Hydrants, including hydrant main intake facing roadway
  - Fire protection system flow meters and alarms
  - Water-demand systems, such as high-water demand processes connected to the supply system
- Required fire flow based on construction type and fuel load information or on calculations that owners/occupants provide
- Water supply system pressure (determined by reading the pressure at hydrants with a pitot gauge while flowing water from them)
- Available fire flow (determined by flowing a hydrant and determining water flow rates based on the pressure readings at the hydrant)
- Reliability of water supplies (determined by reading the water pressure at a variety of hydrants while simultaneously flowing water from them)
- Water supply utilization methods (how water is used and distributed within the facility)

The public works department can provide information regarding the sizes and locations of water mains as well as pressures that can be anticipated serving the occupancy based on the municipality's water atlas, a map book or online database of all waterlines in the jurisdiction.

Property Conservation

While conducting facility surveys, company officers and crew members should identify the building's contents with the highest value, which may include:

- Files and records
- Electronic equipment
- Machinery
- Merchandise
- Antiques
- Irreplaceable items

Some items may require the use of special salvage procedures. See IFSTA's **Structural Fire Fighting: Truck Company Skills and Tactics** manual for additional information on property conservation.

Developing and Managing Preincident Plans

Once the on-site visit is complete, the company officer is responsible for processing the information gathered to develop a preincident plan or forwarding it to those responsible for developing the plan **(Figure 10.17)**. Preincident planning may involve a collective effort at all levels of the organization. The success of the preincident planning process depends upon the ability of the company to conduct adequate preincident surveys and the company officer's ability to process information and complete accurately written reports.

Figure 10.17 A company officer processing preincident survey data to develop a preincident plan.

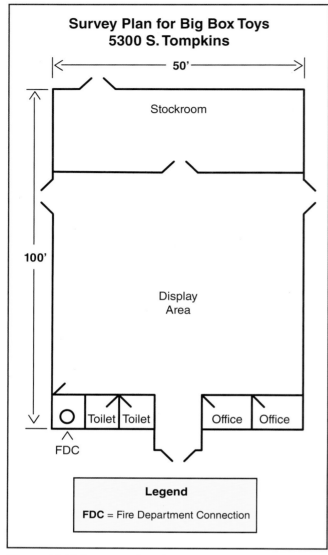

Survey Plan for Big Box Toys
5300 S. Tompkins

50'

Stockroom

100'

Display
Area

FDC

Toilet | Toilet

Office | Office

Legend

FDC = Fire Department Connection

Figure 10.18 A survey plan showing only essential information.

There are two general schools of thought about what should be included in a preincident plan. Each of these approaches has certain advantages and disadvantages. The first approach assumes that all interior structure fires behave in generally the same way and this behavior is predictable unless there is something in the fire environment to cause it to behave differently. Those who subscribe to this approach do not believe that a large volume of data about the building and its contents are necessary. Beyond certain essential information, such as the basic floor plan and locations of utility controls, they only want to know what will make this fire behave differently than any other fire in a similar structure.

This approach is simple to develop, use, and maintain. Some prefer this type of plan because they do not have to filter the essential information they need from extraneous data. Using this approach successfully requires the plan to contain all essential data and enough additional information to make it complete. Even with an essentials-only approach, larger, more complex structures and occupancies require more data to develop a complete plan **(Figure 10.18)**.

The other approach is much more involved and structured because the volume of information gathered on each structure and occupancy surveyed is extensive **(Figure 10.19)**. It is more structured since the same items of information are gathered on every structure and occupancy surveyed, regardless of how different the structures are from each other. Its main advantage is that the likelihood of some critical item of information being omitted from the plan is extremely low. However, it may take the incident commander longer to find the critical information within a large mass of data.

The preincident plan development process includes creating illustrations of the floor, plot plans, elevations of the structure or facility; writing a survey report; converting the report into a preincident plan that can be easily used at an incident; and managing data from multiple plans.

Facility Survey Drawings

Some of the preincident survey information is compiled into a written report, however, a drawing or series of drawings included in the preincident plan more effectively describes the building layout information. The three general types of drawings used to show building information include:

- *Plot plans* — Indicate how buildings are situated in relation to other buildings and streets in the area **(Figure 10.20a, p. 284)**
- *Floor plans* — Show the layout of individual floors, subfloors, and roofs **(Figure 10.20b, p. 285)**
- *Elevations* — Show side views of structures that depict the number of floors in a building and the grades of surrounding ground **(Figure 10.20c, p. 285)**

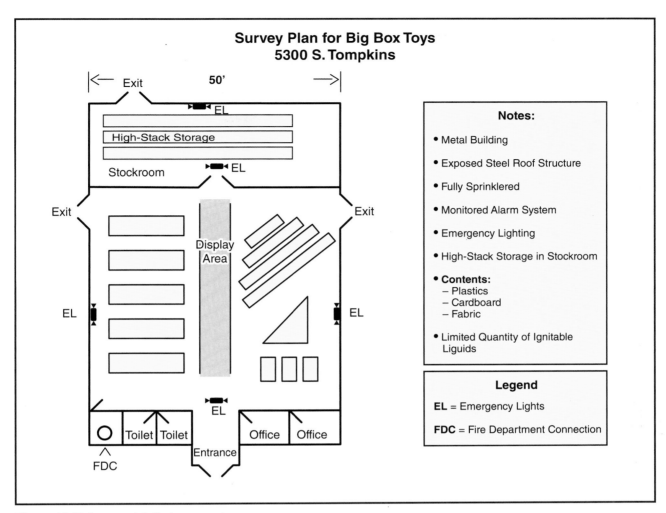

Survey Plan for Big Box Toys
5300 S. Tompkins

|← Exit   **50'**   →|

High-Stack Storage

Stockroom

EL

Exit

Exit

Display Area

EL

EL

EL

EL

Toilet | Toilet

Entrance

Office | Office

FDC

Notes:

- Metal Building
- Exposed Steel Roof Structure
- Fully Sprinklered
- Monitored Alarm System
- Emergency Lighting
- High-Stack Storage in Stockroom
- **Contents:**
  – Plastics
  – Cardboard
  – Fabric
- Limited Quantity of Ignitable Liguids

Legend

EL = Emergency Lights

FDC = Fire Department Connection

Figure 10.19 A more detailed survey plan.

Written Reports

After all drawings and any photographs have been compiled and labeled, a clear, concise written report must be prepared. The report's cover should include the address of the building or occupancy, date of the facility survey, type of building, and name of the submitting officer.

Local policy will dictate the form and content of the written report. If organizational policy dictates that preincident plans contain only information that indicates how this occupancy is different from others, the written report should reflect that information. If policy dictates that the same type of information be included for all occupancies surveyed, the written report should give that information.

Preincident Plans

The preincident plan should contain the essential information that will assist in the development of an initial action plan in conjunction with a tactical worksheet. The plan should be in a format that is easy to access and read. Preplans can be kept in hard-copy format or provided electronically on apparatus equipped with mobile data terminals (MDT).

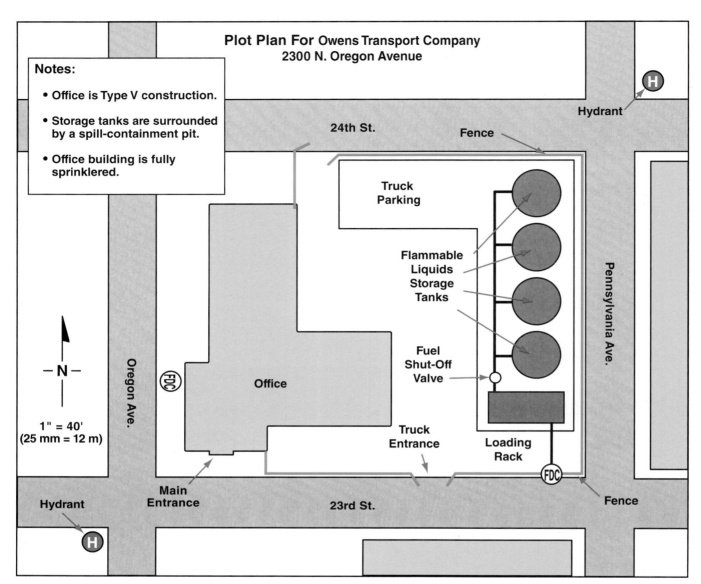

Plot Plan For Owens Transport Company
2300 N. Oregon Avenue

Notes:

• Office is Type V construction.

• Storage tanks are surrounded by a spill-containment pit.

• Office building is fully sprinklered.

24th St.

Fence

Truck Parking

Flammable Liquids Storage Tanks

Fuel Shut-Off Valve

Pennsylvania Ave.

Hydrant

– N –

1" = 40'
(25 mm = 12 m)

Oregon Ave.

FDC

Office

Truck Entrance

Loading Rack

FDC

Fence

Hydrant

Main Entrance

23rd St.

Figure 10.20a A sample plot plan depicting the structure and all adjacent streets, hydrants, structures, and access points.

Managing Preincident Data

The three major tasks with any preincident plan involve gathering the data, entering the data into databases, and keeping the data current. Systems must be developed for managing the data that is gathered during site surveys and then used to produce preincident operational plans. Company officers should be familiar with the system their organization uses and provide feedback up the change of command to improve efficiency in retrieving data and generating reports.

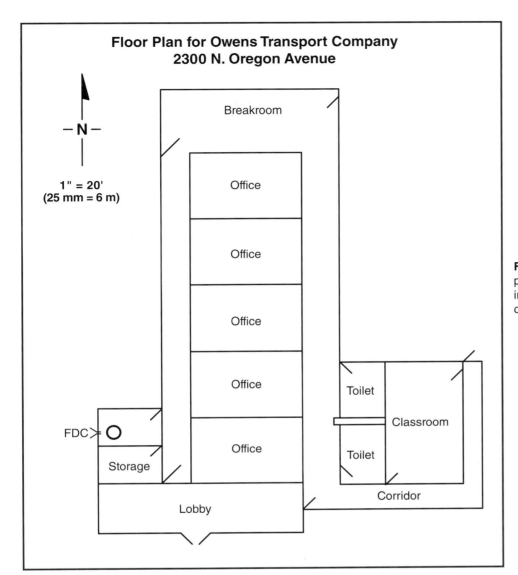

**Floor Plan for Owens Transport Company
2300 N. Oregon Avenue**

−N−

1" = 20'
(25 mm = 6 m)

Breakroom

Office

Office

Office

Office

Office

FDC

Storage

Lobby

Toilet

Toilet

Classroom

Corridor

Figure 10.20b A sample floor plan indicating the access doors, interior wall arrangements, and other information.

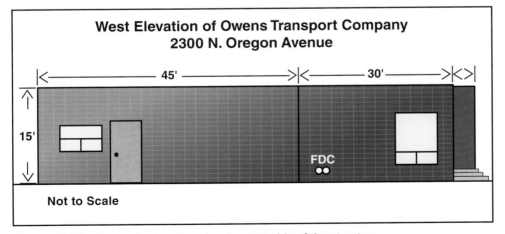

**West Elevation of Owens Transport Company
2300 N. Oregon Avenue**

|← 45' →|← 30' →|←>|

15'

FDC

Not to Scale

Figure 10.20c A sample elevation showing one side of the structure.

Chapter Summary

The safety and effectiveness of emergency operations can be greatly enhanced when emergency responders have comprehensive and up-to-date information about the occupancies in their districts. These surveys provide valuable information on a structure's occupancy type, building construction, contents, and potential fire conditions. Preincident surveys that the company officers and members of their companies conduct are the best way for this information to be gathered and transformed into a plan for use at an incident.

This chapter has described the preincident planning process to include understanding the differences between surveys and inspections. Company officers should understand basic building construction, how to prepare for preincident surveys, how to develop positive public relations, and conduct preincident surveys. Company officers should also know how preincident data is managed and preincident plans are developed.

Review Questions

1. What are the advantages of conducting code inspections and preincident surveys on separate occasions? (p. 264)
2. What are the hazards presented by roofs, lightweight construction, and other building components? (p. 267)
3. How does proper preparation for preincident surveys build a positive relationship with a building or facility's owners/occupants? (p. 269)
4. What elements of a facility or building should be examined during a preincident survey? (pp. 274-281)
5. How is the data from preincident surveys compiled into preincident plans? (p. 283)

Learning Activities

Learning Activity 10-1

Objective 6: Develop a preincident plan.

A company officer must develop a preincident plan by following proper policies and procedures and using data gathered during a preincident survey.

For this activity, you will need access to the following resources:

- A copy of your department's
  — Policies and procedures
  — Preincident survey
  — Preincident plan forms
  — Drawing/sketching tools, including pencils, a pad of paper, etc.
- You may also obtain policies and procedures and other forms by using an Internet search engine.

Conduct a preincident survey on a relatively small occupancy that you have permission to access. Follow the information provided in Chapter 10 to complete a survey of the occupancy, using any forms that your organization or jurisdiction may require. Once you have gathered the information, create a preincident plan following your organization's procedures. If you do not have the procedures, choose one of the approaches outlined in the chapter to create a preincident plan and include justifications for why you chose that approach.

Answer Key:

Answers for this activity will vary; check your answers with a crew member with experience conducting surveys and creating plans. Your answer should include any applicable information, such as:

- Occupancy information
- Access
- Water supply to include estimated fire flow
- Location of utility shutoffs
- Hazards
- Ventilation
- Roof construction
- Building factors – Internal and exterior
- Stairwell features
- Command post sites
- Evacuation sites
- Triage sites
- Suggest street closures
- Elevator operations information
- High value areas (records, computer system data storage)
- Secondary extinguishing systems

  Multistory or large building information may also include:

- Base, staging areas
- Interior command sites
- Lobby controls
- System controls
- Traffic or access plans
- Number of stories
- System inspection current on date of preplan
- Building communications system
- Occupant egress plan

Delivery of Emergency Services I

Chapter Contents

chapter 11

Key Terms

NFPA® Job Performance Requirements

This chapter provides information that addresses the following job performance requirements of NFPA® 1021, *Standard for Fire Officer Professional Qualifications* (2014).

4.5.2   4.6.2

4.5.3   4.6.3

4.6.1

Learning Objectives

After reading this chapter, students will be able to:

1. Recognize approaches to improving firefighter survivability. [NFPA® 1021, 4.6.2]

2. Discuss fire behavior related to incident decision-making. [NFPA® 1021, 4.6.1, 4.6.2]

3. Explain fire behavior considerations prior to fire attack. [NFPA® 1021, 4.5.2, 4.6.1]

4. Identify methods for conducting incident scene operations. [NFPA® 1021, 4.6.1, 4.6.2]

5. Describe postincident activities. [NFPA® 1021, 4.5.3, 4.6.3]

6. Prepare an initial action plan for an emergency incident. [NFPA® 1021, 4.6.1; Learning Activity 11-1]

7. Given a scenario, explain how to execute an action plan [NFPA® 1021, 4.6.2; Learning Activity 11-2]

8. Given a scenario, describe how to conduct a postincident analysis with personnel. [NFPA® 1021, 4.6.3; Learning Activity 11-3]

Chapter 11
Delivery of Emergency Services I

Case History

Engine companies had responded to back-to-back reports of lightning strikes resulting from a heavy thunderstorm. On the radio, the medic unit from the busy fire station reported that it had responded to a walk-in report of a structure fire. Paramedics could see the flames as they left the station and gave an approximate address. As the engine company cleared from another call, it was informed of the fire and dispatched to the call.

Paramedics began initial incident command duties while waiting on the first engine company to arrive. They ordered their driver to put on bunker gear, evacuate Exposure B, and utilize a garden hose to protect the exposure since it was showing signs of heat damage. Paramedics performed a 360-degree check of the structure and observed no signs of occupants from the windows and no vehicles present in the driveway. Exposure D was evacuated, and the occupants confirmed to the paramedics that the residents of the burning home were out of town. These initial actions and findings were reported to the responding units.

Paramedics were already at the hydrant, approximately 250 feet (76 m) from the structure, to establish a water supply when the first engine company arrived. The engine company officer assumed the incident command and ordered the deployment of a hand line for interior attack and a master stream device for exposure protection. The company officer and the paramedics quickly established rehab using the medic crew. Incoming units received further assignments while en route. Due to the initiative of the paramedics, cross training, and common terminology, the company officer was able to make educated, informed decisions that mitigated the incident with no further loss.

The primary role of a fire and emergency services organization is the delivery of emergency services to the community it protects. The emergency services delivered to a community include but are not limited to fire suppression, rescue, hazardous materials response, and emergency medical care activities. To function effectively in support of emergency services delivery, company officers must be highly trained and knowledgeable in:

- Fire behavior and how it relates to incident decision-making
- Incident scene management
- Incident scene operations
- Postincident activities

Because of the risk to emergency responders during emergency services delivery, this chapter describes new approaches to improving firefighter survivability. This chapter also addresses the basic NIMS-ICS model, including the positions and functions that are needed at both small and large emergency incidents. Establishing priorities for incident scene management as well as initial incident size-up considerations and scene control are addressed. It also provides information on the actions necessary to terminate an emergency incident. An incident is terminated once emergency services personnel and investigative authorities have left the scene or the property has returned to the possession of the owner. Finally, this chapter describes postincident activities to include emergency cause determination and postincident analysis and critique.

Firefighter Survivability

To reduce the number of firefighters injured or killed during structural fire fighting operations, a new series of approaches to improving firefighter survivability has been developed and applied to these operations. These approaches include recognizing rapid fire development occupant survivability profiling, crew resource management, and new recommended rules of engagement.

NOTE: While these approaches were primarily developed with structural fire fighting operations in mind, they may also be applied in other situations, such as hazardous materials incidents or wildland/urban interface fires where emergency responders may be endangered.

Occupant Survivability Profiling

Upon arriving at a structure fire, company officers should examine the situation and make an intelligent, informed decision based on the known events or circumstances. This data assists the company officer in determining if building occupants can survive the fire and smoke conditions that are present and whether to commit personnel to life-saving and interior operations **(Figure 11.1)**.

Figure 11.1 The incident commander at this fire must consider the likelihood of occupant survivability given the level of fire spread within the structure.

The environment within a structural fire can exceed 500° F (260° C) within three to four minutes with the potential for **flashover** (approximately 1,110° F [599° C]) to occur within five minutes. The upper human survivability limit is 212° F (100° C) according to the NFPA®. While firefighters have personal protective equipment and SCBA to protect them under such conditions, civilian occupants do not. Occupant survivability profiling is a type of size-up that should be employed to evaluate the potential of an occupant being alive within a structural fire environment. In conducting occupant survivability profiling, the company officers asks the following questions:

1. Are occupants suspected of being or known to be trapped?

2. Is it reasonable to assume that the occupants are still alive?

If the answers to these questions are *no*, then the responders should take a different approach. They should stop what they are doing, analyze the bigger picture, and gather additional information on the situation. The firefighters should focus on fighting the fire first and search for victims later when it is safer to do so. This approach may contradict the traditional view of firefighters racing into a burning building to attempt rescue, but the use of occupant survivability profiling can be paramount to saving the lives of firefighters.

Flashover — Stage of a fire at which all surfaces and objects within a space have been heated to their ignition temperature, and flame breaks out almost at once over the surface of all objects in the space.

Crew Resource Management

Crew resource management (CRM) training should become a part of each fire and emergency services organization's training schedule for all personnel. CRM is a system that optimizes the utilization of all available resources, personnel, procedures, and equipment in order to promote safety and improve operational efficiency. Originated by the air transportation industry, crew resource management has been adopted by other career fields to include the fire and emergency services. CRM training involves a broad range of knowledge, skill, and attitudes to address the following:

- Communications are critical to success at any operation. Using CRM, personnel focus on communications, speak directly and respectfully, and communicate responsibly.

- Situational awareness is the necessity of maintaining a level of attentiveness at an event. Personnel need to recognize that emergency situations can be dynamic and require each individual's full attention.

- Decision making during an emergency relies on the use of risk/benefit analysis. The availability of little or no information can result in a poor risk assessment while too much information can overload the decision maker and interfere with making a decision.

- Teamwork is emphasized during CRM training to improve efficiency and reduce risk.

- Barriers are any factors that interfere with communication, situational awareness, decision making, and teamwork. CRM training helps to identify these barriers and prevent them from impeding an operation.

CRM is designed to create a culture or climate of freedom in which personnel are encouraged to contribute to the safety and goals of mitigating the incident. Using CRM assists personnel in identifying the first indicator of errors occurring; the discrepancy between what IS happening and what SHOULD BE happening! Personnel can then communicate the discrepancy to the supervisor or incident commander in a manner that is forceful yet respectful in order to overcome the problem and save firefighter lives.

Rules of Engagement

In 2010, the Safety, Health, and Survival Section of the International Association of Fire Chiefs (IAFC) released its initial draft of *Rules of Engagement for Structural Fire Fighting – Increasing Firefighter Survival*. This document outlined two sets of rules that should be followed at structural fire incidents, one for incident commanders and one for firefighters. Through the application of these rules of engagement, the IAFC/SHS Section believes that firefighter line-of-duty injuries and deaths can be reduced.

All fire and emergency services personnel should be trained on the *Rules of Engagement for Firefighter Survival*. All personnel who may serve as an incident commander at an emergency scene should be trained on the *Incident Commander Rules of Engagement for Firefighter Safety*.

International Association of Fire Chiefs Rules of Engagement

Rules of Engagement for Firefighter Survival

1. Size-up your tactical area of operation.
2. Determine the occupant survival profile.
3. **DO NOT** risk your life for lives or property that cannot be saved.
4. Extend **LIMITED** risk to protect **SAVABLE** property.
5. Extend **Vigilant** and **Measured** risk to protect and rescue **SAVABLE** lives.
6. Go in together, stay together, come out together.
7. Maintain continuous awareness of your air supply, situation, location, and fire conditions.
8. Constantly monitor fireground communications for critical radio reports.
9. You are required to report unsafe practices or conditions that can harm you. Stop, evaluate, and decide.
10. You are required to abandon your position and retreat before deteriorating conditions can harm you.
11. Declare a May Day as soon as you **THINK** you are in danger.

Incident Commander Rules of Engagement for Firefighter Safety

There are 14 rules of engagement for incident commanders to follow to protect their personnel. These rules include:

1. Rapidly conduct, or obtain, a 360 degree size-up of the incident.
2. Determine the occupant survival profile.
3. Conduct an initial risk assessment and implement a **SAFE ACTION PLAN**.
4. If you do not have the resources to safely support and protect firefighters – seriously consider a defensive strategy.
5. DO NOT risk firefighter lives for lives or property that cannot be saved – seriously consider a defensive strategy.
6. Extend **LIMITED** risk to protect **SAVABLE** property.
7. Extend **Vigilant** and **Measured** risk to protect and rescue **SAVABLE** lives.
8. Act upon reported unsafe practices and conditions that can harm firefighters. Stop, evaluate, and decide.
9. Maintain frequent two-way communications and keep interior crews informed of changing conditions.
10. Obtain frequent progress reports and revise the action plan.
11. Ensure accurate accountability of all firefighter locations and status.
12. If, after completing the primary search, little or no progress towards fire control has been achieved – seriously consider a defensive strategy.
13. Always have a rapid intervention team in place at all working fires.
14. Always have firefighter rehab services in place at all working fires.

Source: © 2012, *The International Association of Fire Chiefs.*

Incident Scene Management

Management of any emergency incident requires emergency responders to gain control of the scene as quickly as possible and maintain that control throughout the incident. Unfortunately, emergency incidents are rarely the same and a variety of problems may exist that will challenge the efficient management of them **(Figure 11.2)**. The following problems may be difficult to overcome:

- Wide- and diverse-area emergency scenes
- Multiple casualties
- Unstable structures or vehicles
- Leaking hazardous materials
- Debris strewn over a wide geographic area
- Witnesses and curious bystanders (spectators) milling about
- Victims mixed with bystanders
- Treatment needs of victims
- Safety for those at the scene

Incident scene management applies to all types of emergency responses and all levels of resource commitment from single-resource situations to multijurisdictional and multiagency disasters requiring many resources. By learning and applying incident scene management at single-resource situations, company officers will perfect the skills that can be applied to more complex situations later.

Figure 11.2 A structure fire, a hazardous materials incident, and a technical rescue illustrate the unique circumstances and challenges a company officer can face at an emergency. *Structural fire photo courtesy of Ron Jeffers. Hazmat photo courtesy of Rich Mahaney.*

National Incident Management System-Incident Command System (NIMS-ICS)

The Incident Command System (ICS) is the basis for safe and efficient incident scene management. As a result of Presidential Directive 5, the National Incident Management System (NIMS) is required to be used. ICS is a component of NIMS.

The first-arriving emergency services personnel establish the NIMS-ICS, make decisions, and take actions that will influence the rest of the operation **(Figure 11.3, p. 296)**. The initial decisions must be based on the organization's incident scene management procedures.

Figure 11.3 A company officer arriving on the scene and assuming command.

Incident Action Plan (IAP) — Written or unwritten plan for the disposition of an incident; contains the strategic goals, tactical objectives, and support requirements for a given operational period during an incident. All incidents require an action plan. On relatively small incidents, the IAP is usually not in writing; on larger, more complex incidents, a written IAP is created for each **operational period** and disseminated to all assigned units. Written IAPs may have a number of forms as attachments.

Operational Period — Period of time scheduled for execution of a specified set of operational goals and objectives as identified in the incident action plan (IAP). An operational period may be 12 hours, 24 hours, or any other arbitrary amount of time. A new IAP is created for each operational period.

Essential to all emergency incident scene management is the management of emergency response resources: apparatus, personnel, equipment, and materials. NIMS-ICS establishes an organizational structure for all types of emergency incidents. Company officers must use NIMS-ICS on all incidents no matter how small or large they are.

Every member of the organization, especially company officers, must be familiar with the system and trained in its application. All agencies with mutual or automatic aid agreements must know and use the same system. This system may require extensive cross-training at all organizational levels among units of the participating agencies. These levels may include: independent EMS providers, law enforcement agencies, and public works.

Common characteristics of the NIMS-ICS are as follows:

- Common terminology for functional structure
- Modular organization
- Common communications
- Unified command structure
- **Incident action plan (IAP)**

    NOTE: The term Operational Plan may be used interchangeably with incident action plan within the confines of this manual.

- Manageable span of control
- Predesignated incident facilities
- Comprehensive resource management
- Personnel accountability

Common terminology for functional elements, position titles, facilities, and resources is essential for any command system, especially one that will be used by units from multiple agencies. The terms in the following lists need to be understood by all fire and emergency service responders. A quick review of the most frequent tools of ICS is listed below.

Organizational Levels

- **Command —** Act of directing, ordering, and/or controlling resources by virtue of explicit legal, agency, or delegated authority; also denotes the organizational level that is in command (incident commander [IC]) of the incident. Lines of authority must be clear to all involved. Lawful commands by those in authority need to be immediately followed.

- **Command Staff —** Incident management personnel who report directly to the incident commander; includes the public information officer, safety officer, and liaison officer.

- **General Staff —** Incident management personnel who represent the major functional Sections.

- **Section —** Organizational level having responsibility for a major functional area of incident management includes:

    — Operations

    — Planning

    — Logistics

— Finance/Administration

— Information and Intelligence

   NOTE: Information and Intelligence may be designated as a section, a branch within Operations, or part of the Command Staff.

- *Branch* — Organizational level having functional/geographic responsibility for major segments of incident operations; organizationally located between Section and Division or Group. Branches are identified by Roman numeral or functional area (such as Command, Operations).

- *Division* — Organizational level having responsibility for operations within a defined geographic area; organizationally between Branch and single resources, task force, or strike team. Resources assigned to a division report to that division supervisor.

- *Group* — Organizational level, equal to division, having responsibility for a specified functional assignment at an incident (such as ventilation, salvage, water supply) without regard for a specific geographical area. When the assigned function has been completed, it is available for reassignment.

- *Unit* — Organizational level within the sections that fulfill specific support functions, such as the resources, documentation, demobilization, and situation units within the Planning Section.

Resources

- *Crew* — Specified number of personnel assembled for an assignment, such as search, ventilation, or hoseline deployment and operations. The number of personnel assigned to a crew should be within span-of-control guidelines. A crew operates under the direct supervision of a crew leader.

- *Single resources* — Individual pieces of apparatus (engines, ladders/trucks, water tenders, bulldozers, air tankers, helicopters) and the personnel required to make them functional.

- *Task force* — Any combination of resources (engines, ladders/trucks, bulldozers) assembled for a specific mission or operational assignment. All units in the force must have common communications capabilities and a designated leader. Once a task force's tactical objective has been met, the force is disbanded; individual resources are reassigned or released.

- *Strike team* — Set number of resources of the same kind and type (engines, ladders/trucks, bulldozers) that have an established minimum number of personnel. All units in the team must have common communications capabilities and a leader in a separate vehicle. Unlike task forces, strike teams remain together and function as a team throughout an incident.

Unified Command Structure

A unified command structure is necessary when an incident involves or threatens to involve more than one jurisdiction or agency. These multijurisdictional incidents are not limited to fires. For example, hazardous materials releases may spread from one jurisdiction to another. Large-scale natural disasters, such as Hurricane Katrina, can easily affect multiple jurisdictions **(Figure 11.4, p. 298).**

Figure 11.4 Large-scale disasters can require multiagency response and the use of a unified command structure. *Courtesy of Chris Mickal/District Chief, New Orleans (LA) FD Photo.*

A unified command may also be appropriate within a single jurisdiction if multiple agencies are affected. For example, a hostage situation may be primarily a law enforcement incident, but if fire or explosion is a possibility, the fire department should also influence the strategic and tactical decisions relating to the incident.

In a unified command structure, representatives of all affected agencies or jurisdictions share the Command responsibilities and decisions **(Figure 11.5)**. They jointly establish the strategic goals for the incident and agree on the tactical objectives that must be achieved. In some agencies or jurisdictions, legal authority to act is vested in those occupying certain positions of responsibility. Unified command allows these individuals to interface with those who have the operational expertise required to resolve an incident.

Company officers must be familiar with the unified command process. Even small incidents, such as a fire in a residential structure that contains an illegal methamphetamine lab, may require the unified command approach. Cross-jurisdictional incidents will also place the company officer either in charge of or as part of a unified command.

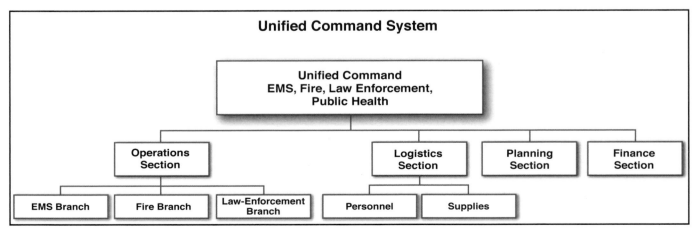

Figure 11.5 An organizational chart that illustrates a unified command system.

Initial Action Plan

NFPA® 1021 requires the Fire Officer I to be able to develop an initial action plan. Lloyd Layman used the term plan of operation to describe the same concept. According to NFPA® 1561, *Standard for Fire Department Incident Management System*, an Initial Action Plan (IAP) establishes the overall strategic decisions and assigned tactical objectives for an incident.

The company officer will need to develop the initial action plan usually consisting of appropriate actions that can be implemented during the initial phase of the incident. Examples may include fire suppression, rescue, water supply, and ventilation. The number of resources initially at the scene will determine the exact implementation. The company officer will need to prioritize these actions based on available resources. The initial CO should not hesitate to call for additional resources if the judgment is made that the resources on-scene or dispatched are inadequate to deal appropriately with the incident.

Many departments will have a tactical worksheet for the company officer to document the initial actions being taken, and this worksheet may serve as the initial action plan. This sheet also serves as a checklist of tasks for the company officer to address **(Figure 11.6)**. A number of helpful worksheets are available in **Appendix C** of this manual.

Figure 11.6 Tactical worksheets are useful tools for documenting initial actions to be taken.

Organizational policies will determine the transfer of command process. For example, when the company officer transfers command to a higher ranking officer, the receiving Incident Commander (IC) should review the initial action plan to determine the actions already taken.

A formal written IAP will be required for long duration events. In addition, the Incident Command System will likely expand to include functions of the Planning Section to assist with the development of the IAP. Company officers, based on their training and experience, may be asked to serve in this role or reassigned to other operational aspects of the incident.

Manageable Span of Control

Span of control is the number of direct subordinates that one supervisor can effectively manage. An effective span of control ranges from three to seven subordinates per supervisor, depending upon a number of variables, with five considered the optimum number **(Figure 11.7, p. 300)**. Supervisors can more easily keep track of their subordinates and monitor their safety if an effective span of control is maintained.

Variables, such as proximity, similarity of function, and subordinate capability, affect the span of control. The number of subordinates can be higher in the following situations:

- Subordinates are within sight of the supervisor and able to communicate with each other
- Subordinates are performing the same or similar functions
- Subordinates are skilled in performing the assigned task

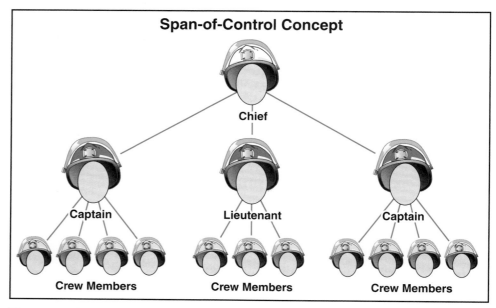

Figure 11.7 Span of control is critical for maintaining effective supervision at an incident.

Personnel Accountability

An essential element of the NIMS-ICS is personnel accountability. Company officers are responsible for knowing where their subordinates are at all times and what tasks they have been assigned. The first-arriving company officer as the incident commander should implement the organization's accountability system soon after arrival on the scene.

Incident Size-up Considerations

Incident scene management should reflect overall incident priorities. These priorities are always considered in the following order:

1. Life safety

2. Incident stabilization

3. Property conservation

To accomplish the incident priorities, the first-arriving company officer must know the type of emergency incident and then gather as much information as possible to make command decisions. Size-up is the ongoing process of evaluating an emergency situation to determine:

- What has happened (nature and scope of the incident)

- What is happening

- What is likely to happen

- What resources are available with the initial response

- What actions are necessary to effect control

- What additional resources will be needed to mitigate the incident

The company officer begins to actively size up the emergency when the alarm sounds and emergency notification is received. If a preincident plan for the emergency location exists, the company officer combines this information with information sent by the telecommunications center. This information may include the description of the incident, weather conditions, and units assigned to the incident. The company officer takes into account the unit's resources, such as the number of personnel on duty and their knowledge, skills, and abilities, plus the equipment and materials that may be needed to control the emergency.

Upon arrival, the first-arriving company officer as the initial Incident Commander will normally:

Figure 11.8 Performing a 360-degree examination of an incident scene can help the Incident Commander understand the "big picture."

- Establish command and communicate who is in command (using NIMS-ICS)

- Perform a 360-degree check or delegate another unit to perform the 360 as part of its size-up **(Figure 11.8)**

- Determine offensive or defensive mode

- Assign tasks

- Begin completing the organization's tactical worksheet(s)

The company officer should be able to determine whether additional resources are needed as well as the number and types of additional resources that will be needed by the time the current resources are operational at the scene. In some departments, operational guidelines define when additional resources should be requested. The lead/reflex time (amount of time to request and obtain additional resources) is a factor in this determination. Once on the scene, the company officer must also determine how the hazard is developing, how rapidly it is expanding, and where it will be in both intensity and location when additional resources are operational at the scene.

A company officer can use any number of size-up processes or models. Decades after Lloyd Layman wrote his influential work *Fire Fighting Tactics*, its principles are as valid as ever, and his traditional model is the one most commonly used today. Layman described the following considerations needed for analyzing any emergency situation:

- Facts — Things that are true

- Probabilities — Things that are likely to happen

- Own situation — Officer's own knowledge about the situation

- Decision — Initial use of resources followed by supplemental resource needs

- Plan of operation — Information compiled into incident action plan

Facts

The facts of the situation are things that are true. Facts are what the officer knows and is actually observing. The majority of this information may be provided by the telecommunications center based on the report of the emergency. Some of these items include:

- Time (month, day, hour)

- Location (address, business name, landmarks)

- Nature of the emergency (fire, hazardous materials release, structural collapse)
- Life hazard (occupants and responders)
- Exposures (adjacent uninvolved property)
- Weather (wind, temperature extremes, humidity)
- Number of potential trapped or injured victims
- Units being dispatched

The number and types of units being dispatched provides the company officer with an idea of the size or complexity of the incident. This information also gives the officer an idea of the number and type of resources that will be available to control the incident.

The company officer combines all of this information with any knowledge gained from building surveys, preincident plans, and training in fire or hazard behavior. If the information available indicates that additional or specialized resources are needed, a request should be made as soon as possible.

Probabilities

Probabilities are things that are not known for certain, but based on the known facts, are likely to happen. Actual observation can transform a probability into a fact. To assist in making decisions, the following questions must be answered regarding the probabilities of a fire emergency situation:

- In which direction is the fire likely to spread?
- Are exposures likely to become involved?
- Are explosions likely and is a secondary explosion likely? Is a secondary collapse likely?
- Is an evacuation of people likely to be needed?
- Are additional resources likely to be needed? If so, what types and how many?

When sizing up a fire incident, many of the decisions in the probabilities phase can be made easier and with greater accuracy if the company officer has some knowledge of:

1. Fire behavior and smoke indicators (from past experience, training, and education)
2. The building or topography involved (from preincident planning)

Unusual Chemical Incidents

Illegal methamphetamine labs are common across North America. They can be found in both urban and rural areas, operating in houses, apartments, sheds, and vehicles. The toxicity of the products, especially when involved in fire, creates hazardous atmospheres that demand the use of self-contained breathing apparatus (SCBA). Other hazards include the likelihood that the site might be booby-trapped and the lab operators may be armed, dangerous, and violent. Another type of unusual chemical incident responders might encounter is chemical suicide in which the victim uses a chemical or chemicals to commit the act.

Own Situation

The first-arriving officer's own situation is one set of facts that is known about the overall incident situation. The following facts are among those to consider:

- Number and types of resources responding to or already at the scene
- Additional resources available immediately, with some delay, and with considerable delay
- Capabilities and limitations of resources
- The officer's ability to deal with the situation based on training and experience
- Abilities of unit members

Decision

Layman identified two or more decisions that must be made in the ongoing size-up process — an initial decision and one or more supplemental decisions based on the three incident priorities. The initial decision may be seen as having three segments:

1. Whether resources at the scene and those en route are adequate for the situation
2. How to deploy the resources already at the scene in the most effective manner
3. What to do with the resources that arrive (immediate deployment or staging)

Supplemental decisions have to be made as the incident progresses and the situation changes. For instance, the IC must decide if the initial deployment of resources is producing the desired results or if the units need to be redeployed. On large incidents (those lasting more than an operational period), consideration must be given to relief personnel, additional supplies and more apparatus. More supplemental decisions will be required and more functional positions of NIMS-ICS may need to be activated if an incident continues for an extended period of time.

Plan of Operation

Information gathered in the size-up process serves as a basis for making decisions about how to manage the incident. Depending upon the nature and scope of the incident, the plan of operation or IAP may be simple or complex. The plan does not need to be in writing on relatively small, routine incidents involving only the initial assignment, but there must be a plan. Large, complex incidents require a written IAP, often with numerous annexes. An IAP normally covers a single operational period.

Scene Control

Scene control means controlling the environment in which responders must work and bystanders or victims may find themselves. Scene control is essential to ensuring the life safety of responders, victims, and bystanders.

Scene control begins with the first-arriving company officer establishing command. Emergencies attract spectators, and maintaining scene control makes it easier to keep them safe. Controlling the movements of nonemergency personnel near a high-hazard area contributes to life safety on the scene.

Perimeter Control

Controlling the perimeter facilitates the use of a personnel accountability system. It also helps in accounting for victims and keeping the scene free of curious spectators.

Establishing three operating control zones (commonly labeled hot, warm, and cold) is the most common and effective way to control the perimeter of an incident scene. The zones can be cordoned off with rope or fire line tape tied to signs, utility poles, parking meters, or any other objects readily available.

There is no specific distance or area that should be cordoned off for each zone or from the total incident scene. Zone boundaries should be established by considering the:

- Amount of area needed by emergency personnel to work
- Degree of hazard presented by elements involved in the incident
- Wind and weather conditions
- General topography of the area

The three control zones can be described as follows **(Figure 11.9)**:

- **Hot zone** — Area where resolving the problem takes place. Only personnel who are directly involved in disposing of the problem are allowed, which limits crowds and confusion at the most critical area of the scene. The size of the zone may vary greatly, depending upon the nature and extent of the problem. Personnel requirements:

  — Trained appropriately to manage the situation

  — Attired in complete personal protective equipment (PPE) designed for the specific hazard

  — Participated in the incident's personnel accountability system

- **Warm zone** — Area immediately outside the hot zone for personnel who are directly supporting the work being performed by those in the hot zone. It is limited to personnel who may be operating hydraulic tool power plants or providing emergency lighting and fire protection. These personnel are in full PPE and ready to enter the hot zone. In hazardous materials incidents, this zone is where a decontamination station is normally assembled.

- **Cold zone** — Area immediately surrounding the hot and warm zones — may include the incident command post (ICP) with a rapid intervention crew (RIC) nearby, public information officer's (PIO) location, rehabilitation area, and staging areas for personnel and portable equipment. The outer boundary of this area would be the control line for the general public (crowd-control line). Examples:

  — Backup personnel available to enter warm or hot zones

  — Witnesses and family members of victims

  — News media accompanied by the PIO or organization representative

Company officers need to communicate effectively with law enforcement personnel about traffic safety needs at the incident scene. Good coordination with the law enforcement agency will help alleviate problems with closing traffic lanes or having law enforcement block roads for incoming fire apparatus **(Figure 11.10)**. In some areas, state and local road crews provide incident response teams to manage traffic flow and safety.

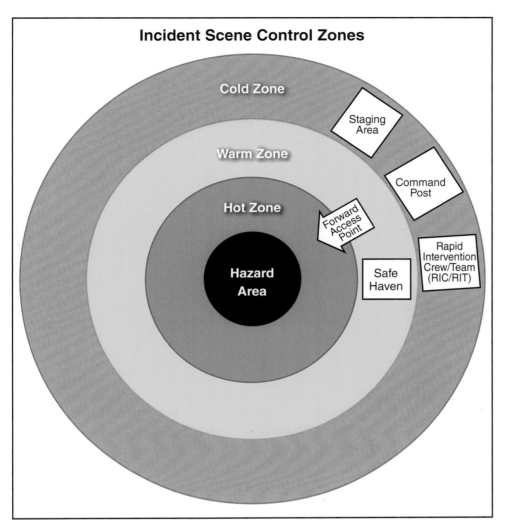

Incident Scene Control Zones

Cold Zone

Warm Zone

Hot Zone

Staging Area

Command Post

Forward Access Point

Hazard Area

Safe Haven

Rapid Intervention Crew/Team (RIC/RIT)

Figure 11.9 Illustrating how control zones are organized for most incidents.

Figure 11.10 Law enforcement personnel can help apparatus respond to an incident by keeping traffic lanes clear. *Courtesy of Ron Jeffers.*

Emergency incidents often do not involve vehicles, nor are they always located on streets or roads. They often occur inside buildings or well off roadways. In these cases, emergency vehicles should be parked so that they do not interfere with the normal flow of traffic.

Each roadway variable requires preplanning to overcome potential barriers. Company officers must be familiar with all types of situations, record the locations and conditions on response maps, inform the telecommunications center of changes resulting from construction or closures, and frequently check the locations for changes.

Crowd Control

In small incidents, when evacuation is unnecessary, cordoning off the area will keep bystanders at a safe distance from the scene and away from where emergency personnel are working. Once cordoned off, monitor the boundary to ensure that people do not cross it. The following actions should be taken to assist:

Figure 11.11 Spectators should be kept away from an incident scene. *Courtesy of Ron Jeffers.*

- *Incident Victims* — People who are involved in an incident should be assessed by emergency medical personnel before being released from the scene. Anyone who refuses treatment or transportation to a medical facility should be asked to sign a release-of-liability form.

- *Spectators* — All spectators should be restricted from getting too close for their own safety and that of victims and emergency personnel **(Figure 11.11)**.

- *Friends/Relatives of Victims* — Victims' friends or relatives should be treated with sensitivity and understanding. They should be gently but firmly restrained from getting too close to the incident, kept some distance from the actual incident, but within the cold zone. A responder or another responsible individual should be assigned to stay with them until victims have been removed from the scene.

On-Scene Occupant Services

On-scene occupant services involve emergency responders seeing beyond the obvious physical effects of an incident on victims and witnesses and being aware of and sensitive to their mental and emotional conditions as well. Company officers should take the following actions to assist occupants:

- Provide medical evaluation and treatment, as needed, and provide shelter from the elements for displaced occupants.

- Contact appropriate relief agencies for further assistance.

- Help those directly involved to notify relatives.

- Explain why forcible entry, ventilation, or victim stabilization is conducted.

- Provide victims with accurate and timely information about the progress of the incident and an estimate of when or if they might be able to reoccupy their property.

- Escort property owners through the damaged area when personnel are available and it is safe to do so.

- Behave professionally since innocent jokes, laughter, or horseplay can be misunderstood by the victims.

Considerations Prior to Fire Attack

By understanding fire behavior, company officers can predict how it will develop and spread and can determine the correct strategy and tactics to apply to a **compartment** or structure fire in order to control, confine, and eliminate it. Company officers must know how fire behavior influences and is influenced by its environment.

For this manual, the discussion of fire behavior is restricted to fires that start in a compartment or confined space of a structure. Compartments may range in size from a small utility closet to one that consists of the entire interior of the structure without interior walls or partitions, such as a warehouse or retail store. How the fire develops and spreads will be determined by the available fuel, oxygen, and the structural configuration of building components, such as the floors, walls, and roof or ceiling assemblies.

Fire Spread

With sufficient fuel and oxygen, a fire will continue to grow and spread. Fire spread results from **heat** transferring from a burning object to other objects of lower temperatures. Heat moves from warmer objects to cooler objects at a rate that is related to the temperature differential of the objects and the thermal conductivity of its materials. The greater the temperature differences between the objects, the more rapid the transfer rate. Heat is transferred from one object to another by **conduction**, **convection**, and **radiation** (**Figure 11.12**).

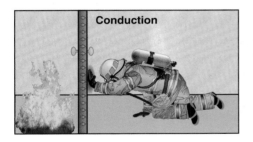

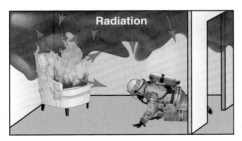

Figure 11.12 Three methods of heat transfer: conduction, convection, and radiation.

The spread of a fire is controlled by its environment. When a fire occurs in an unconfined area, such as outdoors, much of its heat dissipates into the atmosphere through radiation and convection. When a fire is confined within a compartment, the walls, ceiling, floor, and objects in the compartment absorb the radiant heat produced by the fire. Once heat levels rise to a degree in which those objects are at the same temperature, radiant heat energy is reflected back, continuing to increase the temperature of the other fuel in

Compartment — A room or space within a building or structure that is enclosed on all sides, at the top and bottom. The term *compartment fire* is defined as a fire that occurs within such a space.

Heat — Form of energy associated with the motion of atoms or molecules and capable of being transmitted through solid and fluid media by conduction, through fluid media by convection, and through empty space by radiation.

Conduction — Physical flow or transfer of heat energy from one body to another, through direct contact or an intervening medium, from the point where the heat is produced to another location, or from a region of high temperature to a region of low temperature. *See* Convection, Heat, Heat Transfer, Law of Heat Flow, and Radiation.

Convection — Transfer of heat by the movement of heated fluids or gases, usually in an upward direction.

Radiation — Transmission or transfer of heat energy from one body to another body at a lower temperature through intervening space by electromagnetic waves, such as infrared thermal waves, radio waves, or X-rays. *Also known as* Radiated Heat.

Pyrolysis — Thermal or chemical decomposition of fuel (matter) because of heat, generally resulting in the lowered ignition temperature of the material; the pre-ignition combustion phase of burning during which heat energy is absorbed by the fuel, in turn giving off flammable tars, pitches, and gases. Pyrolysis of wood releases combustible gases and leaves a charred surface. *Also known as* Pyrolysis Process or Sublimation.

the space. This process increases the rate of **pyrolysis** of the fuel and the rate of combustion. Hot air and smoke heated by the fire become hotter than the surrounding air, making them more buoyant and causing them to rise. Upon contact with the cooler ceiling and walls of the compartment, heat is transferred to the cooler materials, raising their temperature. This heat transfer process raises the temperature of all materials in the compartment. As nearby fuel is heated, it pyrolizes. Eventually the rate of pyrolysis can reach a point where flaming combustion can be supported and the fire spreads.

When sufficient oxygen is available, fire development is controlled by the fuel's characteristics and configuration. Under these conditions, the fire is said to be *fuel controlled*. Knowing the contents or fuel load is important in your decision-making process and in predicting fire growth. As a fire develops within a compartment, it reaches a point where further development is limited by the available oxygen supply and the fire is said to be *ventilation controlled*. Any action taken to gain access, create openings, or penetrate walls will cause a rapid increase in the amount of oxygen in the compartment and lead to rapid fire development.

Thermal Layering of Gases

Figure 11.13 Company officers and their personnel need to understand how thermal layering of gases impacts their interior fire attack.

Fire Behavior in Compartments

In a compartment fire, heated products of combustion and entrained air become hotter than the surrounding air and rise upwards in a plume. Upon reaching the ceiling, they mushroom, spreading horizontally through the compartment until they reach the compartment's walls. As combustion continues, the depth of the gas layer increases. The difference between hot smoke and the cooler air below causes them to separate into two distinct thermal layers.

Thermal layering of gases (also called *heat stratification*) is the tendency of gases to form into layers according to temperature. The hottest gases will be in the top layer, while the cooler gases form the lower layer **(Figure 11.13)**. Radiation from the hot gas layer also acts to heat the interior surfaces of the compartment and its contents.

As the volume and temperature of the hot gas layer increases, so does the pressure. Gases expand when heated. Higher pressure in this hot layer causes it to push down and out, increasing the pressure in the compartment. The thermal layer fills the room from the top down within the compartment and out through any openings, such as doors or windows. In an opening, the thermal layer will try to rise. The temperature and rate of heat transfer will dictate how fast the layer will move and spread out from the compartment of origin.

The pressure of the smoke and gas in a compartment can affect the movement of air in or out of the compartment. Because of the cool gas layer's lower pressure, air from outside the compartment is drawn into the compartment. The hotter, higher pressure gas layer near the ceiling forces smoke out openings. The pressure is neutral at the point where these two layers meet as the hot gases exit through an opening. The interface of the hot and cooler gas layers at the opening is commonly referred to as the *neutral plane*. This neutral pressure may be visible at openings where hot gases are exiting and cooler air is moving into the compartment. It may also be visible in hallways between the point of ventilation and room fire.

During the development of a compartment fire, pyrolysis of exposed fuels can produce combustible gases, which can gather at locations in the layer away from the fire plume. These pockets of gas may undergo **piloted ignition** from the transfer of heat energy directly from the fire plume itself or ignition as a result of having reached their **autoignition temperature**.

Rapid Fire Development

Numerous firefighter deaths and injuries have resulted from rapid fire development. To protect their crews and themselves, company officers must recognize the indicators of rapid fire development, know the conditions created by each of these situations, and determine the best action to take before they occur. The indicators are:

- Smoke rapidly exiting doors, windows, or other openings
- Doors forced open into the structure as fresh air is rapidly drawn in
- Smoke under pressure pulsing out of openings
- Heavily smoke-stained or cracked window glass
- Rapid lowering of the neutral plane
- Rapid rising and lowering of the smoke layer
- Rapid change in smoke color to black
- Rapid change in temperature within the compartment
- Yellow or orange flames at the ceiling moving away from the main body of fire
- Smoke being sucked back into the structure

Various fire events result in rapid fire development. These events include:

- Flashover
- Backdraft
- Smoke explosion

Flashover

Flashover occurs when all exposed combustible surfaces and objects within a compartment have been heated to their ignition temperature and ignite almost simultaneously **(Figure 11.14)**. During flashover, conditions in the room change from hot gases igniting and burning in the hot gas layer to the potential for flames filling the room floor to ceiling, if sufficient oxygen is present to support the flaming combustion. When flashover occurs, burning gases push out of openings in the compartment (such as a door leading to another room) at a substantial velocity.

Piloted Ignition — Moment when a mixture of fuel and oxygen encounters an external heat (ignition) source with sufficient heat energy to start the combustion reaction.

Autoignition Temperature — Minimum temperature to which a fuel (other than a liquid) in the air must be heated in order to start self-sustained combustion; no external ignition source is required.

Figure 11.14 The moment of flashover when all of the contents and interior of a compartment ignite. *Courtesy of NIST.*

During flashover, several things happen within the burning compartment:

- The fuel in the compartment produces combustible gases through pyrolysis.
- Temperatures rapidly increase from floor to ceiling.
- Additional fuel becomes involved.
- Extremely low visibility in the compartment area is possible.

Elements of Flashover

There are four common elements of flashover:

- **Transition in fire development** — Flashover represents a transition from the growth stage to the fully developed stage.

- **Rapidity** — Although not instantaneous, flashover happens rapidly, in a matter of seconds, to spread complete fire involvement within the compartment.

- **Compartment** — There must be an enclosed space or compartment such as a single room or enclosure.

- **Ignition of all exposed surfaces** — Virtually all combustible surfaces in the enclosed space ignite.

Figure 11.15 The failure of this window introduced additional oxygen into the room and intensified the fire. *Courtesy of Mike Wieder.*

Flashover does not occur in every compartment fire. Two factors determine whether a compartment fire will progress to flashover. First, the fuel must generate enough heat energy to develop flashover conditions. The second factor is ventilation. A developing fire must have sufficient oxygen to reach flashover. With insufficient ventilation, the fire may enter the growth stage but not reach the peak heat release of a fully developed fire.

Changes in ventilation can alter the ventilation flow path and create rapid fire development, placing firefighters in extreme danger. The size, number, and locations of openings as well as the velocity of the air being exchanged influence ventilation. Natural conditions, such as wind direction and velocity, can increase the velocity of the air being exchanged. Heating, ventilating, and air conditioning (HVAC) systems can also assist ventilation efforts.

If a window fails or firefighters open a door or window, ventilation is increased and the additional oxygen will increase the fire and heat release **(Figure 11.15)**. Most fires that grow beyond the incipient stage become ventilation controlled. Intact windows and closed doors may cause the fire to shift to a ventilation-controlled state more quickly. While this process reduces the heat release rate, fuel will continue to pyrolize, creating extremely fuel-rich smoke. Modern, well-sealed, energy efficient buildings do not vent as rapidly as older buildings. This heat retention causes compartment temperatures to rise quickly and a rapid progression to flashover. Careful ventilation is critical.

Rollover describes a condition in which the unburned fire gases that have accumulated at the top of a compartment ignite and flames propagate through the hot gas layer or across the ceiling. It is also a significant indicator of impending flashover. Rollover is distinguished from flashover because it involves only the fire gases at the upper levels of the compartment and not the other fuel packages within a compartment.

Rollover may occur during the growth stage as the hot-gas layer forms at the ceiling of the compartment. Flames may be observed in the layer when the combustible gases reach their ignition temperature. While the flames add to the total heat generated in the compartment, this condition is not flashover. Rollover will generally precede flashover, but it may not result in flashover. Rollover contributes to flashover conditions because the burning gases at the upper levels of the room generate tremendous amounts of radiant heat that preheat the fuel packages in the room and begin pyrolysis necessary for flashover.

Backdraft

A ventilation-controlled compartment fire can produce a large volume of flammable smoke and other gases due to incomplete combustion. While the heat release rate from a ventilation-controlled fire is limited, elevated temperatures are usually present within the compartment. An increase in low-level ventilation (such as opening a door or window) prior to upper level ventilation can result in an explosively rapid combustion of the flammable gases, called a **backdraft** **(Figure 11.16)**. Backdraft occurs in the decay stage, in a space containing a high concentration of heated flammable gases that lacks sufficient oxygen for flaming combustion.

Backdraft — Instantaneous explosion or rapid burning of superheated gases that occurs when oxygen is introduced into an oxygen-depleted confined space. The stalled combustion resumes with explosive force; may occur because of inadequate or improper ventilation procedures.

Figure 11.16 Improper ventilation caused this backdraft. *Courtesy of Bob Esposito.*

When potential backdraft conditions exist in a compartment, the compartment is filled with hot unburned fuel gases and smoke that are above their flammable range. They are only lacking sufficient oxygen to burn. A backdraft can occur with the creation of a horizontal or vertical opening. All that is required is the mixing of hot, fuel-rich smoke with air. Backdraft conditions can develop within a room, a void space, or an entire building. Anytime a compartment or space contains hot combustion products, potential for backdraft must be considered before creating any openings into the compartment.

It is often incorrectly assumed that a backdraft will always occur immediately after making an opening into the building or involved compartment. The mixing of hot flammable products of combustion with air through the action of gravity, air current, pressure differential, and wind effects sometimes takes time so that backdraft may not occur until after air is introduced. Company officers must observe what the smoke is doing: air current changing direction, neutral plane lifting, or smoke rushing out, are indicators of potential rapid fire development. To some degree, the violence of a backdraft is dependent on the extent to which the fuel/air mixture is confined. The more confined, the more violent it will be.

The effects of a backdraft can vary considerably depending on a number of factors, including:

- Volume of smoke
- Degree of confinement
- Pressure
- Speed with which fuel and air are mixed
- Location where ignition occurs

Smoke Explosion

A *smoke explosion* may occur before or after the decay stage. It occurs when unburned fuel gases come in contact with an ignition source. When smoke travels from the fire, it can cool and accumulate in other areas and mix with air. The smoke within its flammable range contacts an ignition source and results in an explosively rapid combustion. Smoke explosions are violent because they involve premixed fuel and oxygen. This explosion is similar to ignition of propane and air within its flammable range.

The key difference between a smoke explosion and backdraft is that with the backdraft, the mixture of smoke and air is extremely fuel rich (generally greater than 10 percent total hydrocarbons). However, a smoke explosion requires fuel and air within its flammable range. The only indication of potential for a smoke explosion is the presence of smoke (generally in an area away from the fire or after fire).

Factors that Affect Fire Development

To assist in their size-up, company officers should know the factors that could affect fire development within a compartment. The factors include but are not limited to the following:

- Fuel type and amount of surface exposure
- Availability and location of additional fuel in relation to the fire location
- Compartment volume and ceiling height
- Ventilation and changes in ventilation
- Thermal properties of the compartment

- Ambient conditions
- Fuel load

Fuel Type

The type of fuel involved in combustion affects both the amount of heat released and the time over which the release occurs. Fires involving the following fuel types will eventually spread to the contents and structure of the compartment, resulting in a primarily Class A fueled fire. Fuel types include:

- Class A or cellulose type fuels are the most common types of fuels found in structures.
- Class B type fuels consist of flammable/combustible liquids and gases.
- Class C type fuels include energized electrical wiring, equipment, and appliances.
- Class D type fuels, combustible metals, are found in limited commercial or industrial occupancies and vehicles.
- Class K type fuels, deep fat fryers, are mainly associated with commercial kitchens.

In compartment fires, Class A fuel combustible materials with high surface-to-mass ratios are much more easily ignited and will burn more quickly than the same substance with less surface area.

The surface area and type of fuel involved influence compartment fires involving Class B flammable/combustible liquids. A liquid fuel spill will increase that liquid's surface-to-volume ratio and will generate more flammable vapors than that same liquid in an open container. The increase of vapor due to the spill will also allow for more of the fuel to ignite, resulting in greater heat over a shorter period of time. Company officers should remember that modern homes and businesses are largely filled with contents made from petroleum-based materials. Black smoke is often present in fires involving materials like foam, synthetics, and plastics.

A compartment fire that results from a flammable/combustible gas leak will begin with a rapid ignition of the gas and an explosion. If not controlled, it will continue to burn at the point of release and extend to adjacent combustibles. Shutting off the fuel source or controlling the leak will reduce or eliminate the Class B fuel, but the resulting Class A fire will continue to burn until extinguished.

Availability and Location of Additional Fuel

Factors that influence the availability and location of additional fuels include the building configuration, construction materials, contents, and proximity of the initial fire to these exposed fuel sources.

Building configuration is the layout of the structure, including:

- Number of stories above or below grade
- Compartmentation
- Floor plan
- Openings between floors
- Continuous voids or concealed spaces
- Barriers to fire spread

Ambient conditions — Common, prevailing, and uncontrolled atmospheric weather conditions. The term may refer to the conditions inside or outside of the structure.

Each element may contribute to fire spread or containment. For example, an open floor plan office may contain furnishings that provide fuel sources on all sides of a point of ignition. Meanwhile, a compartmentalized configuration with fire rated barriers, such as walls, ceilings, and doors, separate fuel sources and limit fire development to an individual compartment.

Fire affects all construction materials, and many contribute to the fuel load of some types of buildings. In wood frame buildings, the structure itself is a fuel source. The orientation of these fuels and their surface-to-mass ratio also influence the rate and intensity of fire spread. Combustible interior finishes, such as wood paneling, can be a significant factor influencing fire spread.

A structure's contents are often the most readily available fuel source and significantly influence fire development in a compartment fire **(Figure 11.17)**. When contents release a large amount of heat rapidly, the intensity of the fire and speed of development will be increased. Synthetic furnishings, such as polyurethane foam, begin to pyrolize rapidly under fire conditions due to the chemical makeup of the foam and its surface/mass ratio, accelerating fire development.

Figure 11.17 Comparing the different types and volumes of fuel sources within a warehouse and a common living room.

The proximity, in relation to the fire, and continuity of contents and structural fuels also influences fire development. Fuels in the upper level of adjacent compartments will pyrolize more quickly from the hot gas layer. Continuous fuels will rapidly spread the fire from compartment to compartment. The location of the fire within the building will influence fire development. When the fire is located low in the building, such as in the basement or on the first floor, convected heat will cause vertical extension through atriums, unprotected stairways, vertical shafts, and concealed spaces. Fires originating on upper levels generally extend downward much more slowly through structural collapse or explosions.

Compartment Volume and Ceiling Height
Fires in a large compartment generally develop more slowly than one in a small compartment. This slower fire development is due to the greater volume of air and the increased distance radiated heat must travel from the fire to contents that must be heated. This large volume of air will support the development of a larger fire before lack of ventilation becomes a limiting factor.

High ceilings may mask the extent of fire. They can allow a large volume of hot smoke and other fire gases to accumulate at ceiling level, while conditions at floor level remain relatively unchanged. This situation is particularly hazardous because conditions can change rapidly if this hot gas layer ignites.

Ventilation

Compartment ventilation significantly influences how fires develop and spread. Pre-existing ventilation is the actual and potential ventilation of a structure based on structural openings, construction type, and building ventilation systems. Normally, all buildings exchange inside air with the air from outside. This exchange may be due to constructed openings, such as windows, doors, and passive ventilation devices as well as leakage through cracks and other gaps **(Figure 11.18)**. These air exchanges are primarily through the heating, ventilating, and air conditioning (HVAC) system.

Figure 11.18 Air can enter a structure through doors, windows, soffits, and cracks in the walls.

When considering fire development, potential openings that could change the ventilation profile under fire conditions must be considered. Under fire conditions, windows can fail or doors can be left open, increasing ventilation into the compartment. When a fire becomes ventilation controlled, the available air supply determines the speed and extent of fire development and the direction of fire travel. Fire will always grow towards ventilation openings as it seeks fresh air.

Thermal Properties of the Compartment

A compartment's thermal properties can contribute to rapid fire development, resulting in flashover, backdraft, or smoke explosions. Thermal properties can make extinguishment more difficult and reignition possible. Thermal properties of a compartment include:

- **Insulation** – contains heat within the compartment, causing a localized increase in the temperature and fire growth
- **Heat reflectivity** – increases fire spread through the transfer of radiant heat from wall surfaces to adjacent fuel sources
- **Retention** – slowly absorbs and releases large amounts of heat to maintain temperature

Ambient Conditions

While ambient temperature and humidity outside the structure can have an effect on the ignitability of many fuels, these factors are less significant inside a compartment. Ambient conditions, such as high humidity and cold temperatures, can slow the natural movement of smoke. Strong winds can place pressure on one side of a structure and force smoke and fire out the opposite side. If a window fails or a door is opened on the structure's windward side, fire intensity and spread can increase significantly. During fire suppression activities, wind direction and velocity can prevent or assist in ventilation activities. Cold temperatures can cause smoke to appear white and give the incorrect impression of the interior conditions. Atmospheric air pressure can also cause smoke to remain close to the ground, obscuring visibility during size-up.

Fuel Load

The total quantity of combustible contents of a building, space, or fire area is referred to as the fuel load (also called *fire load*). A fuel load includes all furnishings, merchandise, interior finish, and structural components of the structure. A company officer should recognize how building contents (fuel load) can contribute to a structure fire. Most structure fires initially involve the contents before spreading to the structure itself. In the early stage of a fire, an offensive attack can quickly extinguish a contents fire and prevent it from spreading. Contents fires that go undetected for many hours will consume all the oxygen in a structure, creating the potential for a backdraft condition when fresh air is introduced.

Fire safety engineers can calculate a fairly accurate estimate of the fuel load of any structure. However, fire officers may only be able to generate an estimate based on their knowledge and experience. For instance, a concrete block structure containing stored steel pipe will have a much smaller fuel load than a wood frame structure used for storing flammable liquids. Your knowledge of building construction and occupancy types will be essential to determining fuel loads.

Recent Fire Behavior Research that Affects Fire Fighting Tactics

Company officers should also be familiar with recent studies into fire behavior and how they relate to the decision-making processes. A variety of agencies conducted these studies and investigated the effects of fire on engineered lumber assemblies, older structures and furnishings (legacy), contemporary structures and furnishings, and floor assemblies involved in basement fires. This new research has a direct impact on structural fire fighting strategies, tactics, and operations as well as on firefighter survivability.

Background on Recent Fire Behavior Studies

The U.S. Department of Homeland Security/Federal Emergency Management Agency (DHS/FEMA) funded a series of fire behavior studies relating to:

- Structural stability of engineered lumber involved in fire
- Legacy and contemporary residential construction
- Engineered floor systems and basement fires

Agencies and organizations involved in conducting, analyzing, and documenting these studies included:

- Underwriters Laboratories Inc. (UL)
- National Institute of Standards and Technology (NIST)
- Chicago Fire Department
- International Association of Fire Chiefs (IAFC)
- Michigan State University

The results of these studies will pay double dividends. First, they can assist the incident commander with risk/benefit assessments during structural fires in both legacy and contemporary construction buildings. Secondly, they provide recommendations for changes to building codes that will influence future construction. The following sections will describe critical results from the studies and their impact on decision-making during structural fire fighting operations.

Structural Stability of Engineered Lumber Involved in Fire

The purpose of this study was to evaluate the structural performance of wood "I" beams and 2-inch by 4-inch (51 mm x 102 mm) wood trusses (lightweight wood construction) under fire conditions in comparison to older, legacy construction techniques using 2 inch by 10 inch (51 mm x 254 mm) floor joists and 2-inch by 6-inch (51 mm x 152 mm) roof supports. A total of nine fire tests were conducted, with seven tests on floor-ceiling assemblies and two tests on roof-ceiling assemblies. While the structural assemblies were designed to represent typical residential construction, the applied structural loads were made heavier than usually used in order to represent the weight of fully equipped fire fighting personnel.

Tactical considerations that resulted from this research study include:

- Protected and non-protected lightweight construction assemblies fail much faster than legacy construction assemblies.

- Legacy construction assemblies commonly fail over a small (local) area, while lightweight construction assemblies commonly fail over a larger (global) area.

- Sight, sound, and touch (sensory) indicators that firefighters use do not reliably indicate impending collapse.

- Data and images from thermal imagers do not reliably indicate impending collapse.

- Preheated wood structural components (especially lightweight construction assemblies) weaken a structure before direct fire involvement.

- Modern roof sheathing is thinner than legacy construction roof sheathing, and it can fail locally well in advance of general structural collapse.

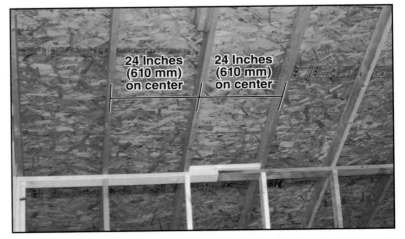

Figure 11.19 Modern roof trusses spaced at 24 inches (610 mm) apart.

- Modern trusses are generally spaced 24 inches (610 mm) apart, and this spacing can contribute to early roof failure and provide large openings that firefighters can fall through **(Figure 11.19)**.

- Plastic continuous roof vents can melt, self seal, and change the ventilation profile and fire conditions in the structure below.

Figure 11.20 Engineered I-joists serving as part of a floor system.

Figure 11.21 A metal gusset plate in a wood truss.

Figure 11.22 Examples of wood and metal hybrid trusses.

Engineered Floor Systems and Basement Fires

This study examined the effects of basement fires on a variety of engineered floor systems (floor joists). Examples of the joists included:

- Dimensional lumber

- Engineered I-joists **(Figure 11.20)**

- Metal plate connected wood trusses **(Figure 11.21)**

- Steel C-joists

- Castellated I-joists

- Hybrid trusses **(Figure 11.22)**

Experiments ranged from examining single floor joists in a laboratory setting to complete floor systems in an acquired structure. Other variables tested to determine their impact on structural stability and firefighter safety included a variety of applied loads, ventilation openings, fuel loads, span lengths, and methods of joist protection.

Tactical considerations that resulted from this study include:

- Collapse times for unprotected wood floor systems were within fire service operational time frames without regard for response times.

- During basement fire size-up, always consider the fire location and amount of ventilation, as floor collapse always started above the fire and the greater the ventilation, the sooner a collapse occurred.

- Inspect the floor from below before operating on it, if possible. Personnel should be trained to recognize the collapse signs that relate to each type of floor system.

- Never rely solely on sounding the floor to determine its stability. Use other methods to improve safety.

- Thermal images might indicate the presence of a basement fire but are not useful in assessing the structural integrity of the floor system above the fire.

- Firefighters should not attack a basement fire from the stairway. This location places them in the flow path of hot gases exiting through the stairway and in a potential collapse zone of the floor system above the fire.

- Temperatures at the bottom of basement stairs were often higher than those encountered at the top of the stairs.

- Ventilating a basement fire requires coordinated ventilation. Basement ventilation experiments create a flow path up the stairway and out the front door, increasing hot gas flow and temperatures to levels that could injure or kill fully protected firefighters.

- Firefighters can find it difficult to determine the amount of floor sag as they move through a structure, making it an unreliable indicator of potential floor collapse.

- The gas temperatures in a room above the fire are a poor indicator of fire conditions below and the structural integrity of a floor system.

- Firefighters should always have charged hoselines available when opening void areas to expose a wood floor system.

Legacy and Contemporary Residential Construction

Larger homes and rooms, more open floor plans, and an increase in synthetic fuel loads indicate that the residential fire environment has evolved over several decades. This study compared legacy (older) residential construction to more contemporary residential construction. Two houses were constructed inside UL's large fire facility:

1. A one-story, 1,200 square foot (111 square m) structure containing three bedrooms, one bathroom, and four other rooms similar to the smaller homes of decades ago.

2. A two-story, 3,200 square foot (297 square m) structure containing four bedrooms, 2.5 bathrooms, and six other rooms. This house had a more open floor plan like more modern homes.

A total of fifteen ventilation experiments were conducted, varying the number and locations of ventilation openings. Tactical considerations that resulted from these experiments include:

- The normal stages of fire development change when fires become ventilation limited. In modern fire environments, it is common to experience a decay period prior to flashover.

- Firefighters need to understand that forcible entry is a form of ventilation. The act of gaining entry into a structure on fire introduces air into the fire environment.

- Once fires become ventilation limited, the amount of smoke forced out of structural gaps or openings is reduced or stopped.

- Adding air to fire without applying water within an appropriate amount of time increases the size of the fire while reducing safety. Greater coordination between ventilation and fire attack must occur.

- Opening the front door of a structure can allow air to rush or tunnel into the structure rapidly.

- During Vent Enter Search (VES) operations, doors should be closed following entry to reduce open venting and increase occupant and firefighter tenability.

- Each new ventilation opening creates another flow path to and from the fire, which is especially dangerous in a ventilation limited fire.

- Even with multiple ventilation openings, the fires remained ventilation limited with each fire responding just as fast or faster to the additional air that was provided. As a result, temperatures inside the structures remained higher than if everything was sealed, rapid fire progression was highly likely, and the need to coordinate ventilation and fire attack was critical.

- Closing doors between the occupants/firefighters and the fire kept temperature and oxygen concentrations within the structure tenable for both parties. Should firefighters become separated from one another, they should enter a room with a door and close it to provide a level of protection until they can be rescued or escape.

- Fire fighting personnel must understand and consider the potential impact of a window failing or being left open could have on the flashover time for the fire.

- Applying water from the exterior did not push the fire along the flow paths nor did it create temperature spikes in rooms adjacent to the fire room. It did push some steam along the flow paths.

- Fires grew until the level of oxygen available within the structures (drawn from surrounding and more remote rooms) fell below sustainable combustion levels. Surrounding rooms had no fire in them even if the fire room became fully involved and had ventilated the structure.

Fire growth theories are generally based on models developed and tested in controlled environments in testing laboratories. However, fire behavior does not always conform to the results found in laboratories. Company officers should use the theories of fire behavior as a baseline to evaluate and predict actual fire behavior and to compare to their experiences and perceptions.

Incident Scene Operations

Company officers must be able to make sound decisions under extreme pressure. Even small incidents can generate a great deal of stress for company officers when they establish the National Incident Management System-Incident Command System (NIMS-ICS). Deploying resources and determining the appropriate strategy and tactics to control the incident can also be stressful. A company officer must employ the following to accomplish incident priorities:

- Proven leadership styles

- Proper resource management

- Supervisory skills

- Knowledge of fire behavior, EMS protocols, rescue operations, and operational tactics

The organization should impress upon its personnel a risk-management philosophy. The IFSTA Principles of Risk Management are as follows:

- Activities that present a significant risk to the safety of members shall be limited to situations when there is a potential to save endangered lives.

- Activities that are routinely employed to protect property shall be recognized as inherent risks to the safety of members, and actions shall be taken to avoid these risks.

- No risk to the safety of members shall be acceptable when there is no possibility to save lives or property.

When applying these principles, there are three key points to keep in mind:

- Team integrity is vital to safety and must always be emphasized.
- No property is worth the life of a firefighter.
- Firefighters should not be committed to interior offensive fire fighting operations in abandoned or derelict buildings that are known or reasonably believed to be unoccupied.

Two basic decision-making processes should be used in coordination with one another. Incident Priorities embraces the three broad incident priorities discussed earlier in this chapter. Lloyd Layman's RECEO-VS represents a historic perspective focusing on key strategies and tactics needed to resolve an incident, primarily fire-related incidents. Both provide a set of criteria that officers may follow to resolve an incident.

Incident Priorities Approach

In the Incident Priorities approach to decision making, the company officer must address the questions posed under each tactical priority:

- Life safety
- Incident mitigation
- Property conservation

Life Safety

The first-arriving CO must consider life safety as the first priority:

- If lives are in danger, what is their survivability profile? Human life is obviously the first priority, but animals should also be considered for sheltering in place, evacuation, or rescue.
  — If rescue is contemplated, the ability to provide safe ingress and egress for both occupants and firefighters must be the first consideration.
  — Rescue of animals, while desirable, does not meet the criteria for taking great risks.
- How many personnel are in need of being sheltered in place, evacuated, or rescue?
- What resources (personnel, equipment, time, etc.) will be needed to accomplish these actions?

Incident Mitigation (Stabilization)

To mitigate an incident, the company officer must ask:

- What type of incident (structural fire, ground cover fire, hazardous materials release, EMS response, or natural disaster) must be mitigated?
- What hazards will responders face?
- What resources are needed and what are available to mitigate the incident?
- What strategies and tactics are available based on the information gathered during size-up?

Property Conservation

To conserve property, the company officer must ask:

- What property (structures, vehicles, environment) is endangered?
- What property can be saved?
- What secondary property can be affected (waterways, sewers, wetlands)?

Layman's RECEO-VS Model

Fire Chief Lloyd Layman created his RECEO-VS decision-making model in the mid-20th Century. Even though these goals are stated in fire-control terms, the model can be adapted for use in all types of hazardous situations. The acronym RECEO-VS identifies a list of strategic goals for an incident. This model employs the information about the emergency incident that was gathered during the initial size-up. This information includes:

- Preincident survey results about a particular structure, facility, or hazard
- Nature of the incident details provided in the alarm dispatch
- Visual and odor indicators that the officer observes upon arrival

  The acronym RECEO-VS stand for:

- **R**escue
- **E**xposures
- **C**onfinement
- **E**xtinguishment
- **O**verhaul
- **V**entilation
- **S**alvage

Along with establishing incident command and performing size-up, company officers determine the strategic goals and objectives used to implement the operational plan (initial action plan). They also select the form of command to assume and the operational mode to use. Tactical worksheets can be utilized to assist with this process.

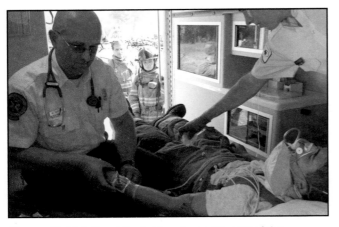

Figure 11.23 Injured firefighters become part of the problem, not the solution, at an emergency.

Rescue

Layman used the term *rescue* to identify the life-safety aspect of emergency incident priorities. In most fire and emergency services organizations, the term is not limited to occupants; it also includes emergency responders. An injured responder cannot rescue occupants or victims and consumes resources needed for victims **(Figure 11.23)**.

Therefore, company officers should neither expect nor allow their personnel to take unnecessary risks at an emergency incident scene. All personnel must conform to NFPA® 1500, *Standard on Fire Department Occupational Safety and Health Program*, and Occupational Safety and Health Administration (OSHA) requirements for 2-in/2-out and initial rapid intervention crew (IRIC) procedures. Company officers should also consider the survivability profile of the incident.

The 2-IN/2-OUT Rule

The U.S. Occupational Safety and Health Administration (OSHA) established the 2-in/2-out rule as part of 29 CFR 1910.134. The sections relevant to 2-in/2-out state:

1910.134(g)(4)

Procedures for interior structural firefighting. In addition to the requirements set forth under paragraph (g)(3), in interior structural fires, the employer shall ensure that:

1910.134(g)(4)(i)

At least two employees enter the IDLH atmosphere and remain in visual or voice contact with one another at all times;

1910.134(g)(4)(ii)

At least two employees are located outside the IDLH atmosphere; and

1910.134(g)(4)(iii)

All employees engaged in interior structural firefighting use SCBAs.

Note 1 to paragraph (g): One of the two individuals located outside the IDLH atmosphere may be assigned to an additional role, such as incident commander in charge of the emergency or safety officer, so long as this individual is able to perform assistance or rescue activities without jeopardizing the safety or health of any firefighter working at the incident.

Note 2 to paragraph (g): Nothing in this section is meant to preclude firefighters from performing emergency rescue activities before an entire team has assembled.

Source: *29 CFR 1910.134*

Life safety takes precedence over any and all other considerations, which means that, if necessary, a building may be allowed to burn for a period of time in order to facilitate a rescue. However, care must be taken to assure safe ingress and egress of occupants and firefighters. The same is true regarding firefighters — they should not be allowed to enter buildings that are already lost or any life-threatening situations to recover a body.

Rescue focuses exclusively on the life-safety priority. As the only company on scene, one of the most important requirements of the rescue process is that the decision to attempt rescue is declared over the radio to alert the responding personnel of the situation and the tactical decisions made. In fire incidents, search and rescue teams must take charged hoselines with them for their protection and that of those being rescued, not for fire attack purposes.

Company officers must be prepared to make some difficult decisions when rescue operations may be required. First, they must determine the level of risk in which responders should be placed during the rescue. They then must decide whether an evacuation should be required. A decision may need to be made on whether survivors can be sheltered in place instead of evacuated in facilities such as pressurized stairwells.

Evacuation. Rescue may also require the evacuation of a building, neighborhood, or community during an emergency operation. Depending on the number of people involved and their conditions, evacuation can be relatively simple or complex. After evacuation is deemed necessary, the next determination is what area needs to be evacuated.

Shelter in Place. The theory of *shelter in place* (also called *safe haven*) refers to those situations when it may be safer or more effective to have occupants remain inside the protection of a building or in a protected portion of the building until the danger has passed. In case of a building fire, occupants who cannot exit should go to a predesignated safe area and wait for emergency responders to rescue them. These areas should be identified during preincident surveys and clearly indicated on preincident plans.

In response to the Americans with Disabilities Act (ADA), many new buildings and those that have undergone major renovation include what are called *areas of rescue assistance*. These areas must meet certain minimum structural requirements (including a means of communication) and fire protection features (fire-rated enclosures and doors) that effectively isolate them from the rest of the building.

Another common application of shelter in place may occur during wildland/urban interface fires. Emergency responders and others in danger of being overrun by a fast-moving wildland fire can take refuge in a structure until the flame front passes. Even if the structure catches fire and eventually burns to the ground, it will provide some measure of protection for occupants long enough for them to survive the flame front and escape the structure before it is completely consumed. Survivors will then be in a previously burned area that is relatively safe. Company officers should be aware of wind shifts and the need to search for secondary places of shelter.

Exposures

Layman used the term *exposures* to describe the need to limit the fire or other emergency to the property or area of origin where the emergency began. Limiting the problem to the area of origin, or property of origin, means taking actions in order to save adjacent structures that are uninvolved or only slightly involved **(Figure 11.24)**. If the first-arriving units have only enough resources to begin to resolve the incident or keep it from spreading — but not both — they should then focus their efforts on keeping the problem from spreading to uninvolved properties or areas until additional resources arrive.

Attacking the source of the problem may be the best way to protect exposures, but if not, it is a lower priority than protecting the adjacent but uninvolved properties. For example, when arriving at a large barn fire with a large liquefied petroleum gas (LPG) tank exposure in an area without hydrants, the first-arriving CO could decide that using a limited water supply to keep the LPG cylinder cool would be a better strategy than attacking the fire that probably could not be controlled with water available in the apparatus' tank water.

Confinement

Confinement is the term Layman used to describe the need to prevent extension of incident effects to uninvolved areas. In a structure fire, the priority is to confine the fire to the area of origin, if possible. If that fails, confinement

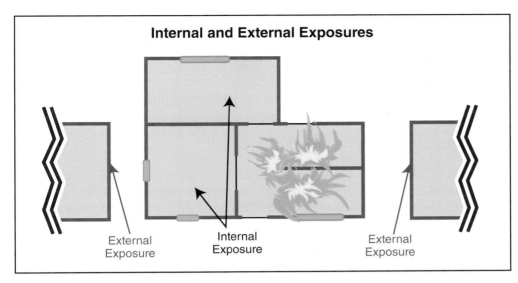

Internal and External Exposures

External Exposure   Internal Exposure   External Exposure

Figure 11.24 Illustrating the concept of internal and external exposures.

should be limited to the compartment or floor of origin with the building of origin being the last option. The principle can be applied to other types of emergencies, such as limiting a hazardous materials problem to the smallest area of the property in which it originated. Remember that it is necessary to confine the fire or hazard before it can be extinguished or eliminated.

Extinguishment

Extinguishment as a fire fighting concept refers simply to mitigating a fire. It can be used as a general concept in terms of mitigation and be applied to any type of emergency, such as performing a rescue, stopping the flow of a hazardous material, or extricating vehicle accident patients.

Overhaul

Layman also included the term *overhaul,* which is to make an incident scene secure from rekindle or other hazards associated with the incident. In this phase of a fire-suppression operation, any and all hidden fire must be found and extinguished, smoldering contents or debris removed, and utilities turned off unless they can be safely restored. Ventilation or forced entry openings should be covered to protect the property from further damage and illegal entries **(Figure 11.25)**.

In the context of RECEO-VS, overhaul can be applied to nonfire emergencies as well. After a hazardous materials release has been stopped, liquids or other contaminants must be cleaned up and packaged for proper disposal. In addition, residues must be neutralized. After a motor vehicle accident, the roadway must be cleared of debris and any spilled liquids must be picked up or neutralized so normal traffic can be restored.

Figure 11.25 Openings to this structure have been covered to prevent illegal entry and protect the structure from further damage.

Ventilation

Ventilation consists of those operations needed to replace a contaminated or heated atmosphere with uncontaminated air. Proper ventilation can help firefighters:

- Reduce the possibility of backdraft or flashover conditions.
- Improve rescue operations by reducing hot gases and poisonous smoke.
- Improve visibility for responders.
- Reduce property damage.

A structure's ventilation system can be used to expel the gases or positive-pressure ventilation fans may be used if the design of the structure permits it. Outside a structure, fans can be used to move and dissipate gases that have accumulated in low-lying areas.

The point to which a fire has progressed determines when, or if, ventilation is used. The ventilation process floats, meaning it can be used when needed during the implementation of the RECEO-VS model. Ventilation must be coordinated with initial fire attack. Introducing fresh air into the building before attack hose lines are in place can cause rapid fire spread. Yet, ventilation must not be started too late in a fire's progression or the full effect of proper ventilation will not be experienced.

Various types of ventilation involve opening doors or windows, cutting holes in roofs, and using mechanical ventilation fans or smoke ejectors to move fresh air into a building or pull out contaminants. In some instances, the building's HVAC system can be used to remove a contaminated or heated atmosphere.

Using a Heating, Ventilating, and Air-Conditioning (HVAC) System for Ventilation

Company officers should have a basic understanding of HVAC systems in order to effectively use an HVAC system to control smoke movement. Firefighters should use the following guidelines:

- Have a qualified building engineer (not emergency responders) operate the system.
- Use the system to limit the extension of fire and smoke to the smallest possible area.
- Never allow the system to spread fire or smoke beyond the area of origin.
- Provide fresh, uncontaminated air to any occupants who are trapped or located in a designated safe refuge area within the building.
- If a building engineer is not able to respond, a system instruction sheet may also assist in this situation.

Salvage

The *salvage* process includes the methods and operating procedures used to save property and reduce further damage from water, smoke, heat, and exposure during or immediately after a fire. Salvage may be accomplished by removing property from a fire area, by covering it, or by other means. It can be applied at any time during RECEO-VS and may occur during the confinement or extinguishment phases or following the extinguishment phase. During the extinguishment phase, limiting the amount of water required for control/extinguishment can increase the effects of salvage operations. Salvage may consist of removing property from a hazardous environment or protecting it in place. Assigning personnel to perform salvage is a judgment decision based on the resources available, completion of other RECEO-VS tasks, and the value or importance of the property involved.

The Operational Planning "P" Model

The Operational Planning "P" was initially developed for the U.S. Coast Guards Oil Spill Field Operations Guide and has evolved for all-risk, all-hazard responses. This model follows a sequence of actions that are critical to using the model, although numerous simultaneous actions are involved in it **(Figure 11.26)**. The incident action plan results from this planning process.

The Operational Planning "P" describes an ICS planning process that focuses on the first five steps of the NIMS-ICS planning process:

1. Understand the situation (size-up)
2 Establish incident objectives and strategies
3. Develop the plan of action (IAP)
4. Prepare and disseminate the plan (make assignments)
5. Evaluate and revise the plan

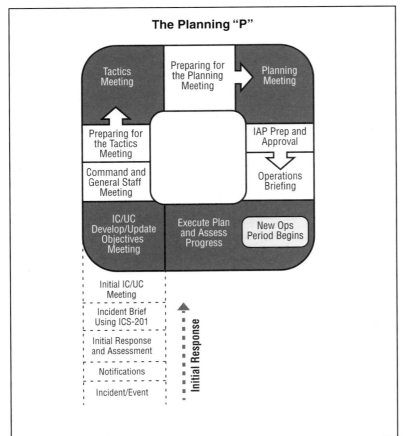

Figure 11.26 The Planning "P" model.

Size-up Application

The size-up process actually begins before an incident is reported and continues throughout the incident. This section discusses the application of size-up theory to three specific time periods: preincident, arrival, and during the incident.

Preincident

The size-up process begins before an incident is reported. The information gathered in the preincident planning process is a critical part of size-up and is collected prior to an incident when the data can be carefully reviewed, analyzed, recorded, and distributed.

Decisions made regarding resources that will be needed to resolve certain hypothetical incidents at specific locations can be translated into generic operational plans for those anticipated incidents. These plans provide facts that will help personnel make decisions during an incident at the surveyed locations. For instance, in jurisdiction containing grasslands, company officers should know:

- Types of vegetation in the area
- How vegetation supports the ignition and growth of fire
- Weather patterns that will aid or hinder fire control
- Topography that the fire will spread over

If the jurisdiction is primarily urban, containing a variety of types of structures, you must understand building construction, including:

- How the building codes classify buildings
- The types of building materials used
- The general interior arrangement of buildings
- How fire will behave within a structure

Company officers should also be familiar with building uses in their response area. Locally adopted building, fire, and life safety codes regulate building use. Referred to as occupancy classifications, these codes place similar types of activities into similar classes.

Before an Alarm

As company officers and their personnel travel to work, they should begin a general size-up of that day's situation. They should observe road maintenance, construction areas, and designated detours. They should review the weather forecast and determine how and to what extent the weather might affect any emergency calls. Company officers should be aware of the possible effects of weather and other factors on the abilities of their units or additional support units to perform effectively and safely. They should consider answers to the following questions:

- Will response time be slowed because of rain, snow, or ice has made the roads slick and dangerous?
- Will detours be necessary because of construction or other factors — parades, demonstrations?
- Will ventilation crews be at additional risk because of wet or icy roofs or high winds?

- Will wind combined with high temperature and low humidity affect the likelihood of large fire development?
- Will these conditions make wildland fires burn more intensely and difficult to extinguish?
- Will extreme weather adversely affect trapped or injured victims?
- In coastal communities, will such factors as tide cycles limit the time available to affect rescue?
- Are there any extremes of temperature that could make it more difficult and perhaps dangerous for personnel working outside?

While Responding

The size-up process continues during the response to an incident. Company officers should continue to gather information and evaluate variables as they respond to the incident scene. The following information should be considered while en route to an incident:

- Review the building's preplan (if available) to prepare for what responders may encounter.
- Observe weather conditions to anticipate the possible effects on fire behavior.
- Observe the amount, color, and movement of smoke that the fire produces.
- Consider every structure to be occupied until determined otherwise.
- Be aware of the resources responding or that may be needed.

Company officers should also evaluate any additional information that the telecommunications center provides via radio during the response. Based on knowledge of the response area, the units assigned, and the information obtained from the radio communications en route, the company officer should be able to determine if the company officer's unit is likely to arrive first and be responsible for establishing the command organization (NIMS-ICS).

On Arrival

The size-up process will probably intensify when the unit arrives at the emergency incident scene. The first-arriving officer may find a scene of utter chaos. In addition to the emergency situation and those directly involved in it, numerous spectators may have gathered at the scene, making it difficult to distinguish them from occupants or victims. These bystanders may be hysterical or irrational and screaming for responders to do something. Some may be attempting to extinguish the fire, assist victims, or perform a rescue, placing themselves in danger.

Upon arrival, the first-arriving company officer must transmit a *condition* or *arrival report* by radio **(Figure 11.27)**. Many fire and emergency services organizations mandate this action in their operations standard operating procedure (SOP). This report should:

- Provide the first impression of the existing hazardous conditions.
- Report the initial actions that the officer and unit take.
- Identify the types and locations of any barriers that could impede access to the scene.

Figure 11.27 A company officer making the initial condition or arrival report.

The next step is to communicate the plan to all on-scene and responding personnel. Communicating the plan usually starts with transmitting the arrival report by radio and formally assuming command of the incident. The first-arriving officer confirms or modifies the location of the incident and specifies the location of the incident command post (ICP) or describes the optional command activity in use.

TACTICAL CHANNELS

Depending upon the organization's radio communications capabilities, multiple tactical channels may be available. These may include channels for mutual aid, RIC/RIT, multi-agency interoperability, as well as for routine communications.

The officer must make every effort to look at the scene from all sides. The officer must focus on the situation and answer the question: *Can the resources at the scene and en route handle this situation?* If the answer is no, or maybe, then additional resources must be requested *immediately.*

Conducting an accurate size-up, implementing the appropriate components of the ICS, and employing sufficient resources are critical to mitigating the incident successfully and in a timely manner. A lack of resources or failure to request additional resources promptly can take immense work and organization to overcome.

Initial Risk Assessment. Based on the initial assessment of the incident scene, company officers must make decisions based on acceptable risk. Risk assessment should be an on-going process throughout the incident. The risk assessment may influence the incident goals and priorities.

Condition Indicators. Initial decisions must be made on accurate and complete information. Visual clues provide the company officer with condition indicators upon which to make the initial report and base the initial decisions. For instance, the presence of multiple unconscious victims may indicate the presence of a toxic or contaminated atmosphere. The lack of a visible cloud could point to a chemical leak or biological contamination. Company officers should seek confirming indicators/factors when making critical decisions.

During the Incident

This phase (between arrival and problem resolution) can be relatively short or last for a considerable length of time. If the problem is relatively small and officers make appropriate decisions, the problem may be resolved quickly. If not, additional assistance may be needed to resolve the situation.

During this phase, the situation either improves or worsens. The initial decisions that were based on the initial size-up may or may not remain valid. The IC must continue to reassess incident conditions and make tactical changes, as needed.

For example, if an emergency situation continues to deteriorate, the IC may need to request additional resources or transition from an aggressive attack to simply containing the situation until additional resources arrive. If the situation gradually improves but will take a long time to resolve, the IC may need to plan for responder rehabilitation and relief and other logistical needs. As the situation improves, the IC should continually reassess (size-up) the resource needs and release those that are no longer needed as soon as possible.

Operational Implementation

Following the initial size-up, the first-in company officer implements the operational decisions that have been made. Goals and objectives must be established, appropriate resources must be assigned, and the need for additional resources must be considered.

The strategic goals of an incident are the overall desired outcomes, and the tactical objectives are the activities used to reach those outcomes. Both are included in the IAP and must be communicated to all incident personnel.

Strategic goals are the overall plans for controlling an incident. They are broad, general statements of the final outcomes to be achieved. These goals apply to all emergency situations:

- Life safety
- Incident stabilization
- Property conservation

Tactical objectives are specific statements of measurable outcomes. Achieving tactical objectives leads to the completion of strategic goals. Units and personnel are assigned specific tasks to accomplish each tactical objective. Some common tactical objectives include:

- Initiate search and rescue.
- Provide a water curtain to protect exposures.
- Contain a hazardous materials spill.
- Use salvage covers to route water from the building's second floor.

Strategic goals and tactical objectives must be constantly evaluated to ensure that they are being accomplished. As goals and objectives are met and situations change, so do the priorities.

Command Options

According to Book I of Fire Protection Publications' **Incident Command System (ICS) Model Procedures Guide**, a variety of command options are available to the company officer at an incident. The first-arriving company officer or member has several command options from which to choose when arriving at the incident, depending on the situation. The establishment of a command post should be a top priority if a chief officer, member, or unit without tactical capabilities (i.e., member is driving staff vehicle with no emergency equipment or member is in an ambulance and arrive at a working fire) initiates Command. At most incidents, the initial IC will be a company officer on a piece of fire apparatus. The following command options define the company officer's direct involvement in tactical activities.

Investigation Option

Upon arrival, an incident may not have visible indicators of a significant event. These situations generally require that the first-arriving company investigate, while other responding companies remain staged. The officer of the first-in company should assume Command and go with the company to investigate, using a portable radio to command the incident **(Figure 11.28)**.

Fast-Attack Option

Situations that require immediate action to stabilize the incident mandate the company officer's assistance to carry out the critical operation. In these situations, the company officer accompanies the crew to provide the appropriate level of supervision. Examples of these situations include:

- Offensive fire attacks (especially in marginal situations)
- Critical life-safety situations (such as rescues) that must be achieved in a compressed time
- Any incident where the safety and welfare of responders are of major concern
- Working incidents that require the company officer to further investigate

Where fast intervention is critical, using a portable radio will permit the company officer's involvement in the attack without neglecting command responsibilities. The Fast Attack option should not last more than a few minutes within the Immediately Dangerous to Life and Health (IDLH) atmosphere and will end with one of the following:

- The situation is stabilized.
- The situation is not stabilized or transfer of Command has not taken place. The company officer should withdraw to the exterior outside of an IDLH atmosphere, and establish a command post. At some time, the company officer must decide whether to withdraw the remainder of the crew — based on the crew's capabilities and experience, safety issues, and the ability to communicate with the crew. No crew should enter or remain in a hazardous area without radio communications capabilities. Interior crews should consist of a minimum of two persons.
- Command is transferred to another officer. When a chief officer is assuming Command, the chief officer may opt to return the company officer to his or her crew or assign this officer to a subordinate position.

Command-Post Option

Large, complex, or rapidly evolving incidents require immediate strong, direct, overall Command. In such cases, the company officer will initially assume an exterior, safe, and effective command position and maintain that position until a higher-ranking officer relieves him or her. A tactical work sheet should be initiated and used to assist in managing this type of incident.

Figure 11.28 A company officer entering a structure with the initial attack crew.

If the company officer selects the command option, the following options are available regarding the assignment of the remaining crew members:

- The officer may place the company into action with the remaining members. One of the crew members will serve as the acting company officer and should be provided with a portable radio. The collective and individual capabilities and experience of the crew will regulate this action. Interior crews must consist of a minimum of two persons.

- The officer may assign the crew members to work under the supervision of another company officer. In such cases, the officer assuming Command must communicate with the officer of the other company and indicate the assignment of those personnel.

- Every effort should be made to maintain company/crew integrity. However, the officer may elect to assign the crew members to perform staff functions to assist Command.

A company officer assuming Command has a choice of offensive or defensive modes and degrees of personal involvement in the tactical activities, but continues to be fully responsible for the command functions. The initiative and judgment of the officer are of great importance. The modes identified are guidelines to assist the officer in planning appropriate actions.

Operational Modes

While all of us recognize that fire fighting can be dangerous and full of risk, one of the first decisions the initial IC needs to make is based on a risk/benefit evaluation. The IC must assess the current conditions and determine whether the potential benefits are worth having firefighters take unnecessary risks. Too often firefighters' lives are jeopardized attempting to put out a fire in a building where there is danger of collapse or where damage is so extensive there is nothing worth saving. Other firefighters are asked to risk their safety to rescue victims with little or no chance of survival.

Should the IC decide the risk is worth the benefits, the next thing that must be determined is how long firefighters can be expected to sustain an interior attack. Modern construction is not designed to maintain its integrity during fire conditions, and building collapse occurs earlier in modern construction than in older, more substantial buildings.

The Incident Commander may not know how long the fire has been burning prior to arrival or the fire's intensity. The length of time firefighters can be expected to sustain an interior attack may therefore be limited. The available resources and needed fire flow should be a part of the IC's considerations. Not enough resources or available water may mean that the risk outweighs the benefits.

Although it may be the hardest decision Incident Commanders are ever asked to make, there are times when attempting to make a rescue or an interior attack may be too great a risk to the safety of the firefighters. Failure to do a risk/benefit evaluation is the ultimate example of not being responsible for the safety of their personnel.

Offensive Mode. In an offensive mode, the Incident Commander shall assess the risk to firefighters and take actions to reduce these risks. Should the IC choose the offensive mode, it means that carrying on an aggressive interior attack is worth the risk and that sufficient resources are available to meet the incident demands.

Defensive Mode. In a defensive mode, the risk versus gain to firefighters is too significant to make an interior fire attack. The probability of saving lives is highly unlikely and the risk to firefighters in attempting to save property outweighs the gain. Therefore, a defensive mode is the most appropriate choice in these situations. Protecting the exposed buildings from further loss and confining the fire to the structure(s) involved is considered a defensive mode.

Indicators for a defensive operation include danger of imminent collapse, the building already is lost, and conditions indicate survival of any victims trapped inside is unlikely or not enough resources are available to effectively deal with the problems. When operating in the defensive mode, the IC needs to maintain accountability of personnel.

Anytime the decision is made to switch from one operational mode to another, particular attention should be given to make sure the switch is communicated to all personnel at the incident and that confirmation of the change is received.

Additional Resource Allocation

The IC should anticipate the need for calling additional resources if it appears that the incident has the potential to be a long-term operation. These additional resources may be held in reserve, used to relieve first-arriving units, or assigned tactical objectives on the incident. One or more staging areas may have to be established **(Figure 11.29)**.

Figure 11.29 Additional resources may be held in reserve at a staging location. *Courtesy of Chris Mickal/District Chief, New Orleans (LA) FD Photo.*

Apparatus Placement and Positioning

The goal of apparatus placement and positioning is to get vehicles that need to be closest to the operation into position. Apparatus that do not need to be close to the incident scene should be positioned to allow room for later-arriving vehicles that are needed to resolve the problem. Incidents that may require priority positioning of special apparatus or equipment may include:

- Structural Fire Scenes
- Wildland Fire Scenes
- Hazardous Materials Incidents
- High-Rise Incidents
- Technical Rescue Incidents
- Aircraft Incidents
- Medical Incidents

Incident Termination

The termination phase of an emergency operation involves a wide variety of activities. If appropriate, these activities may include but are not limited to:

- Conducting medical evaluations of incident personnel
- Retrieving equipment used in the operation
- Releasing appropriate units and returning them to service
- Determining the cause of the incident
- Releasing the scene to those responsible for the property

Postincident Activities

Once an emergency incident has been terminated, the company officer may still participate in two important activities: determine the cause of the incident and prepare a postincident analysis (a PIA or after-action report). Both activities provide information that can be used to reduce loss and improve responder safety. This information can be used to reinforce proper response activities or correct improper activities and to improve future performance.

Securing an Incident Scene and Preserving Evidence

Company officers must be able to establish scene security and ensure physical evidence is preserved. The following sections describe these processes.

Scene Security

A secure perimeter must be established and only those responsible for emergency cause determination should be allowed into the area. For a fire, this can be the same perimeter used to define the hot zone during the suppression or control phase of the operation. Rope or some form of barrier tape may be used to establish this perimeter. For nonfire emergencies, the perimeter may be larger and require the use of apparatus, road barriers, or law enforcement or military personnel to secure it.

The scene should be secured and any evidence preserved until the arrival of appropriate law enforcement officials or fire investigators. Evidence should not be moved or handled unless it is absolutely necessary in order to preserve it and then it must be documented appropriately. Movement of evidence may be necessary if law enforcement officials or fire investigators are not immediately available. Emergency responders should write a description of the evidence and draw/sketch or photograph the site where it was found. Until it can be properly investigated, evidence may need to be protected with a salvage cover or card board box.

Failure to secure the scene may impair or ruin an investigation if the evidence chain of custody is broken. When law enforcement officials or fire investigators are not immediately available, the property must remain under the control of the fire and emergency services organization until all evidence has been collected.

Chain of Custody

The term chain of custody (chain of evidence) is a legal term that refers to the handling and integrity of real evidence (physical materials). The term also denotes the documentation of the custody, including the acquisition or seizure, control, transfer, analysis, and final disposition of the evidence. To be acceptable in a court of law, the chain of custody must authenticate the location of evidence at all times and who had access to it.

Figure 11.30 A company officer photographing evidence at a fire scene.

Evidence must be marked, tagged, and photographed before the organization releases the scene **(Figure 11.30)**. Administrative warrants or a signed consent forms will be needed for re-entering the scene after the initial entry for the emergency.

In most fire incidents, fire and emergency services organizations have the authority to deny access to any building during fire fighting operations and for as long afterward as deemed reasonably necessary. Company officers must know the local right of access laws as they relate to property owners, occupants, or members of the news media. Fire departments can remain at a scene for a reasonable amount of time to investigate a fire. However, the investigation must be a continuation of the initial emergency response.

After a fire incident, a fire officer or emergency responder must accompany individuals entering the premises before it is released. A written log of any such entry should be kept, showing the person's name, times of entry and exit, and a description of any items moved or taken from the scene. A single entry control point should be used to protect the scene and any evidence.

Evidence Preservation

To assist with a fire or criminal investigation, the company officer must identify and preserve any physical evidence. The physical evidence at a scene can include:

- Liquids thought to be accelerants
- Broken glass
- Portions of incendiary or explosive devices
- Liquid containers
- Appliances involved in the ignition of the fire
- Clothing/fabrics
- Tire or foot impressions
- Tool marks on doors or windows
- Bodily fluids
- Cigarette butts
- Papers or documents
- Samples of charred wood, carpet, or other fuel involved in the fire
- Paints
- Hairs
- Metal objects, such as broken locks, weapons, drug paraphernalia, alcoholic containers, and cell phones

Contamination of physical evidence must be avoided during the preservation process. Some of the most common sources of contamination include the:

- Hand tools that firefighters and investigators used
- Protective equipment that firefighters and investigators wore
- Fuel-powered equipment used during fire suppression and investigation operations
- Vehicles driving through the scene
- Friends or family removing evidence

Maintaining the chain of custody is essential for evidence to be of any value in court. Individuals who have possession of items of evidence must be able to attest to the fact that the items were not subject to tampering or contamination while in their custody. Company officers and their personnel are the first persons in the chain of custody. When the investigator takes charge of the investigation, the following evidence information is obtained:

- Name and address of both the current and prior custodian
- Description of any modification, handling, testing, or other alteration that occurred while in the custody of the current custodian
- Condition of the item or its packaging when it was transferred to a new custodian

The overhaul or accessory actions that emergency services personnel perform are the greatest threats to the recovery of evidence or any physical indications of the cause of the incident. Every effort must be made to protect evidence when it is located and identified. Water application and debris movement should be minimized to protect such evidence.

Postincident Analysis and Critique

A Postincident Analysis (PIA) focuses on the activities of the responders without placing blame or finding fault. The analysis is presented to all participants during a postincident critique when the incident's participants review the incident and discuss the outcome. The critique can be considered a training activity since it takes responders through the incident and allows them to see how various activities depend on each other for a successful incident conclusion. The PIA and postincident critique are intended to determine whether an emergency incident was conducted in the safest and most efficient manner.

NOTE: Many organizations have stopped using the word *critique* in relation to a postincident critique, preferring to call it a *postincident analysis (PIA)*. There is a tendency for the meeting to become negative when it changes from a format of critiquing to criticizing.

The information that the company officer, the overall incident commander (IC), and incident safety officer gathered is combined and then analyzed. Those participating in the critique may include the responding units as well as staff officers, branch and division supervisors, and off-duty personnel who were called to the scene.

Analysis

The company officer may be assigned the responsibility of gathering information required to prepare a PIA or components of the PIA if it is a larger scale event. The officer must be objective in the gathering and recording of the data used. Two primary areas of analysis are the application and effectiveness of the operational strategy and tactics and personnel safety. Generally, when an incident is large and complex, two members of the National Incident Management System-Incident Command System (NIMS-ICS) Command Staff are assigned to these topic areas.

Strategy and Tactics. The incident commander will assign an officer to write the postincident analysis dealing with strategy and tactics. This individual may be a member of the Command Staff, a section chief, or other fire officer who was present at the incident.

To develop the postincident analysis, the company should start with a clear description of the site prior to the incident. Next, the officer reviews the actions that the responding units and agencies took over the course of the incident. Information related to the incident may be gathered from the following:

- Interviews of witnesses
- Participants
- News media (photographs and video)
- Strategy and tactics contained in the incident action plan (IAP)
- Communication logs and tapes
- Preincident site plans and inspections
- Structural reports
- Owner/occupant statements

Safety Issues. The responsibility for collecting safety-related information for a postincident analysis is assigned to the Incident Safety Officer (ISO) according to NFPA® 1500, *Standard on Fire Department Occupational Safety and Health Program*, and NFPA® 1521, *Standard for Fire Department Safety Officer*. This officer collects data from interviews of witnesses and participants, response and casualty reports, incident action and safety plans, and communication logs and tapes. The ISO then analyzes the data, reconstructs the incident, and provides recommendations to the organization's health and safety officer and the chief executive officer or manager of the organization. The primary concerns for this portion of the analysis are to identify the following elements:

- Violations of the organization's standard operating procedures/standard operating guidelines (SOPs/SOGs)
- Future topics for company training
- Poorly defined operational procedures
- Unforeseen situations
- Training deficiencies identified through the evaluation of skills demonstrated at the scene

The health and safety officer also evaluates the use of personal protective equipment (PPE), the personnel accountability system, rehabilitation operations, hazardous conditions, and any other issues that pertain to the personal safety of personnel at the incident. A written report containing recommendations is created and forwarded to the chief executive officer or manager of each organization when multiple organizations were involved. Safety of all personnel must be seen as a major responsibility within each element of the NIMS-ICS structure and should get considerable attention before, during, and after any emergency incident regardless of size.

Critique

A postincident critique is a meeting that generally involves all participating units and agencies. The meeting is based on the PIA. In this meeting, honesty is the key to making it work and all egos need to be left outside the room. The goal of the critique is to acknowledge any weaknesses and applaud strengths that were evident in the analysis. Safety issues are highlighted as well as strategic and tactical concerns. The critique results should be recorded and recommendations added to the PIA. The final document should be distributed to interested parties within the organization or other participating agencies.

On small incidents, the critique can involve only the company officer and unit members who participated in the incident. When large-scale incidents occur involving multiple units, jurisdictions, or agencies, representatives of each group should attend rather than all of the participants.

The company officer may want to hold an informal tailboard critique before returning the unit to service. Before leaving the scene, on-scene personnel should gather briefly to discuss what went right and what could or should have been done better **(Figure 11.31, p. 340)**.

A formal critique should be held once all necessary information has been gathered and reviewed. This critique should occur within a week of the incident. This timing ensures that the events are fresh in the minds of the participants and that needed corrections are not delayed.

Figure 11.31 An informal (tailboard) critique being performed immediately after an incident.

Recommended Changes

When the analysis and critique are complete for a multiorganization incident, each organization's chief executive officer or administrative staff should make any necessary changes to the operational strategy, tactics, policies, and procedures. Changes to written policy and procedures are announced to each organization's membership. Any weaknesses in skills must be corrected through additional training. Training may be applied to just the units that participated in the operation or to each individual organization. Recommendations are included in a report for the organization's management staff.

Chapter Summary

Managing an emergency incident scene is one of the most important roles of a company officer. Effective size-up based on sound decision-making and the implementation of NIMS-ICS support the incident priorities of life safety, incident stabilization, and property conservation. The ability to quickly and accurately take command of an emergency situation is a critical skill for company officers. They must be able to quickly identify the nature and scope of the problem, assess the current and future resource needs, and gather the information needed to develop an initial action plan, which must be communicated to all emergency personnel.

When the decisions have been implemented, the officer manages the incident until it is terminated or command is transferred. The officer's final activities involve terminating the incident, preparing the unit to return to service, and returning the property to the control of the owner/occupant.

Company officers must be able to determine the cause of fires, explosions, hazardous materials spills, and other emergencies. Officers must also be able to secure the fire scene and preserve evidence. Company officers must gather information on emergency incidents they respond to for use in postincident analysis. This information should include information regarding the activities of fire and emergency services personnel as well as observations of the incident and statements of witnesses and participants. The PIA is used as the basis for the postincident critique.

Both the analysis and critique are used to improve the way responders operate at similar emergencies. The analysis also provides information that can be used to eliminate hazards or reduce the effect of hazards through the development of codes, changes in personal habits, or the construction of facilities or devices that will protect the population from hazards.

Review Questions

1. What are the three approaches to improving firefighter survivability?

2. What incident size-up considerations are outlined in Lloyd Layman's model?

3. What are some concepts of fire behavior that help company officers determine appropriate strategy and tactics for fire attack?

4. What approaches and models can company officers use to conduct incident scene operations?

5. What are the two most important activities company officers will participate in after an emergency incident has been terminated?

Learning Activities

Learning Activity 11-1

Objective 6: Prepare an initial action plan for an emergency incident.

A company officer must be able to develop an initial action plan that employs accurate size-up and deploys resources effectively.

For this activity, you will need access to the following resources:

- ICS Form 202 used by your department OR you may use the forms provided in the manual's appendix

Prepare an incident action plan using the information provided in the scenario below. Fill out the ICS Form 202 so that all pertinent information is accounted for.

Scenario:

Incident:	Structure Fire
Alarm Time:	22:00 hrs.
Weather:	Temperature - 50°F
	Wind - W 10 mph
	Humidity - 28%
	Forecast - Clear and Stable
First Alarm Response:	Engine 5, Engine 7, Ladder 2, Battalion 6
Available	Second Engine 9, Engine 11, Ladder 4, Utility 1,
Alarm Response:	Rehab 23, Paramedic Ambulance 101, ISO 19, District Chief 19

Engine 5 is dispatched to a report of a structure fire at 9017 West Lisbon Lane. Other responding units are Engine 7, Ladder (Truck) 2, and Battalion 6. Engine 5 is first due at this location, being less than a mile from the incident address. Battalion 6 is on-scene at another incident and will be responding within ten minutes. Upon arrival, fire is visible from the first floor windows at the front of the structure. Smoke is coming from the eves and roof peak. Engine 5 gives an initial report of a working fire, requests a second alarm on the call, and assumes command (Lisbon Command). The dispatch center acknowledges Engine 5 and balances the response with a second alarm, which includes Battalion 19, ISO 19, Engine 9, Engine 11, Ladder (Truck) 4, Utility 1, Rehab 23, and Paramedic Ambulance (PA) 101.

Captain Smith of Engine 5 and his crew advance a 1¾-inch (45 mm) attack line for suppression. He assigns Engine 7 to establish a water supply and Ladder (Truck) 2 to shut off utilities and perform a preliminary search.

District Chief 19 and ISO 19 arrive on the scene. District Chief 19 assumes command, and ISO 19 begins incident safety survey. Engine 9 is ordered to advance a second attack line to the back door of the structure and to report to Interior Division (Capt. Smith). Ladder (Truck) 4 is assigned as ventilation group. The crew from Engine 7 is assigned as a RIT crew standing by at the BC 19 vehicle. Utility 1, Rehab 23, and PA 101 are positioned 50 (15 m) feet upwind from the front of the scene and are available to provide medical/support services. Engine 11 is placed in Staging. Upon arrival, Battalion 6 is assigned to coordinate support services.

Answer Key:

Answers may vary, but should resemble the following:

INCIDENT OBJECTIVES	1. Incident Name LISBON	2. Date TODAY	3. Time 22:03
4. Operational Period **22:03 TO COMPLETION**			
5. General Control Objectives for the Incident (include alternatives) **CONTAIN AND EXTINGUISH FIRE** **PRIMARY SEARCH (WHEN SAFE)** **WATER SUPPLY** **VENTILATION** **SECONDARY SEARCH** **SALVAGE** **OVERHAUL**			
6. Weather Forecast for Period **CLEAR and STABLE, 50°F, HUMIDITY 28%, WIND NW 10 mph**			
7. General Safety Message **SCBA/PPE REQUIRED IN ALL OPERATIONAL AREAS** **ISO 19 PERFORM INCIDENT SAFETY SURVEY** **VENTILATION NOT INITIATED UNTIL APPROVED BY IC** **REHAB 23 POSITIONED 50 FEET UPWIND FROM THE FRONT OF THE SCENE** **PARAMEDIC 101 POSITIONED 50 FEET FROM FRONT OF THE SCENE** **SCENE LIGHTING**			

8.	Attachments (mark if attached)		
☐ Organization List - ICS 203	☐ Medical Plan - ICS 206	☐ (Other)	
☐ Div. Assignment Lists - ICS 204	X Incident Map	☐	
☐ Communications Plan - ICS 205	☐ Traffic Plan	☐	

Learning Activity 11-2

Objective 7: Given a scenario, explain how to execute an incident action plan.

A company officer must be able to implement an action plan at an emergency incident so that resources are deploy efficiently and effectively.

Using the scenario described in Learning Activity 11-1, develop a NIMS-ICS organizational chart for both the initial response (First Alarm) and the balanced response (Second Alarm).

Answer Key:

Answers may vary, but should resemble the following:

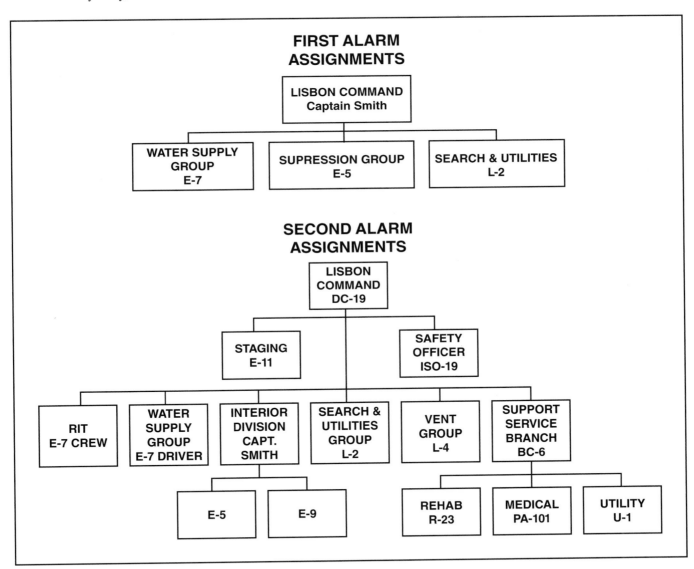

Learning Activity 11-3

Objective 8: Given a scenario, conduct a postincident analysis with personnel.

A company officer must be able to conduct a postincident analysis so that an incident is analyzed accurately and any necessary recommendations can be made.

Review the scenario provided below; it describes the actions taken during the scenario provided in Learning Activity 11-1. Make appropriate recommendations — including operational, safety, and training recommendations—that address any problems that occurred during the fire.

Scenario:

Engine 5 successfully attacked the fire and, during the primary search, discovered a conscious victim on the second floor. The victim was evacuated and treated for smoke inhalation. Engine 9 was ordered to enter the structure from the back door with an additional hoseline and successfully attacked the fire, surprising Engine 5 when the units met upstairs. Engine 5 reported that it had not heard the order for Engine 9 to enter the structure.

Ladder (Truck) 4 successfully performed positive-pressure ventilation from the room. Engine 7 established water supply at the corner of North Banner Road and West Lisbon Lane. Ladder (Truck) 2 shut off utilities to the structure, but then informed District Chief 19 that an excessive amount of radiant heat was threatening a residential structure to the immediate east. District Chief 19 ordered Ladder (Truck) 2 to begin protecting the exposure and did so until the incident ended.

The ISO completed the survey, and the RIT crew from Engine 7 did not receive any orders. Rehab 23 reported that one of the firefighters from Engine 5 complained of being lightheaded. PA 101 found that he had elevated blood pressure and transported him to the hospital for further examination. Engine 11 and Battalion 6 both reported successful operations.

Answer Key:

Answers may vary, but should resemble the following:

Operational recommendations:

- Better communications required between interior attack teams
- Check for radiant heat exposures earlier in operation

Safety recommendations:

- Ensure personnel report potential medical conditions at earliest opportunity

Training recommendations:

- Structural exercises involving two or more engine companies to improve communications and coordinating interior fire fighting operations

The Company Officer II

Chapter Contents

Key Terms

NFPA® Job Performance Requirements

This chapter provides information that addresses the following job performance requirements of NFPA® 1021, *Standard for Fire Officer Professional Qualifications* (2014).

5.2.1	5.4.6
5.2.2	5.5.1
5.2.3	5.6.1
5.3.1	5.6.2
5.4.1	5.6.3
5.4.2	5.7.1
5.4.3	
5.4.4	
5.4.5	

The Company Officer II

Learning Objectives

After reading this chapter, students will be able to:

1. Identify Company Officer II professional qualifications.

2. List Company Officer II roles and responsibilities.

3. Recognize the role of communications in Company Officer II duties. [NFPA® 1021, 5.2.1, 5.2.2, 5.2.3, 5.3.1, 5.4.1, 5.4.2, 5.4.3, 5.4.4, 5.4.5, 5.4.6, 5.5.1, 5.6.1, 5.6.2, 5.6.3, 5.7.1]

4. Describe types and forms of government as they relate to the fire service. [NFPA® 1021, 5.2.1, 5.3.1]

5. Identify local aid agreements. [NFPA® 1021, 5.3.1]

6. Recognize the importance of interagency and intergovernmental cooperation. [NFPA® 1021, 5.3.1]

7. Describe the National Response Plan. [NFPA® 1021, 5.6.1]

8. Explain the role of Company Officer II in evaluating personnel. [NFPA® 1021, 5.2.1, 5.2.2, 5.2.3]

9. Describe the process of managing change issues. [NFPA® 1021, 5.4.1, 5.4.6]

Chapter 12
The Company Officer II

Case History

A captain at a single company fire station with a Mobile Intensive Care Unit (MICU) received a complaint accusing fire department personnel of stealing a female patient's watch at the last address to which they responded. The person making the complaint was the patient's daughter. The citizen was irate, making derogatory comments about the fire department and the personnel that responded.

The captain was successful in calming the citizen down, and he was able ask several questions regarding the alleged incident. He asked the citizen if she had done a thorough search of the bedroom. She stated that she had looked everywhere and the watch could not be found.

The captain asked if it would be all right if he returned to the scene with the MICU crew and together, in the citizen's presence, searched the room again. She agreed, and soon they were searching the room. The captain noticed the bed pressed tightly against the wall. He asked the owner if the bed could be pulled away from the wall to see if the watch had accidentally fallen between the bed and wall. She agreed, and when they moved the bed, the watch fell to the floor. The citizen, obviously embarrassed by her accusations, immediately changed her attitude and apologized.

This incident stresses the importance of handling a situation at the lowest level possible before involving higher levels of supervision. The company officer managed a potentially volatile situation involving a member of the community and brought about a successful outcome, which protected the fire department's reputation.

As company officers advance to Company Officer II, they must retain the knowledge they learned at the previous level in order to apply it at their new level. They may interact more with their organization's upper levels and with their local and regional governmental agencies. They will assume a more advanced set of roles and responsibilities for which they must prepare, such as supervising other officers.

Company officers, in order to function effectively and efficiently, should understand how their governments operate, and they must have a familiarity with other agencies that are involved directly or indirectly in the fire protection process. This interaction may involve planning, training, implementing, monitoring, and evaluating these written agreements. The interagency and intergovernmental agreements usually take the form of automatic aid, mutual aid, outside aid, and multiagency and multijurisdictional incident response and cooperation. Evaluating personnel takes place informally on a daily basis and formally on predetermined schedules. Additionally, company officers act as change agents within their organization.

This chapter briefly describes the selection process for Company Officer II personnel and their roles and responsibilities. It provides a brief overview of communications. It also covers types and forms of government with which company officers must be familiar. It provides basic information about interagency and intergovernmental cooperation. This chapter also addresses evaluating personnel and managing change issues.

NFPA® 1021, *Standard for Fire Officer Professional Qualifications*, General Prerequisite Knowledge Items

NFPA® 1021, *Standard for Fire Officer Professional Qualifications*, item 5.1.1 General Prerequisite Knowledge identifies those knowledge items that candidates should know prior to testing for Fire Officer Level II. These items include the following:

1. The organization of their local government
2. The enabling and regulatory legislation and the law-making process at the local, state/provincial, and national level

This manual may address information pertaining to these two items as they relate to other job performance requirements (JPRs) of NFPA® 1021.

Company Officer II Professional Qualifications

NFPA® 1021, *Standard for Fire Officer Professional Qualifications*, sets guidelines for qualification to the Fire Officer Level II. Candidates for this position should meet the following requirements:

- Fire Officer I as described in NFPA® 1021, *Standard for Fire Officer Professional Qualifications*

- Chapter 5 job performance requirements (JPRs) of NFPA® 1021, *Standard for Fire Officer Professional Qualifications*

Company officer selection methods vary from organization to organization. Each authority having jurisdiction (AHJ) establishes the criteria for selecting and evaluating candidates for company officers. These often include a combination of written testing, interviews, and skills evaluations. Personnel interested in promoting to this rank should become familiar with their organization's promotion policies and procedures.

Company Officer II Roles and Responsibilities

According to NFP® 1021, in addition to the Level I responsibilities, the Level II Fire Officer must also perform the following duties:

- Evaluate personnel performance and create an environment to maximize employee performance.

- Prepare projects and divisional budgets.

- Develop budgets (based on the information provided by Level I Company Officers).

- Evaluate the resource needs of assigned units.

- Understand the purchasing process.
- Maintain records on purchases.
- Conduct a preliminary investigation of a fire scene to include analyzing all available information and determining the point of origin and cause of the fire **(Figure 12.1)**.
- Develop preincident plans for multiunit operations.
- Assign resources to effectively control incidents.
- Conduct postincident analyses using information gathered from all responding units.
- Assist with the development of organizational policies and procedures.
- Provide the media with emergency incident or department activity information.
- Apply planning concepts and project needed resources.

Figure 12.1 A Company Officer II conducting a preliminary fire scene investigation.

To assist with handling inquiries and establishing strategic partnerships, company officers should be familiar with how strategic partnerships affect the delivery of safety, injury, and fire prevention education programs. Level II Company Officers in small departments may report to local authority members or interact with managers in other departments within the jurisdiction.

Company officers may also serve as the point of contact for interagency coordination at incidents involving units or resources from other government levels, other departments within the authority having jurisdiction (AHJ), or emergency responders from other jurisdictions. This coordination requires knowledge of the available resources, the protocols for acquiring those resources, and existing mutual aid agreements.

The Level II Fire Officer must be familiar with the jurisdiction's health and safety policies, potential risks and hazards that result from unsafe practices, and methods for mitigating such risks and hazards. The primary health and safety duties for this officer are analyzing unit accident and injury reports and directing actions and/or recommending steps to prevent their reoccurrence.

Communications

Communications are just as critical for the Company Officer II as they are for the Company Officer I. Like the Company Officer I, the Company Officer II must interact personally with superiors, peers, and subordinates to accomplish organizational goals and tasks. Oral communication skills are necessary for presentations, training, meetings, and at emergency scenes **(Figure 12.2, p. 352)**. Writing skills are vital, and the Company Officer II may be required to develop:

- Written reports
- Press releases
- Memos

Figure 12.2 A Company Officer II conducting a presentation.

- Policies
- Procedures

Company Officer II candidates should evaluate and improve their interpersonal, oral, written, and emergency scene communications skills as part of their advancement training. A review of the information in Chapter 5, *Communications*, can be helpful. Additionally, numerous communications courses are available through colleges and technical/vocational schools.

Types and Forms of Governments

Level II Company Officers must know how governments at various levels function. Critical components of this understanding include:

- How their local government is organized
- Applicable regulatory and enabling legislation
- How laws are enacted at the local, state/provincial, and federal levels
- The functions of other organizations and how their roles and responsibilities relate to the fire service

Local Governments

Most citizens have more direct contact with local government departments and divisions to include fire and emergency services than with any other level. Citizens attend fire board meetings, provide guidance for pre-incident surveys, obtain burn permits, tour fire stations, receive EMS and fire fighting services, and attend fire and life safety presentations. The following paragraphs address local government at several levels:

- Municipal
- County
- District

NOTE: These terms used to describe these government levels are not standard across North America, and their precise meaning varies greatly from one region to another.

Local Governments and the Fire and Emergency Services

Local government affects emergency services organizations in two primary ways. First, governing bodies make decisions that directly relate to these organizations' operations, such as allocating funds, approving or disapproving purchase and staffing requests, implementing ordinances related to fire protection and other emergency services, and reviewing and approving agreements with other fire protection agencies and governments. Second, local governments oversee other departments and agencies with which their emergency services organizations must interact.

Local Lawmaking Processes

NFPA® 1021 requires company officers to understand how local governments enact laws. Their level of understanding can influence their organization's effectiveness in accomplishing its mission. The council, commission, or board with authority over the jurisdiction enacts local legislation. In terms of emergency services issues, the local government will generally consider any information that the organization presents. It is imperative that the organization be aware of the potential effects of such legislation and take an active role in advising the governing body.

Local Government Agencies

In addition to the fire and emergency services organization, a local government is likely to include a variety of departments, each structured to provide specific services. Examples of agencies company officers may interact with include **(Figure 12.3)**:

- Law enforcement
- Building safety
- Water supply agencies
- Public transportation
- Social services
- Municipal/County courts
- Zoning boards
- Public works
- Disaster preparedness

NOTE: Privately owned companies or other government agencies that are not part of the local government may perform some of the functions of the agencies listed above.

Figure 12.3 Local governments are made up of a variety of departments.

State and Provincial Governments

State and provincial legislation affect emergency services organizations because emergency services organizations sometimes interact with state and provincial government agencies. Company officers should be familiar with the structure and operation of this next level of government.

State Governments

In the United States, state and similarly territorial governments are generally modeled after the federal government with three functional branches **(Figure 12.4)**:

- Legislative
- Executive
- Judicial

The term *commonwealth* is also used to describe four states (Kentucky, Massachusetts, Pennsylvania, and Virginia) and one of the territories (Puerto Rico). A commonwealth is a state in which the government functions with the common consent of the people.

NOTE: Territories that the United States currently administers are Guam, Midway, American Samoa, Puerto Rico, and the U.S. Virgin Islands.

Figure 12.4 The branches of state government.

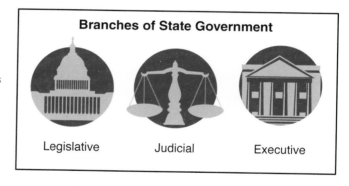

Branches of State Government

Legislative   Judicial   Executive

Provincial and Territorial Governments

Canada is divided into ten provinces and three territories. Territorial governments' power is more limited than those of the provinces. Provincial governments have three branches that include a unicameral legislative assembly (or National Assembly in Quebec), an executive branch that a premier directs, and a court system. Each province also has a lieutenant governor that Canada's governor general appoints; however, the position is largely honorary and carries no real legal authority. The duties of each branch are similar to those of the corresponding sections of U.S. state governments.

The Yukon Territory's political head is the leader of the majority party and carries the title of government leader. In the Northwest and Nunavut Territories, a federal government-appointed commissioner provides political leadership. Each territory has a legislative assembly and a court structure similar to the provincial systems. All three Canadian territories provide fire protection and EMS services.

Tribal Governments

The Aboriginal Peoples of North America (Native Americans) maintain tribal governments to oversee the large areas of land formerly known as reservations **(Figure 12.5)**. These governments have structures similar to the federal government, although the leader is called the chief. In the U.S., the Bureau of Indian Affairs (Department of the Interior) is the primary agency responsible for management of the Aboriginal Peoples of North America lands and resources. Many tribes operate their own fire agencies, and company officers should be aware of their capabilities if near their own jurisdiction.

Figure 12.5 A tribal government office building in Oklahoma.

Agencies of State and Provincial Governments

Company officers must become familiar with the agencies that are active in their state or provincial government. The following agencies may influence U.S. and Canadian fire and emergency services:

- Fire Marshal
- Fire Training Programs
- Fire Commission
- Health Department and treatment protocols (EMS services)
- Forestry Department
- Office of Emergency Preparedness or Homeland Security
- Occupational Health and Safety
- Fish and Game

NOTE: Not all of the agencies listed are found in all states and provinces, and some agencies not listed may be of even more importance than those included here. Also, agencies with the same or similar names may have different responsibilities and objectives in different jurisdictions. Not all of the organizations described are government-sponsored, but each affects the fire and emergency services within the states and provinces.

U.S. Federal Agencies Involved in Fire Protection

The U.S. federal government has established numerous public safety departments and agencies and passed legislation to protect citizens in emergencies and to reduce the risk of life-threatening incidents. These agencies operate within the structure of the government through the support of public funds and under the direction of elected or appointed officials. The legislation that governs these agencies has been introduced and approved under the federal government's lawmaking process. Federal agencies that fire and emergency services may interact with include:

- Department of Homeland Security
  - Federal Emergency Management Agency (FEMA)
    - o United States Fire Administration (USFA)
    - o National Fire Academy (NFA)

- ○ Emergency Management Institute (EMI)
  - — U.S. Coast Guard
- U.S. Department of Agriculture (USDA)
  - — U.S. Forest Service (USFS)
  - — Farm Service Agency
- Department of Housing and Urban Development (HUD)
- Department of the Interior (DOI)
- Department of Labor (DOL)
  - — Occupational Safety and Health Administration (OSHA)
- Department of Health and Human Services
  - — Center for Disease Control and Prevention (CDC)
  - — National Institute for Occupational Safety and Health (NIOSH)
- Department of Transportation (DOT)
- Department of Justice (DOJ)
- Consumer Product Safety Commission (CPSC)
- Nuclear Regulatory Commission (NRC)

Canadian Federal Government and Agencies Involved in Fire Protection

The Canadian federal government is similar to both the United States and Great Britain. Canada is a federation of self-governing provinces and territories with a federal government consisting of three branches **(Figure 12.6)**. Canada's legislature, called Parliament, has two houses: the House of Commons and the Senate.

The most apparent differences between the U.S. and Canadian federal governments exist in the Executive Branch. Although an independent nation, Canada recognizes the Great Britain's sovereign as its official head of state. Thus, the monarch of Great Britain presides in the same role over Canada,

Figure 12.6 The structure of the Canadian government.

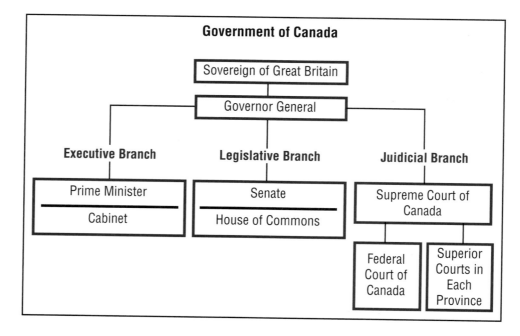

although no real powers are granted to the monarch. An appointed official called the Governor General represents the British sovereign in Canada. The true chief executive of the Canadian government is the Prime Minister, who is assisted by a cabinet of ministers for various governmental functional areas.

The Canadian government enacts laws and establishes and manages agencies that provide for the safety of the citizens. Numerous Canadian federal agencies have some form of interaction with the fire and emergency services. The Canadian fire and emergency services may interact with the following Canadian government agencies:

- Public Safety and Emergency Preparedness Canada (PSEPC)
- Industry Canada
- Public Works and Government Services Canada
- Treasury Board
- Transport Canada
- Environment Canada
- Agriculture and Agri-Food Canada
- Human Resources and Social Development Canada
- National Research Council Institute for Research in Construction (NRC-IRC)

Local Aid Agreements

As described in Chapter 2, Organizational Structure, fire and emergency services organizations may enter into aid agreements with other agencies to provide additional resources to the fire and emergency services organization. Level II company officers may call upon these agreements for assistance during an emergency and/or participate in the agreement development process. In preparing for promotion to Level II, company officers should review the material in Chapter 2.

While Chapter 2 focused on outside aid, this section describes interagency aid agreements. An internal aid agreement may be a simple function of the local government and not require a written document to verify it, although a document may aid in establishing command and control detail. Various departments within the jurisdiction may be required to respond when requested. The following are examples of internal resources:

- **Street Department** — Provides inert materials for controlling hazardous materials spills and signage for long-term traffic control
- **Public Works** — Provides heavy equipment for collapse or trench rescue operations
- **Law Enforcement** — Provides traffic or crowd control or investigative resources
- **Fire and Emergency Services Department** — Provides ventilation for non-emergency services workers entering a confined space, large area lighting for law enforcement, laddering for law enforcement, and/or water removal for public works
- **Emergency Medical Services** — Provide medical support for firefighters and civilians **(Figure 12.7, p. 356)**

Figure 12.7 Within some communities, medical units may be dispatched simultaneously with fire and law enforcement units.

Interagency and Intergovernmental Cooperation

Company officers should be familiar with the interagency and intergovernmental agreements their organization may have with other agencies. This familiarity should include the roles, responsibilities, and requirements of all parties to the agreements.

Formal agreements between the fire and emergency services organization and various levels of government and agencies help ensure a coordinated response during a crisis. These agreements are the result of intergovernmental/agency planning sessions and training simulations. Formal intergovernmental agreements should include the following items:

- Jurisdictional authority
- Agency authority and responsibility
- Funding and reimbursement procedures
- Response procedures
- Communication systems, protocol, and procedures
- Preincident planning and training
- Postincident evaluations
- Notification procedures

Area Contingency Plan (ACP) — A procedure to be put into effect should an emergency occur within a given region or area.

NIMS-based ICS for unified command (UC) should be used as the model for response management in the **area contingency plans (ACP)** to ensure an effective response. Jurisdictions should consider the following items when developing ACPs:

- Jurisdictional responsibilities
- Roles of all government levels in the Unified Command (federal, state/provincial, and local)
- Relationship between the federal on-site coordinators (FOSC) and other officials who also have decision-making authority but are not part of the UC

- Financial agreements
- Information dissemination policies and procedures
- Communications
- Training and conducting exercises
- Logistics
- Lessons learned

National Response Plan

The U.S. National Response Plan (NRP) was created to integrate federal government prevention, preparedness, response, recovery, and mitigation plans into one all-discipline, all-hazard approach to domestic incident management. This plan was developed through an inclusive interagency, interjurisdictional process incorporating the expertise and recommendations of federal, state, local, tribal, and private-sector stakeholders. Similar efforts have occurred in Canada and its provinces.

The NRP and NIMS provide the framework and processes to integrate all the capabilities and resources of the jurisdictions, disciplines, and levels of government and the private sector into a cohesive, unified, and coordinated approach to domestic incident management. This approach accomplishes the following:

- Establishes a common, agreed-upon set of goals.
- Reduces jurisdictional conflicts.
- Creates a forum to critique the team's performance in incident management.
- Creates a controlled environment for the discussion of operational issues.
- Encourages sharing of resources.
- Builds personal and professional relationships between participants.
- Increases understanding and respect between agencies.

While representing the fire and emergency services organization, the company officer must keep the organization's interests in mind while also considering the community's best interests. The officer must know the resources and commitment that the organization can offer and the resources that other agencies or jurisdictions will be required to provide.

Evaluating Personnel

An organization's personnel evaluation program is necessary to maintain complete and documented personnel files. Company officers are typically responsible for evaluating their personnel. **Formative evaluation** is an ongoing process throughout an employee's career. **Summative evaluation** is the company officer's final assessment of the individual's performance. Summative evaluations are conducted at these times:

- At the end of the probationary period
- Annually, as part of a performance review
- For performance improvement or disciplinary purposes

Formative Evaluation — Ongoing, repeated assessment conducted over time to evaluate an employee's performance against an organization's standards.

Summative Evaluation — An assessment of an employee's performance against an organization's standards that are conducted at the end of a given period of time such as a probationary period, annually as part of a performance review, or for performance improvement or disciplinary purposes.

The personnel evaluation program has the following advantages:

- Creates a permanent record of the employee's achievements for the purpose of awards, promotions, transfers, and proposed discipline

- Makes the need for additional training apparent; if warranted, new programs can be developed to address the deficiency if it appears to be widespread

- Helps the supervisor become more familiar with the personnel being evaluated

- Motivates personnel to improve

- Increases upper management's awareness of lower-level supervisors' and managers' abilities

- Illuminates the individual's specific talents, which could be used in other areas of the organization

- Improves the efficiency and/or effectiveness of employees and the organization as a whole

Personnel evaluations should be timely, when the need becomes apparent. If the employee is performing at or above the anticipated level, personal recognition will help to instill pride in the employee. If there is a need to correct a work habit that is not meeting the required standard, immediate attention to the issue will lessen the effect of the work habit and possibly prevent any future problems associated with the act **(Figure 12.8)**.

Discipline may be justified if an employee is either unable to or unwilling to meet the minimum employment standard. Failing to address issues with employees, especially during the probationary period, may result in a number of unwanted situations to include disciplinary actions. Failure to address these issues can:

- Cause other employees to view the supervisor or the organization as being inconsistent with established policies.

- Create resentment within the work force.

- Create the impression that the organization is unwilling to deal with this type of situation.

- Send a message to other employees that nothing will happen to them if they break rules, regulations, policies, and/or procedures.

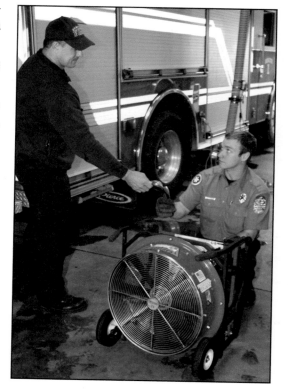

Figure 12.8 Company officers should correct improper work habits as soon as they are discovered.

Managing Change Issues

One management challenge many fire officers may face is managing change in the unit or organization. To successfully manage change, the company officer must know the forces that create and cause change and the change process itself. It is likely that the company officer will be the individual who implements change at the operational level. The company officer must always maintain a positive posture toward the change, even when the officer does not necessarily agree with it. Knowing the types of change and how to overcome resistance to change, implement the change process, and use a follow-up plan can lead to successful change management.

Change can originate from two forces:

1. Internal

2. External

Internal forces originate within the unit/organization, and include changes that are created by the delegation of responsibility, periodic performance reviews, organizational restructuring, and realignment of duties and tasks to meet the changes that external forces drive. External forces originate from political decisions, economic trends, community service demands, changes in technology, and changes in the demographics of the community, among others.

Changes that are perceived as a threat or loss are particularly challenging. Some change is immediate and affects people greatly, while most change is slow and gradual based upon numerous factors. The prospect of change may cause people to go through the four change process stages:

1. **Denial** — People refuse to believe that the change will affect them.

2. **Resistance** — When the threat of change becomes real, people start to resist it.

3. **Exploration** — People gain a better understanding of the potential change through training.

4. **Commitment** — Increased understanding in the third stage leads to an increased commitment.

Change Types

Support for change must come from the top down in order for it to be successful, but those that the change affects must take ownership through involvement and commitment. Consistent communication on the change process helps eliminate fear and can move the change process forward in a positive manner. The types of change that an organization may have to undergo include:

- **Strategic** — Change in the organization's short- or long-range plan

- **Structure** — Change in the organization's design

- **Technology** — Change may include the addition of new equipment, apparatus, communications systems, extinguishing agents, or computerization

- **People** — Change in the skills, performances, attitudes, behaviors, or cultures of the workforce to meet the force of change

Resistance Issues

Research indicates that organizational change can fail because employees resist it. The company officer must understand the reasons employees resist change and the methods used to overcome those reasons. There are several reasons to resist change **(Figure 12.9)**:

- **Uncertainty** — When employees' routines or environments are disrupted, it causes them to feel insecure and unsure how the changes will affect them or other members of the workforce.

- **Loss of control or power** — Employees resent the feeling that they have lost control over their lives.

- **Fear of loss** — Employees experience layoffs, work-schedule changes, or transfers between workgroups.

- **Self-interest** — Employees are more concerned about their own situations than with the organization.

- **Learning anxiety** — Employees experience anxiety when they need to learn a new skill, technique, process, procedure, or equipment operation.

- **Lack of trust** — Employee distrust can be directed toward the organization's leadership and based on prior history or future concerns.

- **Lack of shared vision** — Employees are not aware of or do not hold the same vision for the goals of the organization.

When company officers recognize the resistance to change and take steps to reduce it, they can increase the opportunity for success in the process. Business analysts have determined that resistance to change can be overcome using the following seven basic steps:

1. **Create a climate for change** — Encourage employees to suggest changes and implement those changes.

2. **Plan for change** — Have a plan and prepare to follow it in order to effectively implement change.

Figure 12.9 Common examples of why people resist change.

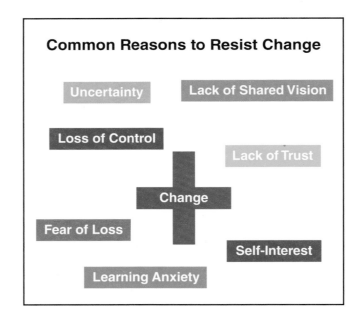

3. **Communicate the advantages and effects of change** — State factually the advantages and effects of change to prevent unfounded rumors from eroding the trust between the supervisor and employees.

4. **Meet the needs of both the organization and employees** — See the change from the employees' viewpoints. Then, focus on their concerns and try to balance the good of the employees with the good of the organization. Share benefits equally in order to create a win-win situation.

5. **Involve employees in the change process** — Involve employees in the change process, keep them informed, focus on their needs, and implement their suggestions.

6. **Provide support for employees during the change** — Make a firm commitment to the change.

7. **Seek the input and support of "opinion leaders" in the organization** — Use informal leaders of the organization to help influence others' opinions.

Change Agents

When company officers assume the role of a change agent, they can affect or cause change. A change agent is a person who leads a change project or initiative. They define, research, plan, build support, and carefully select members of a change team.

Because bringing about change can be time-consuming and involve complex issues and barriers, the change agent must have commitment and persistence. The officer must be able to:

- Commit to the vision that will result from the change.
- Exert all the effort required throughout the project's time frame.
- Employ diplomacy, tactfulness, and political awareness.
- Rely on an ethical foundation that will ensure that the change is morally sound.
- Be a subject matter expert in the area that the change will occur.

In order to affect change, the officer must understand small group relations and interaction. The officer should have an established network within the organization and the community. Relationships in the political arena can also be important to success.

To combat change-induced stress, the officer must have skills that will reduce or eliminate stress. Interpersonal skills are essential and the officer must be able to communicate effectively with individuals and groups. The officer must be able to sell the change to the organization and the community. Finally, the officer must have time management skills and the ability to prioritize the project.

Process Implementation

Even though change can come from both internal and external sources, establishing and following a specific change process benefits the organization. That process needs to include methods for analyzing the current policies that the organization uses, methods for suggesting change from the bottom up and from the top down, methods for implementing change, and a follow-up plan to ensure that the change met the needs it was intended to meet. All company officers should know the implementation policy and process.

Once the need for change has been recognized, resistance has been overcome, and an innovative solution has been agreed upon, it is time to implement the change. Because change is a continuing process, it must be monitored to determine the effectiveness of the new process or procedure. It is important to remember that initial implementation of a change and institutionalizing that change are usually two different things. A model for change has been created to facilitate most forms of change facing an organization; it is based on five steps:

1. **Recognize the need for change** — Clearly state the need for change and establish objectives. Consider the effects the change will have on other parts of the organization.

2. **Identify resistance and address it** — Identify potential resistance to the change and determine the best method for addressing it.

3. **Plan the change interventions** — Recognize that a variety of change agents or interventions exist that can help in implementing the change. Some change interventions include:
   — Training and development
   — Team building
   — Changing or altering the types of tasks members of the organization perform
   — Direct feedback
   — Survey feedback

4. **Implement the change** — Use the appropriate change agent and put the change into operation.

5. **Control the change** — Enforce, review, monitor, and analyze the change model. Take corrective action if change objectives are not met.

Follow-Up Program Plan

The follow-up program is a formal part of the process that continues to monitor the change's effect. The follow-up is applied to behavioral changes made by individuals as well as structural changes to the organization. The follow-up program becomes part of the annual performance evaluation for personnel and the periodic review of programs, operations, or policies.

The change process should be viewed as cyclical rather than linear. The process is continuous and never-ending. The follow-up is the feedback that takes the results and loops them back to the first portion of the process, becoming the current level of performance. As first-line supervisors, company officers monitor the change process as it affects the company personnel and operations. When feedback indicates that the process requires alteration, the company officer should inform the organization's administration.

Reasons That Change Fails

Managers may not always succeed in implementing a change. John Kotter, an organizational researcher, determined in the 1990s that there are eight reasons that change processes fail. They are as follows:

1. The change process is too complex.

2. The change process lacks universal support.

3. Lack of a clear vision and not understanding the importance of having one.

4. The failure to communicate the vision to the organization.

5. Allowing barriers to be placed in the way of the vision and change process.

6. Not planning for and recognizing the short-term results.

7. Declaring completion of the change process prematurely.

8. Failure to make the change a permanent part of the organization's culture.

   To minimize these reasons for failure, the company officer may apply the following strategies:

- Divide the change process into attainable segments and goals and involving a diverse group of people to participate in the process.

- Gain support for the change from the key actors in the organization and community. The *key actors* are influential members, such as the chief of the department, president of the labor organization, branch/division heads, members of the governing board, or heads of other departments, depending on the type of change that is required **(Figure 12.10)**.

- Define the desired results and state them clearly. This definition is the vision statement that allows everyone to understand what the change is, why it is important, and how it will affect the organization and community.

- Communicate the vision to all members of the organization and all customers and stakeholders in the community.

- During the planning process, try to determine the arguments against the change and develop strategies to answer these arguments logically and factually. Take a proactive approach and never allow the arguments to become barriers to change.

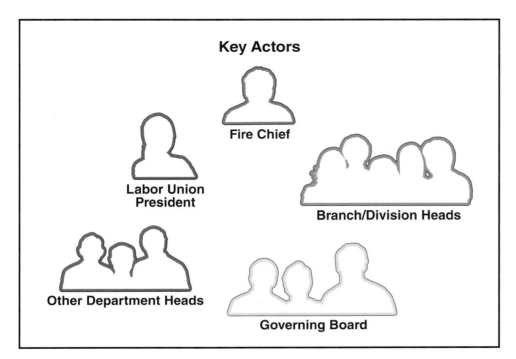

Key Actors

Fire Chief

Labor Union
President

Branch/Division Heads

Other Department Heads

Governing Board

Figure 12.10 Key actors within the organization and community must be supportive of any changes to be made.

- Include limited objectives or milestones in the planning process. When these are attained, celebrate the accomplishment and use the enthusiasm to move onward to the next objective and ultimate goal.

- Ensure that all objectives have been met and that the final goal is complete before declaring victory. Prematurely declaring that the goal has been met will reduce credibility and lessen the team's enthusiasm and motivation.

- Implement the change and monitor the change's results to ensure that it becomes permanent. If the change is insufficient, determine what is lacking and start the process over.

Chapter Summary

Fire and emergency services organizations are an integral part of the local community and their state or province. They must interact with other local, regional, state, and national agencies and departments. Company officers should be aware of their government's structure, and of the other organizations that may be able to assist them. Resources are available from all government levels, depending on the type of emergency or the amount of assistance required. Company officers should establish working relationships with their counterparts in the agencies with which they will interact.

Company officers may interact with local law enforcement personnel at traffic accidents, state/provincial authorities at a hazardous materials spill, or federal officials at a major natural disaster. This interaction must include planning, training, and practice. Company officers must be prepared to establish ICS, recognize and adhere to jurisdictional authority, and request the correct assistance from the appropriate agency or governmental entity. Managing company officers will evaluate personnel and help bring about change within their organizations.

Review Questions

1. What are the professional qualifications for Company Officer II?

2. What are the roles and responsibilities of Company Officer II?

3. What communication skills must Company Officer II demonstrate?

4. In what ways will Company Officer II interact with different types and forms of government?

5. What departments may Company Officer II interact with in accordance to local aid agreements?

6. What items are generally included in formal intergovernmental and interagency agreements?

7. What is the purpose of the U.S. National Response Plan?

8. What are the advantages of having personnel evaluation programs?

9. How can Company Officer II personnel be effective change agents?

Human Resources Management II

Chapter Contents

Key Terms

NFPA® Job Performance Requirements

This chapter provides information that addresses the following job performance requirements of NFPA® 1021, *Standard for Fire Officer Professional Qualifications* (2014).

5.2.1

5.2.2

5.2.3

Human Resources Management II

Learning Objectives

After reading this chapter, students will be able to:

1. Define groups.

2. Describe the characteristics of group dynamics. [NFPA® 1021, 5.2.1]

3. Identify elements of behavior management as they relate to Company Officer II. [NFPA® 1021, 5.2.1, 5.2.2]

4. Explain the role of professional development in fire and emergency service organizations [NFPA® 1021, 5.2.3]

Chapter 13
Human Resources Management II

Case History

A new captain was reviewing the list of required duties on his new job description. One caught his eye: "Responsible for annual appraisals and discipline of subordinate personnel." He suddenly realized that he was about to face one of the most challenging tasks of his fire service career: managing firefighters.

Soon, the new captain had to handle a disciplinary problem involving a firefighter who had played a prank on another firefighter, resulting in a damaged SCBA mask. The entire team closely watched to see how the new captain would react to the situation. The captain knew that if he did not handle this situation correctly it would be highly detrimental to the organization's future work environment.

The captain reviewed the disciplinary policy, looked at the steps, and found there was not a key on what level of discipline applied to what infraction. He finally called another captain for advice. The second captain told the first that he would help him. The second captain said, "Remember, discipline is not an emergency scene, which requires quick decisions based on, often times, little information. You have time to gather all the information needed and can also ask for help. Treat it like a Hazmat scene, slow down, do not rush in, and call technical experts."

The first captain conducted a fact-finding investigation and wrote a report to his battalion chief explaining the findings. He also made a recommendation on discipline based on the policy manual. The chief complimented him on the report and gave him some advice on a few minor changes, then implemented the recommended discipline. The chief went on to explain that administering discipline can be very hard because of personal feelings, but it is a necessary function. He also said that firefighters typically will respond very well to a fair but firm approach to discipline.

Another major challenge was soon upon the newly promoted captain when it was time for yearly appraisals. He sat and looked at the form and debated which was going to be harder: figuring out how to complete the form or coming up with a year's worth of information on each of the firefighters? He learned very quickly that what he thought was a good system to keep notes on subordinates did not provide enough information. He quickly learned to maintain a comprehensive file on all subordinates. He did not have enough to rate anyone high or low. He now understood why he had received "met expectations" many times when he thought he exceeded. "Met expectations" on evaluations did not require any documentation or notes. Furthermore, administration did not challenge this rating and neither did the firefighters.

The new captain felt very prepared for the operational aspects of his new position; however, the human resource aspect of the new job was very much an enigma to him. He later learned that middle level management within the fire service has evolved highly in administrative requirements placed upon it. With decreasing support staff, many captains and battalion chiefs are now faced with having to assist with budgeting and purchasing.

A Company Officer II may manage programs and multiunit emergency incident scenes as well as supervise personnel. Understanding group dynamics is vital for company officers because there is a direct connection between informal group support and formal group success or failure of the unit. Company officers must mesh the goals of both the formal and informal groups by influencing group behavior to meet the goals of both the company and the informal group.

The managing company officer may also evaluate personnel behavior and help personnel achieve their highest level of success. Knowledge of the organization's performance evaluation program and the common errors that can occur when evaluating subordinates is also essential. The company officer should also be familiar with the formal coaching, mentoring, and counseling programs that the organization uses to improve work habits and increase employee success.

This chapter addresses how groups are defined and group dynamics. It also describes key elements of behavior management.

Groups Defined

A group is often defined as a collection of people who:

- Share certain traits.
- Interact with one another.
- Accept rights and obligations as members of the group.
- Share a common identity.

Society is composed of many formal and informal groups. Fire and emergency services organizations are a reflection of their society. An emergency response unit is a subdivision of a fire and emergency services organization **(Figure 13.1)**. For this manual, a group is defined as two or more persons with common goals that may or may not be explicitly stated.

Formal groups usually define common goals in a written document. An emergency response unit is a formal group of responders who interact to meet common goals that the organization's mission, policies, and procedure outline. Informal groups define common goals in a less formal manner. A friendship is an informal group of two persons who interact with the common goal of mutual respect and interests.

Informal subgroups commonly form and exist within formal groups. Informal groups most often form around common interests, such as hobbies, political interests, social interests, religious beliefs, or sports activities. Informal subgroups may have greater influence on the productivity and success of the formal group more than any other factor. The effect may be positive if the members encourage each other to support the unit's activities. The effect may be negative if the individuals regard their informal group's goals as more important than, or contrary to, the goals of the unit.

The organization vests the company officer with the authority to be the formal group's leader. Group dynamics determine the company officer's ability to deal effectively with the informal group. Company officers must learn to balance the relationships within the unit.

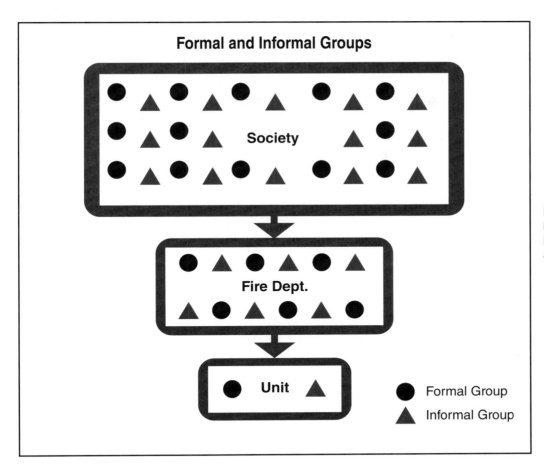

Formal and Informal Groups

Society

Fire Dept.

● Unit ▲

● Formal Group
▲ Informal Group

Figure 13.1 Formal and informal groups are found in society, fire departments, and individual units.

It is beyond the scope of this manual to attempt a complete explanation of group dynamics. Addressing the subject and creating an awareness of group dynamics can help company officers manage their units and the informal groups within them more effectively.

Group Dynamics

The group structure of an emergency response unit is not significantly different from the structure of any other formal or informal group. A group may exhibit the following five essential characteristics (**Figure 13.2**):

- Common binding interest
- Group image/identity
- Sense of continuity
- Shared values
- Roles within the group

The effects of these elements on the group members are what make up group dynamics. A study of group dynamics involves recognizing the internal and external pressures that affect these basic elements and learning to deal with those pressures.

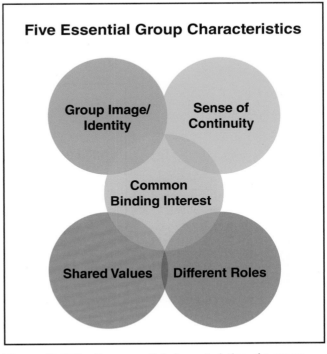

Five Essential Group Characteristics

Group Image/ Identity

Sense of Continuity

Common Binding Interest

Shared Values

Different Roles

Figure 13.2 The five essential characteristics of a group.

Common Binding Interests

Group members must be drawn together by some common interest that is important to them on some level, such as a common hobby, organizational memberships, or religious affiliation. When an individual's interests change, the individual's participation in various groups may change. Some interests are binding for a lifetime, while other interests last only for a given period of time. Emergency responders' interests may change with their personal and professional growth and with their changing goals and aspirations within the organization and the fire and emergency services. Company officers should strive to maintain their subordinates' interest in the unit and its mission, but should recognize that those interests may change over time.

Binding interests within fire and emergency services groups may include **(Figure 13.3)**:

- Desire to serve the community
- Sense of professionalism
- Sense of adventure
- Affiliation with a high-risk profession

From an organizational viewpoint, company officers managing groups must determine, communicate, and support common binding interests. Loss of group cohesion can be a factor in the loss of personnel and support of the unit and the organization.

Group Image or Identity

Group members must share a group image or identity by recognizing their group's purpose and take pride in it. This pride contributes to group spirit and high morale and must extend beyond the unit to the entire organization. Group image is one of the greatest influences on the success of the group. Groups that have a positive self-image, sometimes called *esprit de corps*, tend to be

Figure 13.3 Fire and emergency services personnel are bound by common interests of serving their communities, a sense of professionalism and adventure, and affiliation with a high-risk profession.

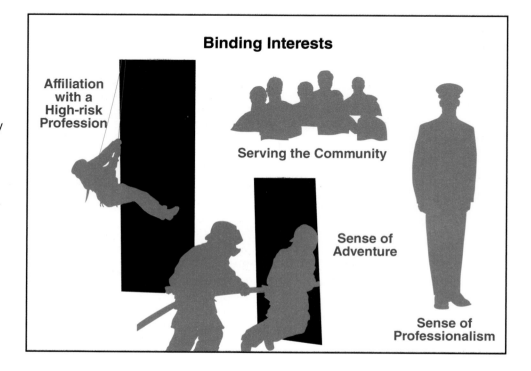

Binding Interests

Affiliation with a High-risk Profession

Serving the Community

Sense of Adventure

Sense of Professionalism

higher achievers. Groups that lack a positive image or identity tend to be poor producers. Company officers must not allow this group spirit to evolve into an unhealthy rivalry with other units. Their subordinates should understand that their first loyalty is to the organization and not the unit.

Sense of Continuity

A sense of continuity is very important to group integrity. If the group's members have doubts about the group's continued existence, then their commitment to the group may diminish. If the members' sense of continuity is disturbed, the group can be fragmented and the members may begin to think and act more independently. Company officers are concerned with how to maintain their subordinates' sense of continuity, even though they are subject to being transferred to another unit or shift. Company officers must continually remind their subordinates that they are part of a larger group or organization.

Shared Values

Common values are sometimes a composite of individual perception of reality, responsibility, and integrity. These values surface as various subjects are confronted on a day-to-day basis in the normal interaction within the group structure. The values shared by group can change gradually as the group accepts new members with differing values. While individuals within the group may share common values, they are likely to have values that differ. Company officers must recognize and respect these differences as long as they are not in conflict with the values of the organization.

The values of the organization also affect group values. The values of the organization usually are reflected in the attitudes and actions of individuals and groups within the organization. For example, organizational values of the fire and emergency services require that emergency responders must be trustworthy and honest. Company officers must exemplify and reinforce organizational values within their units.

Figure 13.4 Informal groups may form within formal groups, such as at this fire station.

Roles within the Group

Individuals assume different roles within each group. In formal groups, the leader is usually either assigned or elected. In informal groups, a natural or indigenous leader emerges regardless of whether any formal selection process is used. In an emergency response unit, the company officer should be the leader of the formal group but is often not the leader of informal groups **(Figure 13.4)**. The company officer must recognize this fact and ensure the organizational and group goals are met.

Role Expectations

A company officer's subordinates expect the officer to be a supervisor. Officers and responders alike are guided in performing their duties by what others expect of them. This is called role expectation. The influences that determine the company officer's perception of his or her role are:

- The role expectations of the organization
- Group members
- The officer's own concept of what it means to be a company officer

The ability to positively influence a group is not dependent upon being its informal leader. Any group member can influence the group to some extent.

A company officer should not ignore informal groups. The company officer should maintain a strong relationship and influence with the informal leader in order to maintain the motivation, satisfaction, and performance of the larger group or team.

Members' Roles

Members, upon joining, agree to follow the organization's rules and guidelines. As group members, they should have an understanding of the group's informal rules and how those rules fit within the organizational rules. Other areas of responsibility for the group members may include:

- Showing mutual respect
- Being dependable
- Operating ethically
- Being goal-oriented

The group members must be ready to acknowledge the authority of the company officer. When group members recognize the officer's authority, the officer will have to exert authority less often. Control over the group will result from a more democratic approach to leadership than a more authoritarian approach. At emergency incidents, the group members will be able to carry out orders, tasks, and assignments with minimum supervision. This approach will permit the company officer to focus on the overall operation and the coordination of major resources.

The Group as Individuals

Company officers must understand that the group's interaction determines the group members' productivity. When group interaction is cooperative, a synergistic effect is created whereby the productivity of the group is greater than could be expected from the sum of individual efforts. When making assignments, company officers should consider the individuals within the unit and their relationships to each other.

Applying Leadership Styles

The company officer may apply situational leadership styles to the group process to gain the best results. The five stages of development are (**Figure 13.5**):

- **Forming** — As relationships within the group grow, trust and respect develop and the members begin to see themselves as a part of the group. They become enthusiastic about the challenges of a new project or task.

- **Storming** — Conflicts may result as members jockey for informal leadership or try to exert their own influence over the group. Company officers can reduce the time spent in the storming phase by actively listening to members and explaining decisions.

- **Norming** — The group establishes its own sets of norms and values that each member accepts and adheres to during this stage.

- **Performing** — The supervisor maintains team spirit as the group accomplishes its objectives.

- **Adjourning** — The final stage is the termination of the group task. It includes acknowledging the group's accomplishments and the participation of the individual members. It is also an opportunity to debrief and determine if any process changes should be made.

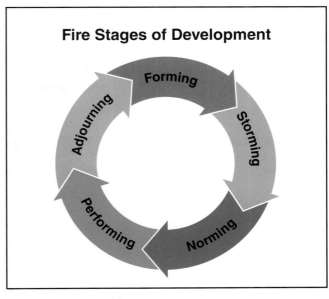

Figure 13.5 Illustrating the five stages of development.

NOTE: Not all groups go through each of these processes at the same rates of time. Some may take longer to move through the process than others. However, the process should not be allowed to go on any longer than necessary.

Behavior Management

Behavior management is one of the most important skills for an officer to acquire and maintain. While group members may respond to peer pressure, the company officer cannot shirk responsibility and depend on peer pressure to correct disruptive behavior. The company officer may still need to privately counsel a disruptive subordinate.

Company officers who fail to control disruptive behavior will lose the respect of the other unit members. Behavior management begins with prevention of disruptive behavior. Prevention requires the officer to communicate behavioral expectations based on the organization's policies, provide a positive example, and create a positive atmosphere in the unit.

The company officer should review the organization's policies to identify the specific policy or procedure that was violated and the policy that describes how violations should be handled. The company officer should also review the labor/management agreement to determine the appropriate steps mandated.

Company officers should follow their organizational policies for behavior management. Company officers should also be familiar with the following ways to assist their subordinates:

- **Counseling** — Guidance starts with a counseling session between the company officer and a new member of the unit **(Figure 13.6, p. 378)**. The officer's expectations are stated positively and behavioral limitations are set. Counseling may also be used for discipline, to determine the cause of inappropriate behavior, and establish a means of correcting it.

- **Coaching** — In coaching, the company officer or designated subordinate guides the individual through any new activities, reinforces correct behaviors, and redirects incorrect behaviors.

Figure 13.6 A company officer counseling a newly assigned unit member.

Figure 13.7 Peer assistance can be a source of help to new crewmembers.

- **Providing peer assistance** — Providing peer assistance may begin with assigning a more experienced member to work with the new member **(Figure 13.7)**.

- **Mentoring** — A supervisor or other superior acts as an advisor or guide (mentor) to the member.

Employee Rights Legislation

In several states, legislation (such as California's "Fire Fighter Bill of Rights") has fundamentally changed the first level supervisor's responsibilities and authorities. Company officers should also be conversant with state statutes concerning employee's rights relating to discipline.

Reviewing Policies

A periodic review of an organization's policies helps address issues that may arise over time. Company officers should review the organization's policies, rules, and regulations as well as the officer's personal expectations with subordinates **(Figure 13.8)**. The policies that are generally addressed include but are not limited to:

- Safety
- Attendance, absenteeism, and tardiness
- Expectations and regulations for responding to emergencies
- Storage and care of PPE
- Station/facility, apparatus, and equipment care, cleaning, and maintenance
- Company-level training participation
- Physical fitness program participation
- Dress/grooming regulations
- Procedures for accommodating visitors or citizen inquiries
- Response procedures for volunteers in personally owned vehicles (POVs)

Counseling

Counseling is a variety of procedures designed to help individuals adjust to certain situations and a means of either reinforcing correct behavior or eliminating improper behavior. Counseling involves resolving behavior issues through such actions as:

- Providing advice
- Recommending career path choices
- Providing professional development opportunities

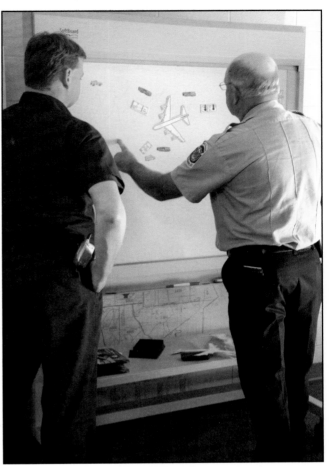

Figure 13.8 A company officer reviewing an aircraft emergency response procedure with a subordinate.

Company officers must not act as a therapist if a subordinate appears to have a psychological/emotional problem. In these cases, the company officer should seek guidance from a superior officer and/or the organization's employee assistance program (EAP). Company officers should learn and practice appropriate counseling and positive reinforcement methods that stimulate and motivate subordinates to perform properly.

Fire and emergency services organizations have a formalized process to follow when documenting behavior issues, which may include completing a counseling form. Company officers should consult with their superiors and follow the specific policies on counseling individuals and completing the appropriate documents. The company officer should use the following general guidelines:

- Meet and talk with the subordinate in private.
- List the exact facts of what behavior the individual is displaying.

- State behavioral objectives that clearly and concisely communicate what is expected of the individual.
- Discuss and agree with the individual on solutions.
- Explain what actions will be taken if the individual does not comply with the objectives and solutions.
- Give a copy of the documentation to the individual and retain the original.
- Follow department policies regarding documentation distribution.

Legal and ethical issues may require or dictate that company officers have supervisory authority before counseling to correct behavior. If the department has a labor/management agreement, it may stipulate that the subordinate has the right to have a union representative present during counseling.

If informal attempts to correct inappropriate behavior are unsuccessful, the CO should review and follow the organization's discipline policy. When disciplinary action becomes necessary, documentation of the situation will be critical in supporting formal action.

Often, company officers who show a sincere interest in a subordinate do more towards solving problems than any action that might intensify the individual's feelings of inferiority or inadequacy. COs should remember that the objective of disciplinary action is to change inappropriate behavior.

Coaching

Coaching is a process of directing an individual's skills performance. For the company officer, coaching is the process of giving motivational correction, positive reinforcement, and constructive feedback to subordinates in order to maintain and improve their performance. The feedback needs to be positive, immediate, direct, and frequent.

One formal coaching model contains the following four steps:
- Describe the current performance level.
- Describe the desired performance level.
- Gain a commitment for change.
- Follow up the commitment.

Coaching can take place in a group setting or individually. The company officer should identify the problem source through observation and questioning and then guide the subordinate(s) to an appropriate solution. Company officers should be able to recognize, constructively criticize, and carefully correct flaws in subordinates' actions **(Figure 13.9)**. They must also effectively praise and positively reinforce those actions that are being performed properly. Company officers should strike a balance between correcting what is performed wrong and praising what is performed right.

Using Peer Assistance

Peer Assistance — A process that involves having unit personnel assist each other in learning teamwork or perfecting new skills.

There may be circumstances where a company officer uses **peer assistance** as a tool to clarify expectations. Some subordinates are intimidated to perform in front of the company officer until they feel confident in their abilities. These subordinates may feel more comfortable practicing with a peer.

Figure 13.9 A company officer coaching two of his personnel.

More experienced or mature unit personnel can often provide peer assistance to new personnel. Unit personnel who have specialized knowledge and skills can provide training in those areas. The peer assistance approach can be used as a basis for a buddy system that pairs an experienced member with a new employee during the probationary period.

Mentoring

Mentoring places a subordinate under the guidance of a more experienced professional, who acts as tutor, guide, and motivator, either formally or informally. A mentor is usually someone, other than the instructor, who guides subordinates' actions in real experiences on the job. Mentors must be chosen carefully and selected for their experience, interest, patience, and communication abilities. Personnel can mentor in the following ways:

- Provide role models for personnel.

- Provide guidance in career planning.

- Assist in gaining specialized training.

- Identify outside resources.

- Suggest opportunities for challenging work assignments.

- Monitor personnel achievements.

Personnel-Evaluation Programs

Company officers should periodically evaluate the personnel who work for them, commonly on an annual basis. Personnel might be formally evaluated in the following situations:

- During their probationary period

- Annually as part of a performance review

- For promotional purposes
- For disciplinary and non-disciplinary purposes

The formal evaluation schedule should not deter company officers from providing ongoing feedback on performance. Performance feedback may be provided on a quarterly or semi-annual basis to allow an individual to alter or improve performance before an annual evaluation. It also allows the supervisor to document the individual's performance during the evaluation period in terms of strengths, weaknesses, and improvements.

The personnel evaluation process should be approached as objectively as possible and with as much information as can be gathered and documented. Evaluations can have a career-long effect on subordinates. Mishandled evaluations can result in loss of motivation, personal resentment, or tarnishing of an individual's professional or personal reputation.

Advantages

Personnel evaluation programs are formal systematic procedures for appraising employees' abilities and accomplishments within the organization. Benefits that can be derived from a well-organized personnel evaluation program include the following:

- A permanent record is made of each employee's strengths and weaknesses that can be used for awards, promotions, transfers, discipline, or termination.
- Additional training needs are identified and weaknesses can be addressed with specific existing training programs.
- The company officer becomes more familiar with the personnel being evaluated, which allows for more effective use of personnel and a better succession system.
- The evaluation program is motivation for improvement by the person being evaluated.
- Upper management becomes more aware of the lower-level managers' and supervisors' abilities.
- Personnel evaluations help identify specific talents of individuals who may be used in other areas of the organization.
- The program improves the efficiency of the employees and the organization as a whole.

Characteristics

Personnel evaluation guidelines can be effective tools in the organization's management. Personnel evaluations must be:

- **Timely** — Conduct performance evaluations linked to specific incidences of unsatisfactory performance or inappropriate behavior as soon as possible following the inappropriate behavior.
- **Stated clearly** — State goals and objectives clearly and concisely.
- **Non-discriminatory** — Apply job-performance standards regardless of gender, race, ethnicity, age, or other classifications.

- **Consistent** — Apply job-performance standards equally throughout the organization.

- **Documented** — Maintain thorough records of each evaluation in the employee's personnel file. Provide a copy to the employee, but maintain confidentiality.

- **Conducted by trained supervisors** — Train company officers to perform personnel evaluations properly.

- **Objective** — Overcome personal bias and base the evaluation on established criteria.

Evaluation Processes

The organization's expectations for job performance should be established during the initial meeting between the company officer and the subordinate. Pre-established job descriptions can be used to describe the employee's duties and responsibilities **(Figure 13.10, p. 384)**. Company officers should ensure that subordinates understand the relevant performance standards upon which they will be evaluated.

The job-performance evaluation is an opportunity to reinforce positive performance or to generate change in an employee's behavior in order to meet the organization's expectations. Accomplishing this change usually involves:

- Focusing on the positive accomplishments of the employee

- Involving the employee in setting goals and objectives

- Creating an atmosphere in which the employee can feel challenged and respected

Fire and emergency services organizations generally have an established probationary period for new employees. The established job-performance expectations provide the basis for performance evaluations during this period. The company officer must continually monitor the job performance of new personnel and provide appropriate feedback.

Following the probationary period, formal, periodic job-performance evaluations are typically established on a recurrent basis. These evaluations allow the company officer and employee to review work quality and established performance goals and objectives. The supervisor may also provide continuous feedback to the employee through informal evaluations. The formal evaluation then reinforces the continuous feedback. To ensure that evaluations are successful, take the following actions:

- Ensure that employees are aware of their roles, authority, and responsibilities.

- Allow employees to contribute to setting or altering performance goals and objectives.

- Conduct the evaluation at a predetermined time, in private, and prohibit interruptions.

- The company officer and employee should both sign the final evaluation. These signatures indicate that the employee has received the evaluation. It does not mean the employee agrees with the content of the evaluation, but indicates the comments that were reviewed with the employee.

CITY OF ELMONT
JOB DESCRIPTION

JOB CODE: 5520   **DATE:**   February 21, 2003
PAY GRADE: 60
JOB TITLE: FIREFIGHTER
DEPARTMENT: FIRE DEPARTMENT
REPORTS TO: FIRE CAPTAIN

This job description identifies the major responsibilities and requirements of this job. The incumbents may be requested to perform job-related responsibilities and tasks other than those stated. Any essential function or requirement of this class will be evaluated as necessary should an incumbent/applicant be unable to perform the function or requirement due to a disability as defined by the Americans with Disabilities Act (ADA).

SUMMARY OF POSITION:

This is skilled fire fighting work in combating, extinguishing, and preventing fires, in answering emergency calls, and in the operation and routine custodial maintenance of fire department equipment, apparatus and quarters. Work involves training for, and participating in, the protection of life and property by fire fighting and rescue activities, under close supervision.

ESSENTIAL JOB DUTIES:

Perform fire fighting duties such as combating, extinguishing and preventing fires, and answering emergency calls with an engine, ladder, or miscellaneous vehicles. Lays and connects hoses, direct water onto burning structures, raises and climbs ladders; uses other fire fighting techniques such as ventilating burning buildings (chopping holes in floors or roofs); administers first aid to injured persons; performs salvage operations; and inspects assigned district to assure knowledge of access, fire hazards, etc. Trains for, and participates in the protection of life and property by fire fighting and rescue activities. Participates in fire drills and attends training classes in fire fighting, first aid and related subjects.

ADDITIONAL JOB DUTIES:

Handles routine custodial maintenance of the fire department equipment, apparatus and quarters.
Enforce safety rules and encourage safety application for employees, conforming to the safety guidelines set by the City of Elmont.

KNOWLEDGE, SKILLS & ABILITIES:

Since this is an entry level classification, most of the qualifications include the ability to: learn fire fighting skills, first aid, and apparatus and equipment maintenance.

Figure 13.10 An example of a pre-established job description for a firefighter position.

REQUIRED EDUCATION, TRAINING & EXPERIENCE:

Graduation from high school or GED equivalent. Required to maintain certification in Emergency Medical Technician/Basic (EMT/B) for the duration of employment with the City of Elmont Fire Department. Must possess a valid Oklahoma driver's license and a driving record acceptable to the City's insurance carrier.

PREFERRED EDUCATION, TRAINING & EXPERIENCE:

Successful completion of fire-related courses in subjects that are applicable to the fire service.

WORKING CONDITIONS/PHYSICAL REQUIREMENTS:

No Tobacco Use Requirement: Only non-tobacco users will be considered for employment with the Elmont Fire Department. All applicants shall agree not to use tobacco of any type while on duty or on premises while employed with the Elmont Fire Department. Violations of these requirement may result in termination.

Such essential functions are performed in and affected by the following environmental factors:
(a)   Operate both as a member of a team and independently at incidents of uncertain duration.
(b)   Spend extensive time outside exposed to the elements.
(c)   Tolerate extreme fluctuations in temperature while performing duties. Must perform physically demanding work in hot (up to 400 degrees Fahrenheit), humid (up to 100 percent) atmospheres while wearing equipment that significantly impairs body cooling mechanisms.
(d)   Experience frequent transition from hot to cold and from humid to dry atmospheres.
(e)   Work in wet, icy, or muddy areas.
(f)   Perform a variety of tasks on slippery, hazardous surfaces such as on roof tops or from ladders.
(g)   Work in areas where sustaining traumatic or thermal injuries is possible.
(h)   Face potential exposure to carcinogenic dusts such as asbestos, toxic substances such as hydrogen cyanide, carbon monoxide, or organic solvents either through inhalation or skin contact.
(i)   Face potential exposure to infectious agents such as hepatitis B or HIV.
(j)   Perform physically demanding work while wearing positive pressure breathing equipment.
(k)   Perform complex tasks during life-threatening emergencies.
(l)   Work for long periods of time, requiring sustained physical activity and intense concentration.
(m)   Exposed to grotesque sights and smells associated with major trauma and burn victims.
(n)   Make rapid transitions from rest to near maximal exertion without warm-up periods.
(o)   Operate in environments of high noise, poor visibility, limited mobility, at heights, and in enclosed or confined spaces.
(p)   Use manual and power tools in the performance of duties.
(q)   Rely on speech, as well as senses of sight, hearing, smell, and touch to help determine the nature of the emergency, maintain personal safety, and make critical decisions in a confused, chaotic, and potentially life threatening environment throughout the duration of the operation.
(r)   Strength to lift, pull or carry objects weighing 50 pounds on a frequent basis and up to 100 pounds on an infrequent basis.

Figure 13.10 Continued.

Legal Considerations

Personnel evaluations must adhere to the guidelines that the AHJ, the state/province, and the federal government provide. Company officers must be familiar with all statutory requirements relevant to personnel evaluations. A number of factors emphasized in recent court decisions that influence the evaluation process include:

- Evaluations must be significantly related to the employee's assigned work behavior or skills. The individual cannot be judged on tasks that are not assigned or the person is not trained to perform.

- Evaluations must include definite identifiable criteria based on the quality or quantity of work or on specific performances that are supported by a documented record.

- Evaluations must be objective and not based on subjective observations.

- Evaluations must be supported by documentation.

The company officer must also be aware of requirements that the labor/management agreement mandates. Union representation, grievance, and reporting procedures may include provisions that:

- Control the evaluation process.

- Require certain actions by the company officer.

- Establish a specific time frame for the process.

Grievance Procedures

Employees file grievances when they perceive they have been unfairly treated. Grievance (complaint) procedures are usually included in the labor/management agreement and/or the organization's policy and procedures manual. The grievance procedure needs to be effective, consistent, and provide an equitable resolution.

All model grievance procedures contain the same general elements, such as:

- Filing period
- Testimony
- Witnesses
- Representation
- Review steps

Discipline

Disciplinary actions consist of corrective measures that are used to get employees to meet standards and adhere to policies. These actions should be taken in a manner that is corrective, progressive, and lawful.

Discipline in the fire and emergency services is designed to do the following:

- Educate and train
- Correct inappropriate behavior
- Provide positive motivation
- Ensure compliance with established policies, rules, regulations, standards, and procedures
- Provide direction

Discipline — To maintain order through training and/or the threat or imposition of sanctions; setting and enforcing the limits or boundaries for expected performance.

Types

There are two basic types of discipline:

1. Positive

2. Negative

Positive (constructive) discipline results when reasonable rules of conduct are established and are fairly and consistently applied. As long as they know what is required, most personnel willingly conform to the rules through self-discipline.

Negative discipline involves corrective action when an employee disobeys the established rules or performance requirements. The company officer is obligated to correct the inappropriate behavior. For relatively minor violations, the company officer needs to promptly do whatever the organization requires in order to correct the behavior, usually through private, informal counseling. If the violations are serious, the company officer should continue the process up the chain of command.

Company officers must recognize that employees are entitled to the following information and considerations:

- Written notice of proposed action

- The reasons for the proposed action

- Copy of the charges and the material upon which the action is based

- The right to respond (either orally or in writing) to the authority initially imposing discipline

Once these requirements have been met, the discipline may be imposed without a hearing unless the employee requests one. If a hearing is held, it is not intended to be an adversarial proceeding but rather informational — to minimize the risk of error in a supervisor/manager's initial decision because information is lacking. The employee, or designated legal or union representative, may provide additional information and respond to the specific charges before the discipline is imposed.

Progressive Discipline

Progressive discipline usually starts with training and/or education. It may be used to correct the first instance an employee fails to meet performance standards or violates the rules of conduct. It then progresses to punitive measures for additional offenses. However, a sufficiently serious first offense (theft, assault, gross negligence) may result in termination. Progressive leadership and participatory management can help to ensure that punitive discipline is seldom used within the organization. Progressive discipline usually involves the following three levels **(Figure 13.11, p. 388)**:

- **Preventive action (Oral reprimand)** — Attempt to correct the inappropriate behavior as soon as it is discovered and prevent it from becoming a pattern or progressing to a more serious offense. Preventive action should start with an individual counseling interview, so that the employee understands which rule was violated and the organizational necessity for the rule. The company officer explains the expectations for the employee in the future and what may happen if another violation occurs.

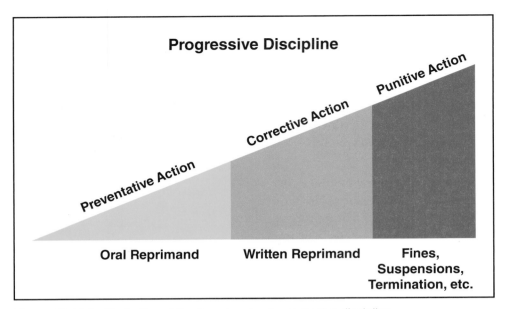

Figure 13.11 An illustration of the three levels of progressive discipline.

- **Corrective action (Written reprimand)** — The second step is applied when an employee repeats a violation for which preventive action was taken or commits a different violation. It may also be used if an employee commits a serious violation as a first offense. Corrective action is always done in writing. This may include giving the employee a letter in person or through certified mail with a return receipt requested.

- **Punitive action** — This step is used when an employee continues to exhibit inappropriate behavior despite earlier corrective efforts or commits a very serious violation of organizational rules as a first offense. The employee is notified that the behavior cannot and will not be tolerated. After meeting the mandated procedural rules and safeguards, the range of sanctions may include:

  — Formal written reprimand

  — Suspension (time off without pay)

  — Demotion (reduction in rank)

  — Termination (dismissal from department/organization)

  — Prosecution (legal action that may result in a large fine or jail time)

NOTE: In some cases, the steps listed here may not be followed due to the severity of the actions. Termination may happen without suspension or demotion.

Most company officers will only be responsible for the first step, preventive action, but they must be familiar with the remaining steps should they become necessary. In most organizations, the administration is responsible for correct and punitive actions. The labor/management agreement may control what actions may be taken.

Professional Development

Professional development is key to growth, not only for the employee but in helping the organization develop future leaders in the organization's succession plan. Company officers need to address the necessary training and education for their employees. This training and education prepares the employees by improving their skills in the current position and prepares them for future promotional opportunities. To accomplish this, company officers need to be sure that they understand what each employee's career goals are.

The training division will also need input for scheduling or delivering courses and/or determining the funding necessary for those courses. Having a professional development plan will assist with those tasks. The training division should maintain a matrix of professional development courses that each department member may require.

Professional Development Plans

Fire and emergency services organizations must provide training and professional development for their personnel. Government and non-government organizations may provide skills training and professional development programs. Company officers should provide career planning and guidance to their personnel. For the purposes of this book, career and professional development is the same thing.

Job shadowing programs may be used to help unit personnel experience different positions within an organization. These programs can be useful in identifying specific areas of interest or duty positions personnel might like to achieve.

Career planning usually occurs within the framework of personnel counseling. Many departments have included career and professional development counseling guidelines in their policies and procedures. These guidelines should be followed; if not, then the process described in this chapter may be used as a general guideline. NFPA® 1021 requires the Fire Officer II to *create a professional development plan* for a subordinate who is preparing for a promotional examination. This plan provides the framework for a more complete career path.

Job Shadowing — A program in which an individual can learn a particular skill set by following an active practitioner in the field.

National Professional Development Models

Recently, more emphasis has been placed on professional development. National fire service organizations, including the International Association of Fire Chiefs (IAFC), have developed several professional development models. The IAFC has published the Officer Development Handbook to assist fire officers, and those aspiring to be fire officers, in preparing and developing for these promotional opportunities.

In addition to the IAFC's Officer Development Handbook, the U.S. Fire Administration/FEMA has also published a National Professional Development Model. This model illustrates the importance of the following components: experience(s), self-development, education, and training.

Career or professional development may be applied to both career and volunteer departments. Volunteer organizations must provide guidance to their members in order for their organization to survive. Helping volunteers with attaining their personal goals is a key element of recruiting and retention. Career or professional development can be divided into three sections:

- Mastering and maintaining current knowledge, skills, and abilities and acquiring new skills required for the current position

- Preparing for promotion to the next rank or level of authority

- Developing a long range plan for career advancement

Planning Process

A career or professional development plan is like a roadmap. It provides people with a visual image that includes their current situation, intermediate objectives, and final goal. Each of these three elements must be identified and entered into the plan. It also becomes part of employees' Individual Development Plan (IDP) that can be included in their annual performance review. Steps in the planning process can include evaluating the current situation, intermediate objectives, and a final goal.

Current Situation. An officer must first measure an individual's current skills and abilities. The company officer may assist the individual with a self-assessment that will determine current skills. The answers to a self assessment's questions will guide the individual and the company officer in making a list of intermediate objectives to reach the final goal. Questions that should be answered in any assessment include:

- What interests me the most?

- What are my personal strengths and weaknesses?

- What is most important to me about my work?

- What knowledge, skills, or abilities do I have that I would like to improve or expand?

- What knowledge, skills, or abilities would I like to acquire?

- What are my immediate goals (within one year)?

- What are my long-range career goals?

- What am I willing to sacrifice to meet my goals?

Intermediate Objectives. The intermediate objectives are the steps needed to attain the final goal. Some intermediate objectives may be goals in themselves within a long-range career plan. If so, then each of these objectives may have objectives of their own. Broad or ambiguous objectives can cause the individual to become distracted or frustrated. Reaching the final goal depends on accomplishing each objective in a reasonable time period.

Final Goal. A final career goal can take many forms. For some, it may be to retire from a career department as a chief, while others may be satisfied to be the best firefighter on the department. Goals are stated in broad general terms over a specified period. The list of objectives must lead to the final goal and provide all the necessary knowledge, training, and skills to attain it.

Current Skills and Abilities

Personnel must be proficient in their current positions before they can advance to the next position or rank. Changes in organizationally-provided services, new technologies, and additional responsibilities for the position may require constant changes in knowledge, skills, and abilities. Officers should be familiar with each assigned person's career goals and assist those people in maintaining and expanding their knowledge, skills, and abilities. After determining what the subordinate knows and what career goals they have, the company officer should take the following steps:

- Evaluate the subordinate's current knowledge, skills, and abilities.
- Compare the results of this evaluation to the current and projected needs of the organization.
- Determine if any knowledge, skills, or abilities should be improved.
- Determine the new knowledge, skills, and abilities the subordinate will need to achieve career goals.
- Advise the subordinate of improvements and additions needed to achieve career goals.
- Suggest sources for training and educational needs.
- Develop a schedule for the completion of the stated goals.

Subordinates may have existing skills that are best used in another job in the department, such as having a degree in fire engineering that could be used in the fire inspections and code enforcement division. Discussing a duty change and providing the subordinate with information to make an informed decision can benefit both the subordinate and the department.

Levels of Capability

Company officers should be familiar with the terms to denote the levels of capability used to describe personnel's ability to perform the tasks associated with their duties.

Competency — Basic skills able to meet minimum requirements.

Proficiency — Higher level of skill performance that is the result of additional practice and experience.

Mastery — Highest level of skill performance when the skill has been internalized due to repetition and experience in performing the skill in actual incidents.

Preparing Subordinates for Promotion

Company officers should be prepared to assist their subordinates in preparing for promotional opportunities **(Figure 13.12, p. 392)**. To help their subordinates, company officers should:

- Know the job and promotional requirements.
- Emphasize the importance of studying the promotional materials.

Figure 13.12 A company officer congratulating a crewmember on a promotion.

- Encourage subordinates to take advantage of study groups and/or practice assessments.
- Follow an established professional development plan.

Chapter Summary

The human resources program is a major segment of any public or private fire and emergency services organization. Company officers should understand group dynamics, which are central to all human interaction groups. Company officers must also be familiar with the various components of a human resources program, including the steps for evaluating and disciplining employees. Effective personnel evaluations will reduce the need for corrective discipline within the unit.

Review Questions

1. How are groups defined?
2. What are the five essential characteristics of group dynamics?
3. What are common methods of behavior management?
4. How do company officers contribute to their subordinates' professional development?

Administrative Responsibilities

Chapter Contents

chapter 14

Key Terms

NFPA® Job Performance Requirements

This chapter provides information that addresses the following job performance requirements of NFPA® 1021, *Standard for Fire Officer Professional Qualifications* (2014).

5.4.1

5.4.2

5.4.3

5.4.6

Administrative Responsibilities

Learning Objectives

After reading this chapter, students will be able to:

1. Identify the development of policies and procedures. [NFPA® 1021, 5.4.1, 5.4.6]

2. Explain budget preparation and development. [NFPA® 1021, 5.4.2]

3. Describe the purchasing process. [NFPA® 1021, 5.4.2, 5.4.3]

4. Develop a policy or procedure that addresses an administrative problem. [NFPA® 1021, 5.4.1; Learning Activity 14-1]

5. Construct a departmental budget that addresses capital, operating, and personnel costs. [NFPA® 1021, 5.4.2; Learning Activity 14-2]

Chapter 14
Administrative Responsibilities

Case History

A new captain realized a personal goal when she was assigned to develop and train a departmental vehicle extrication team. The overall objective was to enhance department morale and rescue training. The captain was ordered to put forward a proposal that would outline procedures for team selection, equipment needs, and training requirements. The proposal was also to reference any issues relating to certification, departmental SOPs, and any impacts on current and future budgets.

The task seemed daunting and unachievable until a more seasoned officer stepped up to assist. This individual's knowledge of administrative systems and processes allowed the young captain to locate the needed information and develop a proposal that the department's chief officers could easily interpret and met the requirements for successful implementation of the plan.

Managing a fire and emergency services organization requires many people. Some activities require highly specialized skills, such as caring for the organization's computers and electronic equipment. Emergency responders can handle other tasks, such as logistics, personnel, or finance management as full-time or part-time duty assignments.

Company officers will be involved in the day-to-day administration of their organizations. Some administrative tasks assigned to the Company Officer II include policy and procedures development, budget development, and purchasing activities. All fire and emergency services organizations must handle some or all of these administrative functions. Larger career organizations may have separate administrative sections that manage them. Small volunteer, combination, or career organizations may depend on outside agencies for support. Company officers must understand these functions in order to manage them internally or monitor external support sources. This chapter provides an overview of policy and procedures development, budget development, and purchasing activities.

Policy and Procedure Development

Policies and procedures that are put in writing outline the organization's expectations based on the organizational model and the strategic and operational plans. They may be called Standard Operating Procedures (SOP), Standard

Figure 14.1 A company officer preparing to review a department SOP/SOG with a crewmember.

Operating Guidelines (SOG), Operating Instructions (OI), Administrative Policies and Procedures, or simply Policies and Procedures **(Figure 14.1)**. The organization should have a process to:

● Evaluate the need for new policies and procedures

● Revise existing policies and procedures

● Effectively implement new or revised policies and procedures

Most company officers will enforce policies, rules, regulations, and procedures. NFPA® 1021 states that the Fire Officer II must have the ability to identify a problem, determine the appropriate solution, and develop a policy or procedure to rectify the problem.

Determining the need for a new or revised policy or procedure includes:

● Identifying the issue or requirement for a policy or procedure

● Collecting data to evaluate the need

● Researching regulations and reports from OSHA, NIOSH, or other agencies

Developing or revising a policy or procedure includes:

● Evaluating the information

● Selecting the best response to the need

● Selecting alternative responses

● Establishing a revision process or schedule

● Recommending the policy or procedure that best meets the need

● Recommending an evaluation process to determine the effectiveness of the new or revised policy or procedure

NOTE: The AHJ then determines the best manner in which to implement the new or revised policy or procedure.

An organization's policies and procedures must be dynamic documents that are continually evaluated for effectiveness. The organization's senior, or command, staff is responsible for establishing and monitoring all policies and procedures. The command staff should be familiar with the content, application, and effects of the policies used to manage the organization. They should also know the proper procedures for performing the tasks assigned to them and to their personnel. Company officers who assist chief officers in the development and revision of policies and procedures should also be familiar with how the policies are applied and enforced.

Budget Preparation and Development

For the Company Officer II level, this chapter will build upon the knowledge and skills provided in Chapter 6, Administration. In this context, budgets refer to the narrow financial budget that details proposed expenditures and expected revenue sources. Some fire and emergency services organizations may have internal budget departments that nonemergency employees staff and a chief officer manages. The Company Officer II should already be familiar with the:

- Organization's budget process
- Types of budgets normally used in public administration
- Types of revenue sources available

Agency Budget Systems

Company officers must become familiar with their agency's budgetary systems. They should also include justifications for the line items in their budget requests that the type of budget system dictates.

Agency policy may require the company officers to compare their budget requests to the previous year's budget. Similarly, the agency may create a projected budget and ask the company officers to compare what they see as their operational needs against what the agency is prepared to budget and then justify any differences. In some budget cycles, company officers are asked to determine their operational needs based on a fixed amount of money that the agency has already determined. When there is not enough funding to cover all operational needs, company officers must offer strong evidence that their requests are justified. Sources for this justification include the following:

- **Organization's financial history** — Primary data source to support the budget request, based on the actual cost of providing the services in previous budgetary cycles. This history includes but is not limited to the cost of fuel, maintenance, utilities, parts, training, and operating supplies. It can be used to justify the operating budget or a capital request, such as the replacement of an apparatus.
- **Actual equipment, material, or service costs** — Average product or item costs according to vendors' catalogs or price lists. Examining the jurisdiction's existing contracts for materials and services can also determine costs.
- **Contractual requirements** — Labor/management contracts and contracts for services that an organization is obligated to provide, such as mutual or automatic aid response.
- **Injury reports and fire losses** — Incidents that resulted in firefighter injuries or fatalities may be indicators of areas where training within the organization needs to be reviewed.
- **New programs or services** — Private sector providers may introduce new programs or services with which the organization wants to become involved.

Formulating Budget Needs

In their role as supervisors, company officers may be responsible for formulating the budgetary needs for their divisions or projects. Company officers submit budget requests to their supervisor, who then submits an official budgetary form to the administration. The line items on a budget form may include **(Figure 14.2, p. 400)**:

- Personnel costs
- New equipment
- Apparatus maintenance
- Repairs to existing facilities
- Supplies and equipment for new or ongoing projects

Budget Form Line Items

FY2013 - 2014 Projection Budget Requests (Apparatus Maintenance Division)	
Line Items	**Projected Costs**
Personnel Costs	1,029,213
New Apparatus/Equipment	5,374,866
Apparatus Maintenance	1,948,233
Repairs (Existing Facilities)	229,290
Supplies/Equipment (Ongoing Projects)	105,000
Supplies/Equipment (New Projects)	701,395
Total	**9,387,997**

Figure 14.2 Examples of common line items within a budget.

Operating Budget — Budget intended to fund the day-to-day operations of the department or agency; usually includes the costs of salaries and benefits, utility bills, fuel, and preventive maintenance.

Capital Budget — Budget intended to fund large, one-time expenditures, such as those for fire stations, fire apparatus, or major pieces of equipment.

If any line item contains an unusual request or proposes a funding increase, the justification should include a budgetary-need summary and any relevant background research. The sections that follow introduce Level II Company Officers to the process of formulating budget needs.

Funding Needs Determination

Company officers must provide an accurate estimate of division and/or project cycle costs. They should estimate each resource cost in their **operating budget** request, and do research to make sure their estimates are accurate. With new equipment for example, company officers should consult the manufacturer's catalogue to determine the price.

Sometimes a purchase, such as a new apparatus, will require that organizations make a large, one-time purchase like those found in **capital budgets**. These budget requests may require greater justification, or other outside funding sources.

Usually, the funding items that company officers identify are meant to be included in the department's operating budget. Completing an operating budget often involves the relatively simple process of updating the requests from the previous year's budget to reflect the current needs. A percentage is usually added to the request that represents the rate of inflation based on the federal government's cost-of-living estimate.

Purchasing Process

To successfully perform its assigned mission, a fire and emergency services organization must acquire resources and services. Purchasing may be the responsibility of a supply, apparatus, or logistics chief; a county or city clerk; or a member of the jurisdiction's central purchasing department. A Company Officer II may also be responsible for purchasing materials or equipment specific to the division's or project's needs. Regardless of their jurisdiction's size, all company officers should understand and follow approved purchasing procedures.

Responsible officers must ensure that the organization receives the exact materials that were budgeted for and ordered, and keep purchasing expenses within the approved budget. In doing so, they must only spend funds on the items for which the money was allotted.

The sections that follow outline aspects of the purchasing process. Some of the information included in these sections may be completed during the budgeting process or afterward.

Determining Purchasing Needs

Determining purchasing needs should have been completed during the budget process. If equipment integral to the operation unexpectedly breaks, then adjustments may have to be made in the budget to purchase replacement equipment.

Needs determined during the budgeting process may be stated in general terms. When the time comes to purchase the items in the budget, the following actions should be performed:

- **Review the standards and regulations that mandate the purchase of specific types of equipment** — Review the legal mandates that the AHJ creates for the operation of fire and emergency services organizations **(Figure 14.3)**.

- **Review the current purchases** — Assess how well current equipment and materials meet the organization's requirements, and determine whether company officers have quick access to them in adequate quantities.

- **Determine the amount of funds available** — Determine whether the organization has the necessary funds for a selected purchase. It may be necessary to locate additional funds, transfer funds from unused accounts, or cancel the purchase.

Figure 14.3 Company officers should review purchasing standards and regulations

Contact Vendors

Company officers should contact available vendors to purchase the resources they need. In some cases, company officers may be limited in the number of vendors from whom they can make purchases. Jurisdictions may have a particular vendor from whom they purchase equipment or services as a matter of policy. Even in these cases, the sole vendor should be contacted. They may be offering special pricing or reduced rates because of contractual agreements with the jurisdiction.

If multiple vendors are available, the purchasing officer should contact them to ascertain which vendor offers the most suitable product at the best price **(Figure 14.4)**. Company officers should understand the organization's policy on soliciting and awarding bids, establishing specifications, and ensuring competitive bidding per applicable laws and regulations.

Figure 14.4 The financial officer may contact multiple vendors to locate the product needed at a good price.

Before purchasing from unfamiliar vendors, company officers should conduct basic research. They can review the business histories of both the vendors and the manufacturers they represent. They should also request a list of the most recent purchasers of the same equipment, then consult those purchasers to ask about their experience with the vendor.

Chapter Summary

The company officer must be familiar with the process used to write and revise policies, procedures, rules, and regulations. The officer must also be able to evaluate the policies and procedures to ensure that they are fair, equitable, and up-to-date. Providing the equipment, apparatus, and operating supplies required to accomplish the organization's mission requires that the company officer be familiar with the concepts of the budgeting and purchasing functions as well as the specific policies and procedures that the AHJ adopts. While each of these functions may not seem as challenging as those encountered at emergency incidents, they are equally important and necessary for providing the services demanded by the public.

Review Questions

1. How does a Company Officer II contribute to policy and procedure development?

2. What sources can be used to justify budget requests?

3. What is the process of determining purchasing needs?

Learning Activities

Learning Activity 14-1

Objective 4: Develop a policy or procedure that addresses an administrative problem.

For this activity, you will need access to the following resources:

● Personnel policy and procedure manual for your department or you may obtain one by utilizing an Internet search.

By using the scenario below or by providing your own scenario, create a document to contain an action plan for the training of the staff you are responsible for in your department that contains: 1) performance goals and 2) developmental objectives for the year ahead. The plan should include procedures to correct problem areas in personnel performance.

Scenario:

It is the beginning of your department's fiscal year and your chief has asked you to prepare the annual action plan to include the extra $10,000 in training funds received from the city council and the implementation of the new procedure to correct the problem of personnel arriving late for their designated shifts. The chief needs the action plan for a presentation at the next month's city council meeting.

Answer Key:

Answers for this activity may vary. Consult an experienced officer in your jurisdiction for assistance. However, you should consider the following questions:

1. When does the performance planning take place?

2. What are each employees' jobs' expectations?

3. What are the priorities for each employee's position within the organization priorities?

4. What are the employee development goals for the year?

5. When does performance review occur and what is included?

6. What achievements are celebrated? How?

7. How are areas for improvement and growth in the year ahead identified?

8. If needed, how have policies and procedures for correcting problem areas in personnel performance been implemented?

Learning Activity 14-2

Objective 5: Construct a departmental budget that addresses capital, operating, and personnel costs.

Using the correct forms and supporting data, company officers must be able to construct a departmental budget to address capital, operating, and personnel costs accurately and completely.

For this activity, you will need access to the following rescoures:

- Your departmental budget. If one is not available, search the Internet for an example to use.

Using the department budget or one found through an Internet search, complete a departmental budget using the information in the scenario provided below.

Scenario:

It is only March, but the time to prepare for the next year's budget is now. The department is in need of replacing the following items:

- 3 sets structural fire fighting bunker gear
- 5 backpack fire fighting pumps
- 1 four-outlet fire hose tester
- 3 Halligan bars
- 25,000 gallons (100 000 L) of diesel

Research the replacement cost of each of these items from at least two different suppliers. Using the department budget, determine how the budget will allow the purchase of these items. Include the goals and objectives for the next fiscal year, if available.

Answer Key:

Answers for this activity may vary. Consult an experienced officer in your jurisdiction for assistance. However, make sure to complete the following actions:

- Prepare budget in proper format (specifications, descriptions, catalogs referenced, item numbers, etc.)
- Justify need for the budget with supporting data and costs
- Suggest an avenue of revenue to support the cost of the replacement items
- Follow department's policies and procedures

Origin and Cause Determination

Chapter Contents

Key Terms

NFPA® Job Performance Requirements

This chapter provides information that addresses the following job performance requirements of NFPA® 1021, *Standard for Fire Officer Professional Qualifications* (2014).

5.5.1

Origin and Cause Determination

Learning Objectives

After reading this chapter, students will be able to:

1. Identify the basic fire investigation process. [NFPA® 1021, 5.5.1]

2. Describe processes of determining a fire's area of origin. [NFPA® 1021, 5.5.1]

3. Explain elements of fire cause determination. [NFPA® 1021, 5.5.1]

4. Recognize cause classifications and motives in post-scene investigations. [NFPA® 1021, 5.5.1]

5. Analyze a scenario to determine the point of origin and preliminary cause of the fire. [NFPA® 5.5.1; Learning Activity 15-1]

Chapter 15
Origin and Cause Determination

Case History

At 11:25 p.m., a fire department responded to a room and contents fire in a single-family, two-story residence. The older, balloon-construction home had fire in the kitchen area, with extension in the outside walls towards the upper floor. After the fire was extinguished and a search of the structure was conducted, the company officer started the determination of origin and cause of the fire.

The company officer started with a search of the outside of the building, determining where the most damage occurred. She then moved into the interior of the structure, working from the least damaged area to the most damaged area. Smoke and fire damage were observed on walls, ceilings, and floors. The observations led the company officer to believe that the kitchen was the area of origin. Upon further evaluation, the company officer went to the corner of the kitchen, where a garbage can was located. After eliminating possible causes and speaking with the homeowner, the company officer determined that discarded smoking materials might have been the cause of the fire. After completing her fire origin and cause determination, the company officer then submitted the findings to the fire department's fire investigation unit for a follow-up.

All fires and explosions should be evaluated to determine their origin and cause. The Company Officer II may make the first evaluation following the mitigation of the incident **(Figure 15.1)**.

NOTE: Emergency responders should avoid disturbing or destroying potential fire cause evidence during suppression operations in order to preserve evidence. The overhaul process should be delayed until the cause of the fire has been determined and any evidence protected.

This chapter addresses fire investigations, area of origin determination, and methods of gathering information during structural, vehicular, and wildland fire investigations. It also addresses making cause determinations to include ignition sources and the material first ignited. Finally, post-scene investigation, including cause classifications and firesetter motives, are covered.

Figure 15.1 A company officer examining a fire scene.

Fire Investigations

A fire investigation normally ends if it is determined that an accident or nature caused the incident, or if there was no loss of life or high content loss. However, the company officer must request a certified fire investigator to evaluate the scene and conduct the fire investigation if a loss of life or high-content loss has occurred or if there is an indication that the incident was intentional or malicious. A fire investigator is an individual who has demonstrated the skills and knowledge necessary to conduct, coordinate, and complete an investigation. The individual may be a Company Officer II or a certified Fire Investigator.

According to NFPA® 1021, this level of investigation is focused on determining if arson has occurred so that law enforcement action can be taken. The officer must know the following:

- Methods that adult and juvenile firesetters use
- Common fire causes
- Isolation of basic origin and cause determination
- Fire growth and development
- Fire investigative documentation procedures

Some of this knowledge should have been acquired as a Company Officer I. This chapter provides a more detailed look at each of these areas and then proceeds into information concerning the motives and methods that arsonists or firesetters use.

The *area of origin* is that area where the ignition source and material first ignited actually came together. Finding the origin of a fire involves knowledge of fire behavior; information gathered from firefighters and other witnesses; and analysis of the physical evidence found at the fire scene.

Area of Origin Determination

Often the area of origin of a fire is readily apparent. If it is not, company officers should use a methodology that typically involves working from the least damaged area to the most damaged area. However, the area of greatest damage should not be assumed to be the origin of the fire. Identifying witnesses, securing the scene, and noting initial scene observations are critical to the overall success of the investigative process **(Figure 15.2)**. Observing fire effects and recognizing and interpreting fire patterns will help determine where the fire originated and how it spread.

Figure 15.2 The officer conducting the fire investigation may interview the members of the unit that extinguished the fire.

> **CAUTION**
>
> The company officer must evaluate scene safety (structural conditions, air monitoring, and presence of other hazards) prior to initiating the investigation.

There are four basic steps in determining the area of origin (**Figures 15.3**):

Step 1: Examine the exterior of the structure or vehicle and the surrounding area. During a wildland fire investigation, start the examination at the outside edge of the burned area and work inward.

Step 2: Examine the interior of the structure or vehicle.

Step 3: Interview witnesses and other first responders. In some instances, it may be necessary or beneficial to conduct the interview before examining the fire scene.

Step 4: Analyze the information gathered using the scientific method.

Structural Fire Scene Examination and Documentation

Company officers may be called to determine the origin and cause of structural fires. The following sections address examining exterior and interior fire patterns and fire pattern analysis.

Exterior Fire Patterns

The examination of a structure fire should start with an examination of the entire incident scene in order to determine its size and scope (**Figures 15.4**). This preliminary scene assessment should begin with the exterior of the structure and continue, if possible, around the entire incident scene, including the roof. During this time, potential physical evidence is documented or preserved. The safety survey is also conducted at this point, and other safety precautions should be followed. Observations should be made regarding the following:

● Building damage (including openings such as broken windows, forced doors, and other damage to the building), as well as structural stability

● Fire and ventilation patterns (**Figure 15.5, p. 410**)

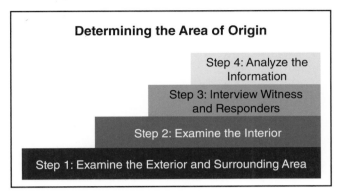

Determining the Area of Origin

Step 4: Analyze the Information

Step 3: Interview Witness and Responders

Step 2: Examine the Interior

Step 1: Examine the Exterior and Surrounding Area

Figure 15.3 The steps in determining the area of origin.

Figure 15.4 The fire investigation should start by examining the exterior of the scene.

Figure 15.5 A fire investigator examining the fire and ventilation patterns visible from the structure's exterior.

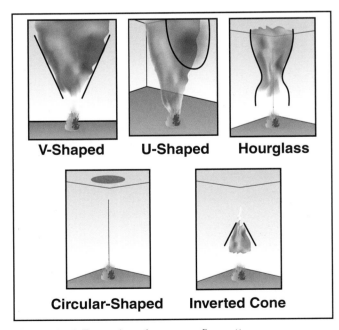

V-Shaped | **U-Shaped** | **Hourglass**

Circular-Shaped | **Inverted Cone**

Figure 15.6 Examples of common fire patterns.

- Methods of ingress and egress (for safety purposes)
- Utility services (such as disconnected meters)
- Tire tracks or footprints
- Discarded containers that responsible parties may have left behind

Fire and products of combustion, fire-suppression efforts, and venting from the interior of the building or ignition points on the outside can cause exterior fire damage. At the same time, venting from the interior could also result in the extension of fire to rooms above the window from which the fire vented. This information assists in the determination of fire growth and development.

Interior Fire Patterns

After the exterior examination has been completed, an interior examination should begin, working from the area of least damage to the areas of greatest damage. With this method, it is possible to use fire indicators to determine the path of fire spread and the area of fire origin.

The patterns found during the interior examination represent the history of the fire from ignition to extinguishment. Part of fire pattern analysis is determining the order in which the patterns were created. The goal of analyzing fire patterns is to determine fire spread from the area of origin. The patterns also provide information about how the fire traveled within the building after ignition and about the fuels involved during the progression of the fire.

NFPA® 921, *Guide for Fire and Explosion Investigations*, describes fire patterns as the "visible or measurable physical effects that remain after a fire." These effects are found in many different forms, including the following:

- Burned or charred materials, including structural components and contents
- Smoke or soot deposits on the surfaces of contents or walls, ceilings, and floors
- Distorted, discolored, or melted materials

Fire patterns are formed on interior surfaces (walls, floors, ceilings, and contents) of a structure as a result of direct flame contact or exposure to heat. Conduction, convection, or radiation can be the heat transfer method that causes a fire pattern (see Chapter 11, *Delivery of Emergency Services I*). Typically, fire patterns have visible boundaries or borders where the fire or products of combustion affected a surface, leaving adjacent surfaces less affected or intact **(Figure 15.6)**.

Fire patterns evolve during a fire's progression. When examining fire patterns, company officers should consider at what point in time the fire pattern was developed. For example, a V-shaped pattern may have been made during the incipient phase of the fire. Should the room or area reach full-room involvement, the V-shaped pattern that the plume above the initial fuel creates could become obscured or unrecognizable. The earlier pattern may still exist, but may not be readily or visibly discernible.

The type of material or surface covering could have an impact on the pattern observed after the fire. For example, combustible surfaces such as wood paneling will demonstrate different fire effects than gypsum wallboard when exposed to the same heat source at a similar distance. When exposed to less energy from the fire, the damage to combustible surfaces may only cause charring or discoloration. On noncombustible surfaces such as brick, plaster, or metals, the patterns may cause surface discoloration, spalling, melting, or distortion **(Figure 15.7)**.

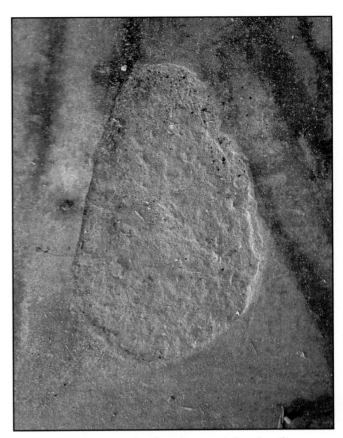

Figure 15.7 An example of spalling and discoloration on concrete caused by a fire.

The physical characteristics of a surface can also affect the type of pattern found. For example, rough surfaces are often more heavily damaged than smooth surfaces of the same material because rough surfaces have greater surface area. The increased surface area and turbulence created as fire gases flow over rough surfaces result in additional damage.

The typical fire patterns include the following types:

- **Plume-generated** – Any of a number of fire patterns created as a result of the plume of hot gases rising above an individual fire.

- **Hot-gas layer** – Fire pattern that radiant heat forms in the hot-gas layer during a fire before flashover; these patterns are found when fires are extinguished before the fire has reached flashover.

- **Ventilation-generated** – Fire pattern that can vary widely in appearance and was created by ventilation introduced to a fire.

- **Suppression-generated** – Fire pattern left as a result of the way the fire was extinguished during fire-suppression efforts.

- **Full-room-involvement** – Fire pattern that occurs after flashover or after a fire has burned for long periods of time, in which almost all vertical and horizontal surfaces in the compartment will show signs of damage.

- **Clean burns** – Fire pattern found on noncombustible surfaces where there has been direct contact with or intense radiant heat on the surface; the direct flame contact burns away any accumulated soot or smoke deposits on the surface, leaving demarcation lines.

- **Pointers or arrows** – Fire pattern created when structural components such as wood studs or trim are exposed to flame; sharp edges of the component are often burned away on the side of the component that faces the heat source. Also refers to a series of burned components that indicate a longer duration on one end of the series to shorter duration on the other.

- **Irregular patterns on floors** – Pattern with no common shape in which the fire followed the path of available fuels.

- **Saddle burns** – Saddle-shaped fire pattern that is the result of fire burning downward through the floor surface above the joist.

- **Protected areas** – Undamaged surface within an otherwise fire damaged area, possibly resulting from objects shielding the surface from the effects of the fire; generally used to refer the fire investigator to where large objects such as furniture were positioned before the fire.

Figure 15.8 The area of origin of a fire. *Courtesy of Donny Howard.*

Fire-Pattern Analysis

The fire effects and patterns represent individual pieces of evidence at a fire scene. Analyzing this evidence results in the correct identification of the area of origin. Taken together, the measurable and visible damage from the fire, combined with the patterns created from the various heat sources involved, retell the history of the fire.

The area of greatest damage may be at or near area of origin **(Figure 15.8)**. However, company officers should not assume that the most damaged area indicates the area of origin. The area of origin is a hypothesis that needs to be tested. For example, a candle left burning on a bedroom dresser ignited nearby combustibles, resulting in a V-shaped pattern and a small area of damage. A window on the opposite wall shows clean-burn patterns, deep char around the window frame, and burned drapes. Is the fire damage at the window the result of ventilation at the window or is the window the area of origin? A hypothesis for each scenario must be developed, and those hypotheses must be tested. Understanding how each pattern was generated and, if possible, the sequence is integral to reconstructing the history of the fire. The company officer should be able to account for the different fuel packages and the effects of ventilation to make the correct judgment about the fire's movement and spread.

CAUTION
If these analysis techniques are above your level of knowledge, skills or abilities, seek help from a more qualified investigator.

Proper documentation is critical to any criminal or civil legal case. Evidence **chain of custody**, complete interview reports, photographs, and certified original copies of documents must be gathered and recorded into an incident investigation report. The following information relating to each item should be recorded:

- Its location
- Name of the party discovering the item
- Where it was discovered
- Time and date of acquisition

Vehicle Fire Scene Examination and Documentation

Determining the area of origin and cause of a fire in a vehicle is similar to searching for the origin and cause of a structural fire. Along with interviewing witnesses and firefighters, examining both the exterior and interior of the vehicle is necessary. Surveying the damage to the vehicle should provide valuable clues to where the fire started.

CAUTION
Vehicles have evidentiary value. Do not unnecessarily loosen, move, or remove parts, components, or switches.

Company officers should complete a systematic examination of the vehicle using the following to determine the fire's origin:

- Photographs
- Written documentation
- Fire pattern analysis
- Comparative analysis of the damage to each area of the vehicle

The vehicle fire scene can be divided into three areas for examination: the scene around the vehicle, the exterior of the vehicle, and the interior of the vehicle. When examining the interior of the vehicle, areas for examination can be further divided into separate compartments using the following to make documentation and comparative analysis easier **(Figure 15.9)**:

- Engine Compartment
- Cargo Compartment
- Passenger Compartment

Figure 15.9 During a fire investigation, the investigating officer should examine the vehicle's engine, passenger, and cargo compartments to determine the area of origin.

NOTE: The passenger compartment may also be subdivided into separate areas such as front passenger and rear passenger area. Further division of the passenger compartment may prove helpful, such as driver's side and passenger side.

Company officers should follow a specific methodology when conducting a vehicle fire investigation. This methodology should include the following:

- Obtaining information about the vehicle's history and documentation
- Conducting a scene examination
- Documenting the scene
- Conducting fire pattern analysis
- Examining the exterior of the vehicle
- Examining the engine, cargo, and passenger compartments
- Examining the high-voltage battery compartment (hybrid vehicles)

Vehicle Investigation Scene Safety

Company officers must be aware that significant safety hazards may exist at the scene of a vehicle fire, both outside and inside the vehicle. These safety hazards may be different than those normally found inside a structure. Company officers should ensure that they are wearing the appropriate personal protective equipment when completing a vehicle fire investigation.

Some safety hazards found at a vehicle fire scene include:

- Trip hazards
- Spilled liquids
- Vehicle stability issues
- Broken glass, both inside and outside the vehicle
- Unburned fuel in tanks or containers
- Sharp edges on damaged metals or plastics
- Airborne particulates
- Undeployed airbags
- High-voltage batteries
- Alternative fuels

Competent Ignition Source— An initial energy source that can produce enough heat and energy, over a long enough period of time to raise the temperature of a fuel to its ignition temperature.

Today's passenger vehicles may have additional fuel loads and **competent ignition sources** more than older model vehicles have **(Figure 15.10)**. Some of these additional fuels include an increase in the plastic components found throughout the vehicle. Additional competent ignition sources may include the updated vehicle electrical systems to incorporate systems, such as satellite radio, DVD players, navigation systems, telephones, and additional charging ports for consumer electronics to name a few.

Scene Examination

Investigation of the vehicle should also involve an examination of the scene and surrounding areas. In ideal situations, the vehicle should be examined where the fire occurred. Sometimes the vehicle may have been moved prior to the examination. If possible, document the area through photographs, written notes, and a sketch of the scene. A diagram should be completed showing the vehicle position in relation to other objects.

Figure 15.10 Engine compartments can provide many competent ignition sources, such as the battery, electrical harness, and ignition system.

Documenting the Scene

Documentation of any relevant potential physical evidence is crucial. Photographs of the fire scene should show the following:

- Nearby vegetation
- Other vehicles
- Fire damage to other items
- Nearby structures
- Foot prints
- Tire tracks
- Relationship of the burned vehicle to other objects

Company officers should also determine and document the vehicle's rest angle when it burned. Determining the rest angle (such as sideways in a ditch or parked on a hill) will assist in understanding the fire patterns. Examining such things as re-solidified aluminum can determine the vehicle's rest angle. Tilting the vehicle until the aluminum is plumb will give you the angle the vehicle was at when the aluminum melted. If the vehicle is no longer aligned with the melted aluminum, it must be determined when and why the vehicle's angle was altered and whether the move occurred during the fire, suppression, or post-fire. Photographs and notes should be taken during the determination process so that the findings are documented.

Fire Pattern Analysis

A systematic examination of the fire patterns and fire effects present on the exterior and interior portions of the vehicle should be documented and analyzed in an attempt to identify the compartment and area of origin. A proper analysis of these fire patterns will provide information about the fire's intensity, movement, and origin. A comparative analysis of the fire patterns present on each exterior body panel and the wheels may assist the investigator in determining the area or compartment of origin.

Radial fire patterns show movement on the vehicle's body panels, such as the hood, fenders, doors, roof, and trunk. These fire patterns may appear as "ripples" extending from a particular compartment as the fire progresses across the vehicle body panels.

Vehicle Exterior

The exterior of the vehicle may reveal fire patterns on the body panels and windshield. An examination of these fire patterns may assist the investigator in determining which compartment the fire originated in.

Photographs should be taken in a systematic manner of the exterior of each side of the vehicle, including the top and undercarriage, if possible. Safety of the investigator is paramount, and the vehicle should be stabilized prior to entering or reaching under the vehicle.

Photographs should be taken of each panel and wheel on the exterior of the vehicle. Written documentation should also be completed for each exterior section of the vehicle. The company officer may find it helpful to use a pre-designed checklist to accurately document the exterior of the vehicle.

The exterior documentation of the vehicle should include the following:

- Tire type, condition, size, tread depth, and notes regarding the condition of the wheel itself
- Door position: open/closed or locked
- Window position: broken, up, or down, and condition (glass on interior or exterior of vehicle)
- Body or fire damage to each body panel
- Fire debris from vehicle on ground

Figure 15.11 The fire in this car started in the engine compartment, penetrated the windshield at its base, and then spread to the vehicle's interior. *Courtesy of Donny Howard, Yates & Associates.*

Engine Compartment

The engine compartment should be photographed from different angles before examination. Additional photographs may be required to illustrate damage (or lack thereof) to specific parts of the engine.

Company officers should remember that an engine compartment fire may spread into the passenger compartment through pre-existing holes in the bulkhead. In addition, passenger compartment fires may spread (although typically at a slower rate) to the engine compartment through these same holes.

An analysis of the remaining glass in the windshield may assist the company officer in determining fire spread. Damage to the lower portion of the windshield indicates directional fire spread from the engine to the passenger compartment **(Figures 15.11)**.

Damage to the top section of the windshield may indicate that the fire spread from the passenger compartment into the engine compartment because the interior of the passenger compartment is similar to a compartment in a structure. As the fire plume develops and impacts the combustible head liner, a ceiling jet is formed that will impact the top portion of the windshield.

Hot surfaces may exist in the engine compartment or on the underside of a vehicle, including the manifold and other portions of the vehicle exhaust system. These surfaces may be hot enough to ignite the vapors of ignitable liquids routinely found in motor vehicles, such as gasoline, brake fluid, and oil. In addition, the temperature of exhaust systems may increase substantially for the first few minutes after a vehicle has been shut off. This increase in temperature may be sufficient to ignite the vapors of a leaking ignitable liquid.

Cargo Compartment

The cargo compartment of vehicles should also be photographed from several different angles, if possible **(Figures 15.12)**. Documentation of the cargo compartment should include the following:

- Damage to interior of compartment
- Documentation of personal effects, including their condition
- Damage to spare tire (if applicable)
- Damage to wiring
- Fire pattern analysis

Passenger Compartment

Before examining, the passenger compartment of the vehicle should be photographed from several different angles. Company officers may find it helpful to photograph the interior of the vehicle from each door and from front to rear and rear to front **(Figures 15.13)**. Photographs of the underside of the roof and floor must be taken as well as any personal effects within the vehicle. Additional photographs may need to be taken during debris removal.

Wildland Fire Investigation

Wildland fires may involve ground cover ranging from grasslands to forests **(Figure 15.14a and b, p. 418)**. The fire may originate in the ground cover and spread to stored materials and structures.

From its point of origin, a wildland fire burns outward in all directions. On flat ground with a consistent fuel bed and no wind, a fire would burn equally in all directions and the point of origin would be in the center of the circular burn pattern. However, wildland fires rarely occur in these conditions. In reality, wind, topography, **aspect**, and fuel variations affect the fire's spread rate and direction of travel.

The area of origin may display evidence of slower and less intense fire growth than at the head or leading edge of the fire. More unburned materials are left in the area of origin, and the effects of flame on the fuels are considerably less there than at the head. Conversely, if a fire were to begin in a brush pile, intense burning might be noted at the area of origin.

Figure 15.12 This photograph shows that heat and smoke penetrated into the cargo compartment, but the evidence shows the fire started elsewhere in the vehicle.

Figure 15.13 One of numerous photos taken of a pickup truck's interior following a fire. *Courtesy of Donny Howard, Yates & Associates.*

Aspect — The direction - north, south, east, or west - in which the slope faces.

Figure 15.14a An example of a grass fire.

Figure 15.14b An example of a forest fire.

Radiant heat from burning materials affects other adjacent fuels. As the fire burns past a given area, the flames scorch or char surfaces exposed to the fire. But the backsides of grass stems or tree trunks are protected, even though the fuel is consumed and turned to ash. White ash is a product of more complete combustion, and it appears on the exposed sides of the remaining debris.

Witness Interviews

During the investigation, company officers may need to gather information from the following witnesses:

- Those who discovered, reported, or observed the fire or conditions prior to the fire
- Emergency responders
- Anyone else identified as having relevant information, such as the owner, neighbors

During the interviews, the company officer will look for pertinent information that consists of who, what, when, where, why, and how. These are the six basic questions that should be asked of every witness **(Figure 15.15)**.

NOTE: If the subject being interviewed, or about to be interviewed, is suspected of a fire-related crime, the company officer should consider having an agency authorized fire investigator or a police officer conduct the Miranda Rights. This should be accomplished before initiating the interview or, if that suspicion is generated during the interview, before asking any further questions.

Figure 15.15 An investigating officer interviewing a witness.

Cause Determination

After evaluating scene safety and locating the area/point of origin and protecting evidence, company officers may be required to determine the specific cause of the fire. While the company officer examines the evidence, one responder may take notes while another sketches the scene or photographs evidence. If the company officer cannot determine the specific cause or if the fire appears to be the result of a malicious or negligent act, an agency authorized fire investigator should be called.

Ignition Sources

Once the origin is identified, the investigator should look for heat sources that might be potential sources of ignition. A competent **ignition source** must have the three following qualities:

- Sufficient temperature to ignite the first material
- Sufficient heat energy transfer to result in the ignition of the first material
- Sufficient time to transfer the required heat to the first material

Company officers may find a heat source that is recognizable, such as an electric space heater or coffeemaker **(Figure 15.16)**. In other cases, the heat source may have been altered, is unrecognizable, or has been completely destroyed by the fire.

Potential forms of heat of ignition include:

- Heat, sparks, ember, or flames from outside, open fires
- Heat from fuel-fired or fuel-powered equipment (gas, liquid, or solid fuel)
- Heat from electrical equipment
- Heat from hot object
- Heat from explosive or fireworks
- Heat from other open flame, sparks, or smoking materials
- Heat from natural source (lightning, spontaneous combustion)
- Heat spreading from separate fire source

Ignition Source —
Mechanism or initial energy source employed to initiate combustion, such as a spark that provides a means for the initiation of self-sustained combustion.

Figure 15.16 Sometimes the heat source that started a fire can be recognized, such as this coffeemaker.

Material First Ignited

Identifying the **material first ignited** is a key component in making a fire cause determination **(Figure 15.17)**. The first material must have the following three characteristics that parallel the characteristics of the ignition source:

- Capable of being ignited by the heat energy of the identified ignition source
- Close enough to the ignition source to receive energy transfer from the ignition source
- Capable of absorbing and retaining sufficient heat energy transferred from the ignition source to begin the combustion process

Figure 15.17 The investigating officer photographing evidence of the first material ignited.

Post-Scene Investigation

Up to this point in the investigation of a fire incident, the investigation has primarily focused on the fire scene. If the origin and cause are easily determined, the analysis phase of the fire investigation can be simple and may be completed during the scene examination. However, the post-scene investigation can be complex and time-consuming when the determination of the origin and cause is not readily made during the examination of the scene. In most cases, calling in an agency authorized fire investigator may be necessary.

Material First Ignited —
Fuel that is first set on fire by the heat of ignition. To be meaningful, both a type of material and a form of material should be identified.

Once the examination of a fire scene is complete, the investigation involves the examination, organization, and analysis of data with the ultimate objective of determining the fire origin and cause. In addition, it may be necessary to determine who or what was responsible for any of the following:

● Cause of the fire
● Cause of damage to property at the incident
● Cause of bodily injury or loss of life
● Degree of human fault

NOTE: Different parties may be responsible for different aspects of the incident.

Cause Classifications

At the conclusion of an investigation, the company officer will typically determine a classification. The following are four generally accepted classifications of fire cause **(Figure 15.18)**:

● **Accidental** — Fires that do not involve a deliberate human act to ignite or spread the fire into an area where the fire should not be.

● **Natural** — Fires, such as those that lightning, storms, or floods cause, where human intervention has not been involved in the ignition process.

● **Incendiary** — A fire deliberately set under circumstances in which the responsible party knows that the fire should not be ignited.

● **Undetermined** — The classification used when the specific cause has not been determined to a reasonable degree of probability. This classification may be used as an interim classification as the fire investigation is proceeding, or it may be the final outcome if additional information cannot be obtained that identifies the specific cause. This classification may refer to situations in which each of the specific components of the ignition sequence is not specifically identified. However, it is not necessary to have all of the pieces of the ignition sequence identified to classify the cause of the fire. A cause classification other than "undetermined" should be assigned if sufficient information is available.

Figure 15.18 Once the area of origin, the heat source, and the first material ignited are determined, the officer must select the correct fire cause classification.

Motives

Identification of the motive may provide assistance in the identification of the party responsible for setting an incendiary fire. The following sections describe the most common motives and motive indicators associated with incendiary fires.

NOTE: A potential motive should not influence the origin and cause determination. Analyzing elements of motive may help in identifying potential suspects.

Revenge

Fires set because of personal or professional vendettas fall into the largest category of arson fires and account for fifty percent of the total arson problem. Generally, the victim is able to provide information regarding the suspect's identity. Personal property is often the target, and ignitable liquids are seldom used because usually the fire is not planned in advance. Revenge fires usually occur as a more impulsive reaction to some other incident. Normal targets are vehicles, storage rooms, outbuildings, or fences.

Vandalism

Vandalism fires are usually set by two or more individuals (often juveniles). Schools are prime targets, and other common locations include vacant buildings, trash containers, and vegetation. If vandalism is found on the interior of a scene, entry to the building was probably forced. Before the fire, vandals usually do other property damage or paint graffiti.

Profit (Fraud)

Monetary gain is the primary motivator for this type of incendiary fire, and total destruction of property is the ultimate goal. Firesetters motivated by fraud attempt to cause the most possible damage in the least possible amount of time. For that reason, multiple fires and ignitable liquids are common. Holes broken in walls or ceilings and/or trailers are often used to assist in the fire spread; time-delay ignition devices are also common. Property owners often set elaborate fires that require significant preparation. Firesetters with a motive for profit or fraud generally have unlimited access to the interior of a structure without fear of discovery.

Crime Concealment

Arson used as a tool to destroy evidence of another crime is most generally associated with burglary, homicide, and embezzlement. The attempt to cover a burglary is most common with the fire set at the location where evidence, such as fingerprints or blood, was believed to have been left. Usually the location is at the point of entry or where an item has been removed. The fire is generally set with combustibles on hand and rarely involves ignitable liquids because a burglar usually enters a structure with the intent to steal and not to set a fire. The fire is set after entry and after the fire setter has decided that incriminating evidence was left behind.

Homicide concealment fires, however, often involve the use of ignitable liquids in an attempt to destroy the body and the evidence of the manner and cause of death. These fires are generally set on and around the body.

Embezzlement fires are set to erase or destroy a "paper trail;" therefore, the paperwork and surrounding area are the origin for the fire. Often the paperwork is used as the fuel with ignitable liquids sometimes added to assist in the destruction of the documents.

Excitement (Vanity)

Some firesetters commit arson in order to have the private satisfaction of being the one who created a situation requiring the response of the fire service and law enforcement. Fires started for the sheer excitement of creating a fire scene provide some people with a feeling of empowerment over society. The spur-of-the-moment fires, however, develop as a recognizable pattern over a period of time. Examples of pattern development include any of the following evidence:

- **Dates and day of the week** — Paydays, normal work days, or days spent consuming alcohol are believed to help stimulate these individuals in fire setting.

- **Time of day** — The time of day or night may correspond with travel to and from work or other activity. Most excitement fires are set during the hours of darkness.

- **Type of structure** — The arsonist is often consciously or subconsciously attracted to a certain type of structure (such as schools, churches, vacant structures)

- **How the fire is set** — The arsonist rarely plans to set a fire; therefore, combustibles on hand are usually used. An arsonist often becomes comfortable with a certain method and tends to stay with the method that has worked in the past.

- **Where the fire is set** — The arsonist tends to set these fires in similar locations (such as under a crawl space) as prior fires at that location resulted in the required emergency response and lack of detection.

Arsonists who seek recognition or wish to be viewed as heroes may set and "discover" fires. These individuals are always present at the fire scene and often attempt to assist in fire fighting activities. They may be from any background; however, some have been employed as security guards, volunteer firefighters, and reserve law enforcement officers. These same individuals may often be seen at multiple fire scenes, and if their presence is observed, their background should be investigated for past examples of fire setting behavior.

Pyromania

Pyromania — Psychological disorder in which the sufferer has an uncontrollable impulse to set fires, either to relieve tension or produce a feeling of euphoria.

Pyromania, as properly defined, is not a motive because it is a mental state and a recognized psychological disorder. True pyromaniacs are rare in number and set fires as a release of tension or to produce a feeling of euphoria. These fires are seldom set with ignitable liquids and often set to paper products in vehicles, in alleys, or behind buildings. Over a short period of time, this type of individual will regularly set multiple small fires within several blocks of each other.

Extremism (Terrorism)

An individual or group of protesters may target a government, an ethnic or religious group, or a facility that operates in opposition to their cause. Fires or explosions are carried out with the intent to advertise or advance the arsonist's purpose. Although arsonists wish for their identity to remain unknown, they want their group or cause to be identified as the responsible party. Graffiti or signs may be left at the scene, and phone calls or letters to the press are common. Fires and explosives are usually set to the exterior of buildings or are propelled (such as a Molotov cocktail) into the interior through broken windows or doorways.

Juvenile Firesetters

Most small children under the age of 7 years experiment with fire out of curiosity, usually resulting in accidental fires **(Figure 15.19)**. Between the ages of 8 and 13 years, the majority of fires that children set is the result of psychosocial conflicts, such as revenge, anger, or need for attention. The last phase of juvenile firesetter is the crisis phase, between 15 and 18 years of age, and usually involves the arrest and detention of the fire setter. These firesetters have a long history of playing with fire or intentionally using fire for revenge or to gain attention.

Figure 15.19 Young children are often curious about fire.

Setting fires is simply an end in itself that brings pleasure to the firesetter. The majority of juvenile firesetters are male, and many have poor social skills. The company officer should be aware of the presence of the same juveniles at fires and visiting the fire station.

Chapter Summary

Determining the true cause of a fire can be difficult. The area of origin may not be obvious, the structure or vehicle may be destroyed, or the fire suppression activities may have eliminated much of the evidence as to the cause. The company officer must gather together as much information as possible from witness and participant interviews, inspection histories of the facility (if available), and physical evidence to determine the point of origin. The company officer can focus on the potential cause of the fire after eliminating the less likely scenarios. If the information indicates that the fire was intentional and malicious, the officer should request the assistance of fire investigators from the jurisdiction, county/parish, state/province, or national government. Every effort should be made to determine the true cause of the fire and, if it is determined to be intentional, locate the firesetter so criminal charges can be pressed.

Review Questions

1. What is needed to find a fire's area of origin?

2. What are some ways that area of origin determination differs between structure, vehicle, and wildland fires?

3. What are the three qualities of a competent ignition source and of the material first ignited?

4. What are the four generally accepted classifications of fire cause?

Learning Activities

Learning Activity 15-1

Objective 5: Analyze a scenario to determine the point of origin and preliminary cause of the fire.

Company officers are frequently called upon to determine the probable cause and determine the location of the origin of fires in their response areas. The first level of fire investigation that is the responsibility of a company officer is to determine whether the fire was the result of an accident or naturally occurring event. The second level involves an investigation that requires a greater understanding of fire cause and involves a determination of whether the fire was intentional or malicious. The company officer at this level should be focused on determining if the crime of arson might be responsible for the fire.

Given the following limited scenario information, describe how the point of origin and preliminary cause of the fire could be determined, including what further information is needed to make those determinations.

Scenario:

Anytown Fire Department Engine 5, commanded by Captain Smith, has been dispatched to a reported structure fire at 02:30 hours, February 15th, at 9120 West Olive Avenue. West Olive Avenue is a one-way street with east-bound traffic only. Engine 7 and Ladder (Truck) 4 are also assigned to the alarm. Engine 5 is the first unit on the scene and is positioned on the northeast corner of the structure. Captain Smith finds that light smoke is coming from the open front door of the building and flames are visible through a window located next to the door. The structure houses the Fish Shack, a small fishing, tackle, and bait shop. Captain Smith orders a 1¾ inch (45 mm) attack line to the front door to begin suppression operations. While preparing to enter with the attack crew, he notices a small fire burning in the northeast corner of the front showroom. As the crew enters the room, he sees flames behind the west service counter at the back of the room. This is a small fire inside of a large plastic trash receptacle located against the west wall. He has the hose crew advance and extinguish this fire after they put out the fire in the northeast corner. Ladder (Truck) 4 arrives and is positioned at the front of the structure. Captain Smith assigns L-4 to shut off utilities and check the rear of the structure. While they are doing this, they notice that the rear door that leads to a storage area is open and a small fire is burning in the southeast corner in a pile of cartons and paper. Engine 7 arrives, lays a 5 inch (130 mm) supply line from the hydrant 200 feet (60 m) west of the structure to E-5, and positions beside E-5 to the east of the structure. Captain Smith orders E-7 to advance a 1¾ inch (45 mm) attack line from E-5 to the rear door and extinguish the fire that L-4 located.

With all fires extinguished, Captain Smith begins the investigation. The front door shows no signs of forced entry. In the front of the structure, located behind the west service counter, he finds an empty can that contains a trash can of lighter fluid. Also found in the bottom of the trash receptacle with other debris are the remains of six matches taped together around what appears to be a burnt cigarette filter. Further examination at the front of the store finds a similar device in the northeast corner of the front of the store in a rack of burned clothing. Continuing to the stock room at the rear of the building, Captain Smith locates newspapers that have been tightly wadded on top of the cardboard and paper that had burned in the southeast corner. During his investigation, Captain Smith finds a small natural gas jet on the tackle repair table in the "ON" position. This table is located on the east wall of the stock room.

The incident structure's dimensions are 24 X 48 feet (7 X 14 m) with a wall at the midpoint of the structure. A doorway in the middle of this wall has display counters on either side. There is a non-rated door in the middle of this wall that leads to the stock room. There is a plate glass front door set in a metal frame and a steel door at the rear of the structure. Each of the doors is located at the midpoint of the front and rear walls.

There are display windows on either side of the front door and small high windows located on the rear wall. Parking is located on the east side of the structure with a vacant lot on the west side. An alley is to the rear of the structure.

Answer Key:

Answers for this activity may vary. Consult an experienced officer in your jurisdiction for assistance. However, you report should address some or all of the following considerations:

Color of smoke, where smoke is coming from, who else is on the scene, other companies responding, observers/witnesses, size and type of structure, where fire is coming from, where fire can be seen from windows, stage of fire, vehicles/cars present in driveway/parking areas, how fire attack was started, where is majority of fire coming from, structure ventilation, other officer reports, utilities disconnected, burn pattern, lack of pictures on walls and or furniture, empty fuel containers, sounds observers heard, structure contents, structure dimensions, forced entry detected or not, other access to structure via alley/street/sidewalk, etc.

Delivery of Emergency Services II

Chapter Contents

Key Terms

NFPA® Job Performance Requirements

This chapter provides information that addresses the following job performance requirements of NFPA® 1021, *Standard for Fire Officer Professional Qualifications* (2014).

5.6.1

5.6.2

5.6.3

Delivery of Emergency Services II

CHIE

Learning Objectives

After reading this chapter, students will be able to:

1. Identify multi-unit emergency scene operations. [NFPA® 1021, 5.6.1]

2. Describe elements of developing and implementing operational plans [NFPA® 1021, 5.6.1]

3. Explain the purpose and processes of postincident analyses and critiques. [NFPA 1021, 5.6.2, 5.6.3]

4. Develop a postincident analysis. [NFPA® 1021, 5.6.2; Learning Activity 16-1]

5. Conduct a postincident critique. [NFPA® 1021, 5.6.2; Learning Activity 16-2]

Chapter 16
Delivery of Emergency Services II

Case History

As large grass fires swept through the city, company officers became more adept at tracking resources with the Incident Command System. On some of the early fires, divisions manage the span of control. The company officers soon realized that on some large, fast-moving grass fires, all available resources assisted the division at the head of the fire, overwhelming that division's supervisor.

One day, at a particularly large fire, several large heads broke out. A major gust front came through, sending the fire in the opposite direction at forty miles per hour (64 kph). The incident commander began setting up task forces when resources first arrived on scene. The incident had almost 100 units from 30 departments on scene by the end of the day. Twelve task forces within three divisions were created to handle the span of control. The Incident Commander set up five or six unit task forces either as they arrived on scene or brought them out of staging that way. This organization allowed the company officer to keep track of numerous units over a five- or six-mile incident. The management of the large fire fighting force, which was established early in the incident, with the use of the Incident Command System, helped save many homes.

Level II Company Officers should be prepared to establish or assume incident command at emergency incidents where multiple resources are employed. Company officers must also be prepared to transfer command to a chief officer, as necessary, later in the incident. They must produce operational plans that effectively utilize all resources to mitigate an incident. Producing operational plans involves the application of information gathered from the following:

- Preincident surveys
- Knowledge of the jurisdiction's ICS procedures
- Knowledge of incident scene safety policies
- The strategy required to control incidents using the various available resources

This chapter looks at multi-unit emergency scene operations, operational plan development, and the expansion of an ICS, including the command positions and functions at multiple alarm incidents.

NOTE: For the purpose of this manual, the term "Operational Plan" may be used interchangeably with the term "Incident Action Plan" as discussed in Chapter 11. Additionally, the term unit may be used in this manual to refer to a company or resource as opposed to the use of the term in the NIMS-ICS documentation.

Multi-unit (Multiple Alarm) Emergency Scene Operations

An increase in the complexity of an incident increases the complexity of the incident command system employed at the scene. Large scale incidents require additional apparatus (units) and personnel in order to mitigate incidents commonly referred to as **multiple alarms**. These units can include pumpers, aerial, rescue, hazardous materials, and support apparatus and vehicles (**Figure 16.1**). The Company Officer II must be able to coordinate the functions of these units to mitigate the incident.

Figure 16.1 An example of a large scale incident. *Courtesy of Ron Jeffers.*

Incident Command System

Company officers should receive ongoing training in NIMS-ICS throughout their careers to be prepared to participate in or apply the system at each level of operation or supervision. Each Company Officer II should be trained, at a minimum, to ICS Level 200, although ICS Level 300 is recommended. If additional review of NIMS-ICS is required, please review Chapter 11, *Delivery of Emergency Services I*, and the NIMS-ICS documents available from the Federal Emergency Management Agency (FEMA).

Each incident should only have **ONE** Incident Commander, including when a unified command is appropriate. The Company Officer II should be prepared to assume command of the incident, be assigned a task responsibility with assigned crew personnel, or assume a supervisory (division or group supervisor) position within the command structure. As the complexity of an incident increases, the Company Officer II may transfer command to a more experienced or higher ranked officer.

The Company Officer II as the Incident Commander

As the IC, the Company Officer II has assumed command, conducted size-up, assigned task responsibilities for the incidents, and developed an initial plan of action. As the incident progresses, the Company Officer II must also track the resources on the scene, consider personnel accountability, and plan the release of those resources once the incident has been mitigated. Another option the Company Officer II must consider is the transfer of command.

Most units arrive at the incident fully staffed and ready to be assigned an operational objective; command will assign other personnel to duties or tasks as needed upon their arrival. To manage these resources, a tracking and accountability system used by the organization should be implemented. This system may include the following elements:

- Procedure for checking in at the scene
- Way of identifying the location of each unit and all personnel on scene
- Procedure for releasing units no longer needed

Resource Management

The Company Officer II, in the role of the Incident Commander, must be able to locate, contact, deploy, and reassign the units assigned to the emergency incident. These actions are accomplished through the ICS procedures that assign personnel or single resources to *crews*. As units arrive at the scene, the IC assigns them to the part of the incident where they are most needed. Other units may be held in a staging area until needed or until they are released from the incident. If staging has not been implemented, company officers should check in with the IC and wait for an assignment.

Units will communicate using the radio communication system or through direct face-to-face communication. Units assigned to the incident must contact the IC to ensure that they have complete communication with the command post. Face-to-face communication occurs as personnel without radios arrive at the incident and are formed into crews.

Tracking system visual aids may be a worksheet or dry erase board and can be used to manage the arriving units **(Figure 16.2)**. The tracking system should be easy to use and contain necessary information about each unit's activities. The visual aid may contain the following information:

Figure 16.2 Many departments use a visual tracking system, such as the one shown to manage arriving units and personnel. *Courtesy of Ron Jeffers.*

- Assigned radio frequencies
- Assigned units
- Activated ICS functions
- Site plan may include:
  — Staging areas
  — Logistics location
  — Control zones
  — Rehab

Personnel Accountability System

Each organization should employ a standardized system of accountability at every incident. This system should also be compatible with any mutual aid departments. The system should identify and track all personnel working at the scene. All personnel must be familiar with the system and participate in it.

The system must also account for those individuals who respond to the scene in vehicles other than emergency response apparatus. Accountability is critical in the event of a sudden change in the emergency incident (such as structural collapse or a lost firefighter) so that the IC knows who is at the incident, where each person is located, and who and how many may be trapped or injured.

The IC is responsible for the personnel accountability system. The system may be assigned to another officer or Command aide, if one is available, as part of the planning section. Common types of personnel accountability systems used at the emergency incident include:

- Tag systems
- SCBA tag systems
- Bar code readers

Figure 16.3 A Company Officer II checking in with a crew prior to returning a unit to service.

Demobilizing Resources

When the Incident Commander determines certain resources are no longer needed at an incident, those personnel and units should be demobilized. The IC should implement a demobilization plan for releasing units that is in accordance with the organization's policies. NFPA® 1584, *Standard on the Rehabilitation Process for Members during Emergency Operations and Training Exercises*, identifies rehabilitation procedures for demobilizing personnel.

Before leaving the scene, the company officer should inspect these units to ensure that they are ready to return to service (**Figure 16.3**). If critical equipment such as a breathing apparatus is not available, the unit may remain out of service until the equipment can be replaced.

Decontamination may be necessary before placing units or personnel back into service. This task can take place at the incident site or when the unit returns to the station. Small tools, medical equipment, and personal protective equipment must be decontaminated in accordance with local policy and NFPA® 1581, *Standard on Fire Department Infection Control Program*. Contaminated clothing and equipment should not be cleaned in kitchen or bathroom sinks or showers.

Transferring Command

The transfer of command should be done in person at the incident command post, if possible. If this is not possible, it is normally accomplished over the radio. The first IC provides the relieving officer with a situation status report (incident briefing), which is the current incident status. This action can be assisted through the use of an organization-approved tactical worksheet or ICS Form 201 that has documented the action taken up to transfer of command. The officer assuming command should acknowledge receipt of the information by repeating it back to the current IC. Once this has been completed properly, the recipient is ready to accept control of and responsibility for managing the incident. The former IC can then be reassigned to an operating unit or retained as an aide or a member of the Command or General Staff.

The Company Officer II as the Group/Division Supervisor

ICS is designed to permit the control and allocation of any number of units or agencies at an emergency incident. Company Officers II must be familiar with the ICS and where they may be reassigned responsibilities and supervision in a multiunit incident.

Command Organization

The Command organization must develop at a pace that stays ahead of the tactical deployment of resources. The IC must direct, control, and track the locations and functions of all operating units in order to efficiently manage the incident. Building a Command organization is the best support mechanism the IC can use to balance managing personnel and incident needs.

Strategic Level

The strategic level involves the overall command of the incident. The IC is responsible for the strategic level of the Command structure. Strategic level responsibilities include the following:

- Determination of the appropriate strategy
- Establishment of overall incident objectives
- Setting of priorities
- Development of an Incident Action Plan
- Obtainment and assignment of resources
- Planning
- Prediction of outcomes
- Assignment of specific objectives to tactical level management units

Tactical Level

A tactical level assignment comes with the authority to make decisions and assignments within the boundaries of the overall plan and safety conditions. The accumulated achievements of tactical objectives should accomplish the strategy as outlined in the Incident Action Plan. Tactical level supervisors are responsible for supervising:

- Operational activities toward specific objectives
- Grouped resources
- Operations in specific geographic areas or function

Task Level

Task level refers to those activities assigned to specific resources that result in the accomplishment of tactical level requirements. Company officers generally supervise task level activities in order to accomplish tactical objectives.

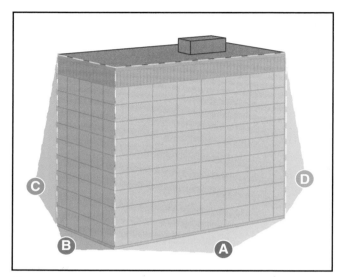

Figure 16.4 Designating the Divisions of a building.

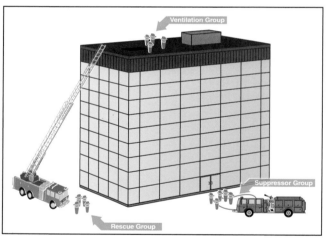

Figure 16.5 Examples of functional Groups at a structural incident.

Basic Organization

The basic structure for an initial response incident involving a small number of units requires only two levels of the Command structure. In this situation, the IC directly handles both strategic and tactical levels. Emergency response units report directly to Command and operate at the task level.

The terms Divisions and Groups are tactical level management components that assemble units and/or resources for a common purpose. Divisions are the organizational level having responsibility for operations within a defined geographic area. The Division level is organizationally between Single Resources, Task Forces, or Strike Teams and the Branch. For situations where the incident has an odd geographical layout (no obvious North, South, East, or West), the front of the building is designated Division A, and the remaining sides are designated B, C, or D in a clockwise manner **(Figure 16.4)**. During radio communications, the phonetic designations of *Alpha*, *Bravo*, *Charlie*, and *Delta* should be used for clarity.

NOTE: In this manual, the abbreviation DG will be used when referencing a Division/Group hereafter. The term DG Supervisor will refer to the person in charge of a Division/Group. In Wildland ICS, DIVs may be used for Division/Group Supervisors.

In multistory occupancies, floor number will usually indicate Divisions (Division 6 indicates 6th floor). When operating in levels below grade, a descriptive term, such as Basement Division 2 or Parking Garage Division 4, may be used.

Groups are an organizational level responsible for a specific functional assignment **(Figure 16.5)**. The Group level is also organizationally between Single Resources, Task Forces, or Strike Teams and the Branch. Examples are Salvage Group, Search Group, Rescue Group, Haz-Mat Group, and Medical Group.

Establishing Divisions/Groups (DG)

Major incidents often have more tasks than available resources can accomplish. There is a tendency to start performing these tasks immediately upon arrival and postpone establishing ICS. This major error results in confusion and a lack of direction and coordination, increasing the risks to emergency personnel and reducing the likelihood of a successful operation.

The IC should assign DGs based on the following factors:

- Situations that will involve a number of units or functions beyond the IC's span of control
- When units are involved in complex operations
- When units are operating from tactical positions that Command has little or no direct control over (for example, they are out of IC's sight)
- When the situation presents special hazards and close control is required over operating units (for example, unstable structural conditions, heavy fire load, marginal offensive situations)

When establishing DGs, the IC will assign each unit:

- Tactical objectives
- A radio designation (Division/Group)
- The identity of resources assigned to that DG

Span of Control

Complex emergency situations may exceed one officer's capability to effectively manage the entire operation. Creating tactical-level DGs to manage incident-related functions or direct operations in specific geographic areas or functions should reduce the span of control. Establishing DGs reduces the ICs span of control and makes it feasible to communicate with those Supervisors rather than multiple individual company officers.

NOTE: Company officers should remember that an effective span of control ranges from three to seven subordinates per supervisor, depending upon the variables just mentioned, with five considered the optimum number.

In fast-moving, complex operations, a span of control of no more than five DGs is recommended. In slower moving, less-complex operations, the IC may effectively manage more DGs. When the span of control is exceeded, the IC should establish Branches or an Operations Section.

Division/Group Supervisors

With effective DGs in place, the IC can concentrate on overall strategy and resource assignments, allowing DG Supervisors to supervise the assigned resources. The IC determines strategy and assigns tactical objectives and resources to each DG. Each DG Supervisor (in the context of this section, the Company Officer II) is responsible for the tactical deployment of assigned resources to complete the assigned tactical objectives. DG Supervisors must communicate their needs and progress to their immediate supervisor.

A DG Supervisor may be assigned initially to an area/function to evaluate and report conditions and advise Command of needed tasks and resources. This DG Supervisor then assumes responsibility for directing resources and operations within an assigned area of responsibility. DG Supervisors should not limit themselves to staying with their original crew, but they should be positioned where they can effectively supervise all the units assigned to them. Whenever practical, DG Supervisors should take a member of their crew to assist them with managing their DG tasks. Remaining crew members should be formed into a company or crew under supervision of an officer or acting officer or assigned to another company or crew.

Figure 16.6 An officer completing a tactical worksheet during an incident.

Communications

Using DGs reduces the overall amount of radio communications. When practical, communications within a DG unit should be conducted face-to-face between company officers and the DG Supervisor. This method reduces unnecessary radio traffic and increases the ability to transmit critical radio communications. Regular transfer of command procedures should be followed in transferring DG responsibility when necessary.

The safety of fire fighting personnel represents a major reason for establishing DGs. Each DG Supervisor must maintain communication with assigned units to control both their location and function. DG Supervisors must constantly monitor all hazardous situations and risks to personnel and take appropriate action to ensure that units are operating in a safe and effective manner.

Developing and Implementing Operational Plans

NFPA® 1021 requires the company officer to develop operational plans to ensure that the assigned resources and assignments mitigate the incident while complying with safety protocols. These operational plans (also called incident action plans) are developed during an actual incident after the first operational period. A variety of forms are available for use at an incident to assist the company officer in developing the IAP. The tactical worksheet discussed in Chapter 11 serves as the foundation for initial action plan **(Figure 16.6)**.

ICS Forms

NIMS–ICS provides a number of forms to document the actions taken during an incident (see **Appendix C**). The primary forms that are contained in most IAPs include:

- **Incident Objectives (ICS 202)** — Clearly stated and measurable objectives to be achieved in the specific time interval

- **Organization Assignment List (ICS 203)** — Description of the ICS table of organization, including the units and agencies involved

- **Assignments List (ICS 204)** — Specific unit tactical assignments divided by Branch, Division, and Group

- **Incident Radio Communications Plan (ICS 205)** — Lists the basic radio channel assignments for use during the incident

- **Medical Plan (ICS 206)** — Provides information on the location and staffing of the incident medical aid station, the types of ambulance resources available, the location of on-site ambulances, and the contact information for hospitals that are available to the IC

Operational Plan Components

Once size-up is completed, the IC determines the incident priorities, selects an overall strategy, and establishes tactics for meeting that strategy. Even at small incidents that do not require a written IAP, the IC must create and communicate to responding and on-scene resources the strategy, tactics, and support activities required for control of the incident. The IC must also include safety and any special environmental considerations. The IC must also be familiar with the local agreements and operational guidelines.

Factors of Command

Company officers should be able to accurately allocate resources to mitigate a wide variety of incident types. These may include but are not limited to:

- Structure, vehicle, and wildland fires
- Hazardous materials incidents
- Mass-casualty incidents
- Automobile accidents
- Technical rescues
- Natural disasters

At the onset of an incident, the company officer acting as the IC has certain resource allocation considerations that are common to most incidents. Depending upon the type of incident, local policies and procedures, and locally available resources and information, these may include but are not limited to:

- Assume Command – Assume command, announce Incident Command Post location, and establish an effective Incident Command Post.
- Situational Awareness – Rapidly evaluate the situation (size-up), continually update, and/or obtain briefing from the previous IC.
- Incident Communications – Identify, develop, initiate, maintain, and control the communications process, as well as establish a communications plan.
- Incident Objectives, Strategy, Develop IAP – Based on the tactical priorities, identify incident objectives, an overall strategy, and develop an incident action plan.
- Deploy Resources – Assign resources consistent with plans and standard operating procedures, standard operating guidelines, and the incident action plan.
- Develop Incident Organization – Develop an effective Incident Command organization based on incident objectives and initiate/maintain a worksheet.
- Review, Evaluate, and Revise the IAP as needed – Review, evaluate, and revise (as needed) the Incident Management plan based on conditions, actions, and needs.
- Continuity, Transfer and Termination of Command – Provide for the continuity, transfer, and termination of Incident Command.

NOTE: Consider the safety of those on scene, both emergency response and nonemergency personnel.

Postincident Analysis and Critique

Just as a Company Officer I develops and conducts a PIA for single unit activities, NFPA® 1021 requires the Company Officer II to develop and conduct a postincident analysis for multiunit incidents. Much of this topic was addressed previously in the Postincident Analysis and Critique section of Chapter 11, *Delivery of Emergency Services I*. A review of that section can assist the reader with the following sections.

The postincident analysis (PIA), evaluation (PIE), or review (PIR) determines the strengths and weaknesses of the organization's response to an emergency. It provides a training tool as well as the basis for future planning for emergency responses. The postincident analysis also motivates change in policies and procedures that may be outdated or ineffectual in meeting the current needs of the response area. The Company Officer II should realize that the PIA is the foundation for strengthening the emergency response activities of the organization.

Postincident Analysis

The PIA is a compilation of all factual data obtained from key positions to include statements and communication tapes. The Incident Commander (IC) or a designated incident staff member(s) should compile the PIA. The PIA should be completed for major incidents or those that involve:

- Line-of-duty injuries and deaths

- Unusual situations

- Situations that the IC or Staff Officers deem necessary

  The PIA objectives are the following:

- Provide an opportunity for participants to objectively and constructively review operations.

- Identify effective procedures (strengths) for future emergency operations.

- Identify areas requiring improvement (weaknesses) and recommend changes.

  The analysis should focus on participant activities, incident elements, and the decisions made with the intention of controlling the incident. The PIA is not intended to place blame or find fault with the participants. It must not be used to punish any of the participants or be perceived as a fault-finding process.

Data Collection

The PIA is a critical and objective assessment of the emergency incident based on all available information about the incident. Information sources may include the following:

- Preincident survey or fire and life safety inspection report

- Size-up

- Incident Action Plan

- Command and general staff records

- Outside agency reports

- Interviews

- Site plan

- Incident safety plan
- Personnel accountability system
- Weather reports
- Communications records
- Miscellaneous reports
- NIMS-ICS forms

The information from each of these sources is then compiled into a chronological report of the incident. Photographs and sketches can help to illustrate the situation both before and after the incident **(Figure 16.7)**.

Figure 16.7 A company officer selecting photos for an incident report.

Analysis

To prepare the postincident analysis, the company officer must combine a thorough understanding of the elements of postincident analysis with previously acquired knowledge relating to:

- Building construction
- Fire protection systems and features
- Water supply
- Fuel loading
- Fire growth and development
- Departmental dispatch procedures
- Strategy, tactics, and operations
- Customer service

With all the information compiled into one report, the company officer must then look for the strengths and weaknesses in the response. The company officer can develop a checklist of questions to help focus on each aspect of the incident. The following areas should be considered and addressed:

- **Dispatch** — answers to the following questions:
  - Was the response time within the organization's minimum/maximum time criteria?
  - How can the response time be reduced?
  - Were there any extenuating circumstances that resulted in an increased response time (weather, traffic, road construction)?
  - Was all available information communicated to the responding units?
- **Initial Attack** — answers to the following questions:
  - Was the initial assignment adequate to mitigate the incident?
  - What additional resources were required to mitigate the incident?
  - Was the ICS properly implemented?
  - Was the ICS adequate for the incident?

- Was all relevant information communicated from the incident scene to other responding units?
- What improvements could be made to the initial attack?
- What weaknesses should be corrected?
- What procedures need to be updated or changed?
- What strengths can be used as examples for similar situations?

- **Subsequent Resource Assignments** — answers to the following questions:
  - Were additional resources requested in time to be effective?
  - Was a Staging Area established and a Staging Area Manager (SAM) assigned?
  - Were IC duties delegated according to the ICS?
  - Were communications with automatic and mutual aid units and other support resources adequate?
  - Were there any difficulties in dealing with outside agencies or jurisdictions?
  - What can be improved when dealing with outside agencies or jurisdictions?

- **Private Fire Protection Systems** — answers to the following questions:
  - How effective were the fire protection systems?
  - How well did the responding units use these systems?
  - Could the systems have been used to better advantage?

- **Health and Safety** — answers to the following questions:
  - Did the activity assign an Incident Safety Officer?
  - How were personnel and accountability conducted?
  - Did the activity necessitate for a REHAB; if so, was the location adequate?
  - Did the operation identify operational periods and work/rest cycles?
  - Was the 2-In/2-Out program placed in operation?
  - Were there rapid intervention teams and/or a backup assigned if needed?

- **Post Fire Activity** — answers to the following questions:
  - Was the property properly secured or turned over to the fire investigator after suppression forces vacated the area?
  - Did the fire investigations unit respond in a timely manner?

Once these and other questions are answered, the company officer develops a set of recommendations based on the results of the analysis. The recommendations should be included in the PIA and an executive summary that is provided to the organization's administration. If a critique is warranted, the company officer should recommend that one be held.

Postincident analysis can also help identify new service demands or needs for a fire and emergency services organization within a community. When discovered, these should be categorized, documented, and reported to the department's administration for review and consideration.

Postincident Critique

Postincident critiques can be informal or formal. As mentioned in Chapter 11, the company officer and unit members can hold an informal critique following any single-unit incident. This critique usually occurs immediately after termination of the incident and prior to leaving the incident scene **(Figure 16.8)**. By discussing the incident while at the scene, the unit members can provide their impressions of the initial attack, suggest alternative approaches to the attack, and learn methods to improve their actions at similar incidents. In inclement weather, the critique can take place at the station after returning from the incident. An informal critique can be used as a training exercise for the unit.

Figure 16.8 An informal postincident critique following a high-rise incident.

Postincident critiques should always be positive in nature, taking into account the different personalities present. When necessary, constructive criticism must be communicated to correct operational deficiencies. Simply state the facts and focus recommendations on improving emergency responses and interagency relationships.

The formal critique is held if the PIA indicates that it is necessary or if the incident involves an interagency or interjurisdictional response. Critiques for incidents involving only units from one jurisdiction should include all incident participants. If the incident was interjurisdictional, representatives of each agency or jurisdiction should be in attendance.

Provide copies of the analysis before the critique to allow the participants time to read the report. The critique should be held in a space large enough to accommodate the attending participants as well as work space, audiovisual aids, and privacy. A set agenda and sufficient time are important to a productive critique.

Following an overview of the incident, each agency representative should present a brief report of its participation in the incident in order of arrival. The PIA recommendations can be reviewed, and procedures for implementing them can be developed. Any additional recommendations can also be discussed and addressed.

The greatest failure of both the postincident analysis and postincident critique is the failure to learn from and apply the results and recommendations. Whether the critiques are informal or formal, the participants must be assured that any necessary changes will be made and that successes will be celebrated.

Chapter Summary

The company officer will be able to manage multi-unit operations using the basic concepts of the Incident Command System. Deployment of the initial assignment and requests for additional assistance can ensure that the appropriate resources are available to control the incident. The company officer should be capable of providing assistance to the Incident Commander or managing Divisions/Groups, as assigned.

Company officers should realize the importance of the postincident analysis and critique. Both provide an opportunity for the organization, unit, officer, and unit members to improve the way they respond to emergency incidents. If unit members and other participants view the PIA and the critique as a learning experience and not as punishment, the results will be evident in the quality of service that the organization provided.

Review Questions

1. What are some responsibilities of Company Officer II acting as Incident Commander?

2. What resource allocation considerations must be made when developing and implementing operational plans?

3. What types of information should be gathered for a postincident analysis?

Learning Activities

Learning Activity 16-1

Objective 4: Develop a postincident analysis.

A company officer must be able to conduct a postincident analysis (PIA) after emergency incidents. When properly developed and written, a PIA will help identify the strengths and weaknesses of the organization, and should be used as a training tool, as well as the basis for future emergency response planning. The PIA should also motivate changes in policies and procedure that have become outdated or ineffectual due to the current needs of a given response area.

In the development of a postincident analysis, several questions should be addressed. Answer the following questions provided below.

1. What is a postincident analysis (PIA) and why is it prepared?

2. List the objectives of a postincident analysis.

3. List some information sources available to a company officer when collecting data for a PIA.

Answer Key:

1. The postincident analysis is a written document that is compiled by the Incident Commander (IC) or a designated member of the Incident Command Staff or general staff, such as the Incident Safety Officer (ISO). The PIA should be written for all incidents regardless of size. The analysis is intended to focus on the activities of the participants, the elements of the emergency, and the decisions made that were intended to control the incident.

2. a. Provide an opportunity for participants to objectively review operation in a constructive manner.

   b. Identify effective procedures (strengths) for future emergency operations.

   c. Identify areas needing improvement (weakness) and recommend changes to improve effectiveness.

3.
- Preincident survey or fire and life safety inspection report
- Size-up
- Incident Action Plan
- Command and general staff records
- Outside agency reports
- Interviews

- Site plan
- Incident safety plan
- Personnel accountability system
- Weather reports
- Communications records
- Miscellaneous reports
- NIMS-ICS forms

Learning Activity 16-2

Objective 5: Conduct a postincident critique.

A company officer must be able to lead a formal or informal postincident critique. The critique should be positive in nature and should focus on recommendations and constructive criticism.

Read and answer the following questions about conducting postincident critiques.

1. When should a postincident critique be conducted for incidents involving single units?
2. When is it necessary to conduct a formal critique?
3. Who should be invited to a formal critique if units from only one jurisdiction participated?
4. Who should be invited to a formal critique when the incident involves a number of jurisdictions and agencies?
5. What item should be provided before a formal postincident critique?
6. What is considered the greatest failure of a postincident critique?

Answer Key:

1. The postincident critique can be conducted immediately following a single-unit incident.
2. A formal postincident critique is held if the postincident analysis indicates that it is necessary or if the incident involves an interagency or interjurisdictional response.
3. All units that participated from the jurisdiction should be part of the critique.
4. If the incident was interjurisdictional, representatives from each agency should be in attendance.
5. Copies of the analysis should be provide to be read before the critique
6. The greatest failure of a postincident critique is the failure to learn from the results and recommendations of the process.

Safety Investigations and Analyses

Chapter Contents

chapter 17

Key Terms

NFPA® Job Performance Requirements

This chapter provides information that addresses the following job performance requirements of NFPA® 1021, *Standard for Fire Officer Professional Qualifications* (2014).

5.7.1

Safety Investigations and Analyses

Learning Objectives

After reading this chapter, students will be able to:

1. Identify risk management as it relates to the duties of Company Officer II. [NFPA® 1021, 5.7.1]

2. Describe health and safety investigations. [NFPA® 1021, 5.7.1]

3. Explain processes for analyzing safety and health reports. [NFPA® 1021, 5.7.1]

4. Analyze scenarios and make recommendations based on member history. [NFPA® 1021, 5.7.1; Learning Activity 17-1]

Chapter 17
Safety and Investigations and Analyses

Case History

Within six months of putting their new engine in service, firefighters assigned to the company experienced an unusually high rate of leg and back injuries. A company officer, serving as the department's Medical Liaison Unit commander, sought to determine the cause of the injuries. The officer's initial research determined that no significant changes in the company's operations had occurred. After further investigation, the officer believed that the change in injury rate must be related to the new apparatus. The officer also observed that all the injured firefighters were less than six feet in height.

Comparing the new engine to the previously assigned apparatus, the officer came to the conclusion that the only significant operational difference was the inclusion of transverse hose beds (cross-lays) on the new engine. The height of the transverse hose beds was approximately 30 inches (76 mm) higher than the approved specifications for the apparatus. As a result, the nozzles on the transverse hose lines were out of reach for anyone less than six feet tall.

The company officer directed members of the crew, less than six feet in height, to demonstrate how they pulled the hose from the transverse beds. He watched the firefighters climb up the side of the engine, using the discharge gate handles as footpads. The handles were chrome plated and slippery. As the officer watched, two of the crewmembers slipped off of the handles, causing the firefighters to fall into postures that put their backs and legs in unusual positions.

The investigating officer found that the manufacturer had received a change in specifications from the department's apparatus design officer. A committee of engine captains, engineers, and firefighters had determined the official specifications, and the chief officer in charge of apparatus maintenance had approved them. A different department committee, tasked with preparing the city for the upcoming Insurance Services Office (ISO) survey, recommended the design change.

That committee had determined that the extension ladder specified for the new design triple combination was not long enough to receive full credit from ISO and recommended that the ladder length be increased. However, the committee had not reviewed the potential consequences of the design change.

In making the change, the manufacturer had placed the longer ladder in the same position as the originally designed ladder, but it extended two feet further forward. The additional length put the ladder in front of the originally designed transverse hose beds. The manufacturer then raised the hose beds by 30 inches (76 mm) to clear them from the ladder.

At the recommendation of the Medical Liaison Officer, the department shops installed folding footpads under the transverse beds to provide safe positions that allowed firefighters to pull hose from those beds. The investigating officer also recommended that all apparatus specification changes be reviewed by the design committee for that apparatus.

Figure 17.1 An emergency medical technician examining a firefighter injured during an emergency. *Courtesy of Ron Jeffers.*

The fire and emergency services are high-risk professions. Emergency responders enter hazardous conditions and situations to protect other citizens, eliminate the hazards, and restore the incident scene to a safe environment. While accomplishing these tasks, fire and emergency services responders sustain injuries and numerous casualties **(Figure 17.1)**. While the numbers of injuries and deaths have decreased in the past decade, they still require an increased focus on ways that fire and emergency services organizations can provide a safe work environment and reduce responder casualties.

The Company Officer II may be tasked with investigating and analyzing the accidents, injuries, health exposures, and fatalities that members of the organization may sustain. The Company Officer II may also be assigned other tasks, such as acting as the organization's Health and Safety Officer (HSO) and managing the health and safety program. To perform these duties effectively, the officer must have an understanding of risk management as it is applied to health and safety. An overview of that topic is included in this chapter. Additionally, the steps for performing an accident investigation and analysis are included to help meet the primary safety responsibility of the Company Officer II.

NOTE: Company officers may be assigned to their organization's health and safety committee. For this manual, the term HSO will be used to represent those individuals. The role of the HSO in the risk management process is defined in NFPA® 1521, *Standard for Fire Department Safety Officer.*

Risk Management

While risk management in the broad sense considers, among other things, liability issues and damage to equipment and property, the terms **hazard** and **risk** are applied to the fire and emergency services personnel in this chapter. The hazards are those that an individual faces while performing firefighter or emergency responder duties. These hazards can occur during the following:

- En route to a scene
- While operating at a scene
- When returning from a scene
- In the organization's facilities
- In apparatus
- While at nonemergency operations

Each fire and emergency services organization should operate within the parameters of a risk management plan. The organization's chief executive officer is responsible for the development of an organizational risk management plan. Responsibility for accomplishing this task may be delegated. All organizational personnel must be familiar with the plan. The HSO must be capable of performing multiple skills to include training, investigating, evaluating, analyzing, implementing, and communicating. In each task, the HSO applies the concepts of risk management.

Hazard — Condition, substance, or device that can directly cause injury or loss; the source of a risk.

Risk — (1) Likelihood of suffering harm from a hazard; exposure to a hazard. The potential for failure or loss. (2) Estimated effect that a hazard would have on people, services, facilities, and structures in a community; likelihood of a hazard event resulting in an adverse condition that causes injury or damage. Often expressed as *high*, *moderate*, or *low* or in terms of potential monetary losses associated with the intensity of the hazard.

Risk Management Model

An understanding of the concepts of risk management and system safety is essential to fire officers and especially the personnel who serve as the organization's HSO. These concepts are the basis for the majority of the organization's safety and health program. Company officers who investigate and analyze accidents within the organization will benefit from an understanding of the risk management model.

NFPA® Standards Related to Risk Management

There are a number of NFPA® standards that address risk management. These standards include:

- NFPA® 551, *Guide for the Evaluation of Fire Risk Assessments*
- NFPA® 1250, *Recommended Practice in Fire and Emergency Service Organization Risk Management*
- NFPA® 1500, *Standard on Fire Department Occupational Safety and Health Program*
- NFPA® 1521, *Standard for Fire Department Safety Officer*
- NFPA® 1600, *Standard on Disaster/Emergency Management and Business Continuity Programs*

To understand how the risk management model works, it is necessary to understand the risk management model incorporated in NFPA® 1500. The fire service has successfully used this model for decades.

According to NFPA® 1500, the fire and emergency services organization should adopt an official written risk management plan that covers the following:

- Administration
- Facilities
- Training
- Vehicle operations
- Protective clothing and equipment
- Operations at emergency incidents
- Operations at nonemergency incidents
- Other related activities

The plan serves as documentation that risks have been identified and evaluated and that a reasonable control plan has been implemented and followed. At a minimum, the plan should include risk:

- Identification
- Prioritization
- Evaluation
- Control techniques
- Monitoring

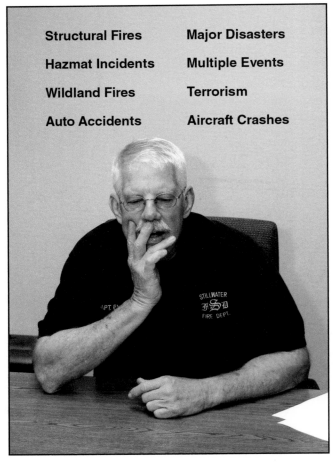

Structural Fires | Major Disasters

Hazmat Incidents | Multiple Events

Wildland Fires | Terrorism

Auto Accidents | Aircraft Crashes

Figure 17.2 Some of the many potential emergency operations the fire and emergency services must be prepared to face.

Personnel-Risk Analysis

The company officer is responsible for the safety of all personnel assigned to the unit or under the officer's command at an emergency incident. This responsibility exists throughout the work shift and includes emergency and nonemergency situations. The officer uses the risk management model to determine the appropriate responses to the health, safety, and wellness risks that the unit faces.

Risk Identification

To identify the risks, the company officer compiles a list of all organizational emergency and nonemergency operations and duties. The officer should include consideration of the worst possible conditions or potential events, including major disasters, multiple events, pandemics, and acts of terrorism as well as those operations occurring more often **(Figure 17.2)**.

Sources of information can include:

- The organization's internal records on accidents, injuries, illnesses, fatalities, physical fitness tests, and daily attendance reports

- Incident response reports that provide the basis for an understanding of the most frequent types of emergency responses

- National averages and trends available from a number of sources

U.S. and Canadian Safety Information and Statistics Sources

National sources for information and statistics on safety-related risks include:

- The Centers for Disease Control and Prevention (CDC)

- National Institute for Occupational Safety and Health (NIOSH)

- Occupational Safety and Health Administration (OSHA)

- Fire Department Safety Officers Association (FDSOA)

- National Fire Protection Association (NFPA)

- U.S. Fire Administration/National Fire Academy (USFA/NFA)

- National Fallen Firefighters Foundation

- National Fire Fighter Near-Miss Reporting System

- Fire Fighter Close Calls.com

    In Canada, there are other systems to include:

- Canadian Centre for Occupational Health and Safety (CCOHS)

- Industrial Accident Prevention Association (IAPA)

- WorkSafe British Columbia (WorkSafe BC)

continued

Risk Evaluation

Once the risks are identified, they should be evaluated in terms of frequency and severity. OSHA refers to frequency as incidence rate, and addresses the likelihood of occurrence. If a particular type of injury or accident occurs repeatedly, it will likely continue to occur until a job hazard or task analysis identifies the root causes and effective control measures are implemented (**Figure 17.3**). The root cause is the most basic reason and the source or origin for the accident. For example, the HSO or company officer might develop and implement guidelines for proper lifting techniques and physical fitness requirements, provide mechanical lifting aids, or establish a requirement for a minimum number of personnel needed to lift a specific weight.

Severity addresses the degree of seriousness of the incident and can be measured in a variety of ways, such as lost time away from work, cost of medical treatment, and number of personnel injured. **Appendix D** contains the formula for calculating frequency and severity. Incidents of high frequency and high severity should be given the highest priority in the risk analysis, while those of low frequency and low severity should receive the lowest priority.

NOTE: There are a number of matrices available. Company officers should utilize the one that their organization uses.

Figure 17.3 An HSO monitoring a lifting operation being performed by two firefighters.

Risk Prioritization

The results of the frequency and severity assessments help establish priorities for determining action. Any risk that has both a high probability of occurrence and serious consequences deserves immediate action and is considered a high-priority item. Nonserious incidents with a low likelihood of occurrence are lower priorities.

Risk-Control Techniques

After the risks have been prioritized, it is time to apply risk control measures. Several approaches can be taken in risk control, including the following:

- **Risk avoidance** — Avoiding the activity that creates the risk. The activity may be at an emergency scene or during routine daily activities.
- **Risk transfer** — Physically transferring the risk to someone else or purchase insurance. Transfer of risk can be difficult for a fire or emergency medical services (EMS) organization.

- **Control measures** — Implementing effective control measures (risk reduction) is the most common method used for risk management. While control measures will not eliminate the risk, they can reduce the likelihood of personnel injury or mitigate the severity. Effective control measures include the following:

  — Safety, health, and wellness programs

  — Ongoing training and educations programs such as drivers training

  — Administrative controls such as well-defined standard operating procedures or guidelines (SOPs/SOGs)

Implementation of a Risk Management Plan

Implementing the risk management plan requires communication, training, and application. The plan, produced in written form as part of the organization's SOPs/SOGs, is distributed to all organizational personnel. After ensuring that the plan is effectively communicated to all staff, training sessions will be conducted with all members of the organization. The application of the plan takes place daily as personnel follow the prescribed policies and procedures. The risk control techniques must become second nature to all personnel.

Monitoring a Risk Management Plan

Monitoring ensures that the system is dynamic and facilitates periodic reviews of the program. Additionally, monitoring leads to the evaluation of the effectiveness of the program and possible revisions. Any process-related problems have to be revised or modified. Revisions should be made as identified or needed. However, the plan should be reviewed as a whole at least once annually.

Evaluation of a Risk Management Plan

When applying evaluation techniques, the company officer or HSO compares the plan's desired results to its actual results. Data for making these comparisons include:

- Injury and fatality reports, including Worker's Compensation Insurance reports

- Safety training records

- Medical evaluation reports

The results of the comparisons may indicate an increase, decrease, or no change in the risks and determine the effectiveness of the risk management plan. A decrease in the risk indicates the plan is being effective. If there is no change or an increase in the number of injuries, then the implemented risk control techniques must be reviewed and alternate solutions applied (**Figure 17.4**). Smaller agencies may require more than a single year's data to allow accurate comparison.

When the risk management plan is initially implemented, an increase in some types of injuries may occur. For instance, at the beginning of a mandatory physical-training (PT) program, there may be a temporary increase in on-the-job injuries. This increase may be due to improper warm-up techniques, improper exercise techniques, and inadequate training. An analysis of the types and frequency of these injuries will need to be made to determine the root cause and the appropriate response.

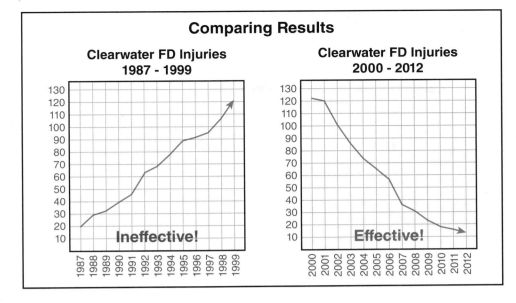

Comparing Results

**Clearwater FD Injuries
1987 - 1999**

Ineffective!

**Clearwater FD Injuries
2000 - 2012**

Effective!

Figure 17.4 Comparing results of a safety program over given periods of time can determine the effectiveness of the program.

Company officers should determine if the cost/benefit is appropriate. A single, minor injury due to an awkward placement of an apparatus compartment may not justify the cost of altering the apparatus to prevent future injuries. Training relating to use of the compartment may be more cost effective.

Revision of a Risk Management Plan

The risk management plan should include procedures for making revisions. The revision process should focus only on those risks that require revision and not the entire plan. Company officers should understand why revisions may be necessary and be able to recognize them in the plan evaluation.

Some reasons for revisions may include the following:

- Increase in injuries, fatalities, or loss due to the target risks
- Increase in risk-related costs
- No apparent change in the risk results
- Ineffective cost/benefit
- Ineffective training

When a negative trend becomes apparent, the plan must be revised. The plan must continually provide the organization with a means to create a safer working environment. Otherwise, the status quo that existed before the plan will re-establish itself and an unsafe environment will develop.

Health and Safety Investigations

Company officers are responsible for reviewing and analyzing injury, accident, and health exposure reports. They are also responsible for identifying unsafe work environments or behaviors and taking approved action to prevent reoccurrence. This duty may be assigned to the HSO or it may be the responsibility of all company officers.

The company officer must also be skilled in investigation and analysis techniques. Determining the cause of accidents, injuries, illnesses, and exposures requires good investigative skills.

Figure 17.5 A fire apparatus following a single-vehicle accident while responding to an emergency. *Courtesy of Ted Boothroyd.*

Accident Investigations

Accidents are unplanned, uncontrolled but usually avoidable events resulting from unsafe acts and/or unsafe occupational conditions, either of which may result in injury, death, or property damage **(Figure 17.5)**. Accidents may result from:

● Adverse conditions in the environment (weather, terrain, or situation)

● Equipment/material malfunction (design, age, lack of maintenance)

● Human error (ignorance, carelessness, or mental/emotional/physical difficulties)

To reduce the potential for accidents to occur or to reduce the severity of accidents, each organization must develop and implement an accident investigation policy and procedure. The policy should define accidents, establish the authority for investigating each type of accident, and establish a procedure for accident investigation. The HSO and the organization's safety and health committee will have the ultimate authority for accident analysis. The company officer will have the responsibility for doing the initial accident investigation based on the procedure. According to NFPA® 1500, investigations should not be limited to accidents but should also include job-related injuries, illnesses, fatalities, and health exposures.

Conducting Accident Investigations

When an accident occurs, an investigation is conducted to determine the root cause of it. Accident investigations should be objective, impartial, and directed toward fact-finding, not fault-finding. Workplace accidents are investigated to identify:

● The culture, habits, behavior, or condition that caused the accident (root cause)

● Previously unrecognized hazards

● Apparatus/equipment defects or design flaws

● Additional training needs

● Improvements needed in safety policies and procedures

● Facts that could have a legal effect on an accident case

● Trends

When conducting a workplace accident investigation, the company officer should interview all participants and witnesses and document all relevant factors. The human factor is prominent among these. For a thorough and comprehensive investigation, the company officer should understand the impact of training, education, and experience on the occurrence of accidents.

Understanding Human Factors

Safety research has shown that accidents happen frequently to some people and infrequently to others, indicating that accidents are not uniformly distributed throughout the workforce. Workers who fail to control the factors leading to an accident because of mental, psychological, or physical reasons will be involved in accidents more often than other workers.

Human factors are an individual's attributes or personal characteristics that cause the individual to be involved in more or fewer accidents than other people. Often, an organization can mitigate negative human factors through motivation, training, or technical revision. Human factors that often contribute to accidents have been classified into three broad categories **(Figure 17.6)**:

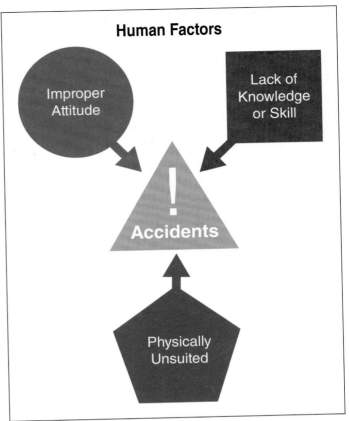

Figure 17.6 The human factors that contribute to accidents.

- **Improper attitude** – This category includes willful disregard, recklessness, irresponsibility, laziness, disloyalty, uncooperativeness, fearfulness, oversensitivity, egotism, jealousy, impatience, obsession, phobia, absentmindedness, excitability, inconsideration, intolerance, or mental unsuitability in general. Readjusting any of these attitudes or personality traits through counseling, coaching, mentoring, training, or discipline can lead to accident reduction.

- **Lack of knowledge or skill** – This category includes insufficient knowledge, misunderstandings, indecision, inexperience, poor training, or failure to recognize potential hazards. These problems can be reduced or eliminated through training, coaching, and mentoring.

- **Physically unsuited** – This category includes problems of hearing, sight, weight, height, illness, allergies, slow reactions, disabilities, intoxication, or physical limitations in general. Correcting these physical limitations can often reduce accident rates. If they cannot be corrected, personnel should not be assigned to tasks in which their limitations might create a hazard or be potentially dangerous to themselves or others.

Mitigating the human factors that lead to accidents often depends upon a number of other factors. Some of these factors include:

- Time and resources committed to developing and implementing safety
- Policies and procedures
- Safety training
- Certification on the safe use of equipment

During an investigation, company officers collect basic information about the participants, event, or incident. The investigation should provide the company officer with the following information:

- *General information:*
  — Date and time of incident
  — Type of incident, illness, injury, exposure, fatality
  — Location and emergency response type
  — Names of witnesses and their accounts of the situation
- *Employee characteristics (participant):*
  — Name and unit assignment (company/shift)
  — Age and gender
  — Rank/function
  — Personal protective clothing or equipment in use
- *Environmental information:*
  — Weather and temperature
  — Day or night conditions
  — Noise and visibility
  — Terrain
- *Apparatus/equipment information:*
  — Type of equipment involved
  — Age and condition
  — Location
  — Maintenance history
  — Distinguishing characteristics

The investigation report should contain a narrative description of the incident. This narrative includes observations on the part of the officer, eyewitness reports, participant interviews, and information from other sources, such as law-enforcement reports and dispatch information.

Injury, Illness, and Exposures

The first priority when dealing with any injury, job-related illness, or health exposure is to provide medical assistance to the affected individual. The health and safety of the individual takes precedence over investigating the cause. Once the victim is stabilized, transported, or treated locally, the company officer can gather the initial information needed for the investigation.

The investigation process is identical to the one used for accidents: asking the same general questions of the victim, witnesses, and participants **(Figure 17.7)**. Gathering incident specific information is important for all incidents.

While an injury is often obvious when it occurs, job-related illnesses or the symptoms of health-related exposures may not become evident for hours, days, weeks, or longer. Maintaining accurate information on the emergency response is essential. When it is likely that an exposure will not produce symptoms of an occupational illness, it may be more appropriate to enroll the employee in a medical surveillance program (including a base-line medical evaluation) to document any health changes that may be related to the exposure.

Figure 17.7 A Company Officer II questioning crewmembers about an accident.

Job-Related Illnesses and Health Exposures

Job-related illnesses and health exposures can result from a number of situations during the work shift and at various work sites. Some situations and illnesses may include:

- **Headaches** — result from stress, noise, or physical back strains

- **Nausea** — results from exposure to flu or viruses, contaminated food, or stress

- **Virus** — results from exposure to others carrying the virus

- **Hepatitis**— results from contact with the body fluids of an infected person

- **HIV** — results from contact with the body fluids of an infected person

- **Allergies** — results from exposure to pollen, dust, mold, or mildew

- **Hearing Loss** — results from exposure to loud or continuous high noise levels

- **Stress** — results from noise exposure, heat, high levels of activity, or situations involving fatalities or casualties

Gathering information on these types of illnesses and exposures requires a great deal of effort. The root cause may not be obvious at first, especially due to delayed symptoms. The company officer may have to research incidents, situations, and personal attendance histories over an extended period of time. Off-duty situations that may have resulted in the illness or exposure must also be considered. It may be difficult to determine if the employee was exposed to a virus during a response, at the station, or at home.

Analyzing Safety and Health Reports

Analysis of safety and health reports provides the organization with an opportunity to prevent future accidents, injuries, illnesses, or exposures. Once a specific root cause has been determined and documented, specific policies or procedures can be developed to mitigate it. The Company Officer II may be responsible for determining the cause through analysis and recommending a solution. Determining the cause is accomplished through analyzing accident, injury, illness, and health exposure reports.

NOTE: NFPA® 1021 does not mention fatalities, other than as part of the accident investigation. The organization's chief officers, the jurisdiction's medical examiner, and OSHA and NIOSH investigators usually investigate fatalities involving fire and emergency responders.

Accident Report Analysis

Accident data must be analyzed after all of it is collected. A careful analysis of an accident report can have some very positive effects on workplace safety in the future. The analysis must be conducted in an objective and impartial way. The point is to glean useful information from the report to determine the root cause and not to find fault or fix blame. The report should be carefully scrutinized to see whether any patterns emerge or whether there were common elements in the sequence of events leading to the accident.

All workplace accidents are the result of unsafe acts, unsafe conditions, or both. The point of the accident analysis is to determine how these factors combined to create one root cause and what can be learned from the particular incident. Unsafe acts may result from the following:

- Inadequate training and supervision
- Improper attitudes of the individual(s) involved
- Well-intentioned attempts to save time by cutting corners
- Careless attitudes that reflect the low morale of those involved

Unsafe conditions are common at most emergency incident scenes and during emergency responses. SOPs should be designed to reduce the risks to fire and emergency responders in these situations. The procedures may prove inadequate if the circumstances were beyond those anticipated in the SOPs. Unsafe conditions also exist during training exercises and daily non-emergency activities.

When analyzing an accident report, attempts should be made to find answers to a number of basic questions. Some of these questions are as follows:

- Who was involved?
- What was involved?
- What were the circumstances?
- What was the root cause?

The analysis will provide a number of potential responses to the root cause. The analysis may indicate a need for:

- More personnel
- Additional or better equipment
- More training
- Additional funding
- Realignment of resources
- Mutual aid agreements
- Purchase or creation of new training programs
- Shifting of the risk to the private sector
- Changes in building codes, traffic laws, or building design

Allocating more money does not solve every safety problem. A certain amount of risk is inherent in fire fighting and other emergency response activities. Making changes in an emergency responder's personal behavior or changing the organization's culture will require conscious effort on the part of the administration and membership of the organization.

The company officer's duty is to change the attitude and behavior of responders. In the area of safety, company officers have a responsibility to take action. The company officer must:

- Be a role model by providing personnel with an example of correct safe behavior

- Insist that subordinates adhere to the organization's safety policies and procedures

- Support and enforce all safety-related decisions that the administration makes

Injury, Illness, and Exposure Report Analysis

Analyzing injury, job-related illnesses, and health exposures is much the same as analyzing accident reports. Pertinent information is gathered, the root cause is determined, and, if indicated, a recommendation for change is made. The primary difference in the process is the length of time that may exist between the incident and the investigation. In many cases, such as exposure to hazardous chemicals or a bloodbourne disease, an investigation may have to start years after the initial exposure. The investigating officer must do thorough research and fact-finding in order to provide an accurate report.

Recommendations Based on Analysis

After completing the analysis and determining the root cause of the accident, injury, job-related illness, or health exposure, the officer should identify a solution to resolve the problem. The officer then writes a report outlining the problem, the investigation process, and one or more recommended solutions. Most investigations result in an obvious solution, while others may require multiple solutions. In some cases, contingency recommendations should be developed.

One area that can have a long-lasting effect on the safety and health of emergency responders is the wellness component of the safety and health program. Statistics verify that cardiac arrest (heart attacks) and strokes are the leading cause of fire and emergency responder fatalities. While the wellness program may be of little help to the victim of a heart attack or stroke, it can be a strong preventive for others.

An effective wellness program, including proper nutrition, physical fitness, periodic medical evaluations, ceasing tobacco use, and stress relief and control, will help to reduce this needless loss of life. The company officer should not hesitate to recommend this program as a solution when it is evident that physical and/or psychological stress was the root cause of the injury or fatality.

Chapter Summary

The Company Officer II may be responsible for reviewing and analyzing injury, accident, and health exposure reports. The officer can affect changes that will result in a safer work environment. Knowledge of the risk management model, the organization's health and safety program, and the steps required to investigate and analyze the information and determine trends are basic to the officer's success in providing a safe environment.

Review Questions

1. How does Company Officer II use risk management to improve an organization's safety?

2. How do accident investigations differ from job-related illness or exposure investigations?

3. How is accident report analysis similar to injury, illness, and exposure report analysis?

Learning Activity

Learning Activity 17-1

Objective 4: Analyze scenarios and make recommendations based on member history.

The company officer has the responsibility to investigate and analyze causes of accidents, injuries, and health exposures of the company. Once analyzed, corrective action must be taken to remove the factors that lead to these events.

Using the scenario below, outline a risk management plan for the fire department. The plan should address the type of risk that is presented in the scenario and what the department can do to improve safety

Scenario:

You are a company officer of the Anytown Fire Department assigned to Fire Station 7, A shift. Fire Station 7 is located near a large housing development, over 3 square miles (8 square km) in size, and is situated in a wildland/interface environment. Anticipating an emerging threat posed by the possibility of brush and forest fire potential, the fire department stationed Brush Unit 7 in Fire Station 7.

David Dent is the senior firefighter on your shift and is the designated D/O for BU-7. He has been trained to operate fire department engines and aerial devices. Though national statistics indicate that brush units suffer the same accident rate as other fire apparatus, BU-7 has been involved in three accidents with only a small number emergency calls. Firefighter Dent has been the driver/operator in all three accidents. No other accidents have been reported when other driver/operators are assigned to the vehicle. Though none have been resulted in an injury, you believe that additional investigation and analysis are needed. The vehicle accidents have occurred often enough that you have become very concerned and believe that a more serious event could happen.

During the time that BU-7 has been in service, it has responded to 317 emergency calls. These calls by shift are:

- 102 - A Shift
- 99 - B Shift
- 116 - C Shift

Of the 102 emergency calls that BU-7 has responded to during A Shift, Firefighter Dent has been on duty and assigned to this vehicle for 95. Each of the other operators of BU-7 has as many responses in the unit as Dent.

Firefighter Dent is approximately 5 feet 5 inches (1.6 m) in height and wears glasses, but his vision is corrected to 20/20. The other drivers assigned to BU-7 are much taller.

BU-7 is a four-wheel drive vehicle on a standard pickup truck frame that has had a commercial fire body installed on the back. The cab is slightly higher than a normal pickup truck, and due to the size of the fire body, oversized mirrors have been installed. These mirrors are of the type used on large trucks. The mirrors can be adjusted inward and outward, but will not move up or down.

Accident Description Narrative: While responding to a reported brush fire, BU-7 struck a stop sign on the northeast corner of Carol Avenue and Hatfield Road as it was making a right turn. The stop sign was knocked over and run over by BU-7. The vehicle suffered damage, mostly scraped paint, to the right door and right side of the fire body. Firefighter Dent stopped the vehicle and checked it for damage, and finding it minor, proceeded to the fire for fire suppression activities. Dent claimed that when he looked to the right, the mirror on the passenger side partially blocked his vision, causing him to misjudge the proximity of the curb and sign.

Accident Cause Narrative: The accident occurred while Firefighter Dent was attempting to make a right turn. The vehicle was turned too early and the rear of the vehicle went over the curb and struck the stop sign. Firefighter Dent stated that he was traveling at about 45 miles per hour (72 km/h). The posted speed limit is 25 miles per hour (40 km/h).

Once you have analyzed the information provided, write a brief synopsis of how you would address brush unit driver safety for this department to reduce/eliminate such accidents

Answer Key:

Answers for this activity may vary. Consult an experienced officer in your jurisdiction for detailed feedback. However, your outline should address the following:

- Consideration for varying physical heights of various drivers has not been taken in regards to the placement of the mirrors on the vehicle
- Improper mirror placement on the vehicle is the major factor in the three accidents
- Identification of the risk – mirror placement on the vehicle
- Recommendation includes changes to equipment to include replacing the mirrors with adjustable left-to-right, up-to-down mirrors

Appendices

Contents

Appendix A
NFPA® 1021 Job Performance Requirements (JPRs) with Chapter and Page References

NFPA® 1021 JPR Number	Chapter	Page Numbers
4.2.1	5	107-117, 129-136
4.2.2	5	107-117, 129-136
4.2.3	5, 8	112-117, 194-206
4.2.4	4	82-89
4.2.5	4, 5	82-89, 90-98, 111-112
4.2.6	3, 4	63-77, 82-89, 90-98
4.3.1	9	212-217
4.3.2	5, 9	107-117, 212-217
4.3.3	5, 9	112-128, 212-217
4.4.1	5, 6	112-128, 147-151
4.4.2	6	147-151, 154-160
4.4.3	6	147-153
4.4.4	2	32-46
4.4.5	6	154-160
4.5.1	9, 10	217-255, 264
4.5.2	9, 10, 11	217-255, 264-285, 307-320
4.5.3	11	335-340
4.6.1	10, 11	281-285, 307-335
4.6.2	2, 7, 11	47-49, 170-185, 292-294, 307-335
4.6.3	6, 11	147-151, 335-340
4.7.1	7	170-185
4.7.2	7	170-185
4.7.3	7	170-185
5.2.1	3, 5, 12, 13	56-63, 112-117, 351-357, 359-360, 372-388
5.2.2	12, 13	351-352, 359-360, 377-388
5.2.3	12, 13	351-352, 359-360, 389-392

NFPA® 1021 JPR Number	Chapter	Page Numbers
5.3.1	12	351-359
5.4.1	3, 12, 14	56-63, 351-352, 361-366, 397-398
5.4.2	12, 14	351-352, 398-402
5.4.3	12, 14	351-352, 400-402
5.4.4	5, 12	117-128, 351-352
5.4.5	5, 12	117-128, 351-352, 397-398
5.4.6	12, 14	351-352, 361-366
5.5.1	12, 15	351-352, 407-423
5.6.1	12, 16	351-352, 359, 430-437
5.6.2	6, 12, 16	144-147, 351-352, 438-441
5.6.3	12, 16	351-352
5.7.1	12, 17	351-352, 448-459

Appendix B
Fire Flow Calculations

Calculating Fire Flow Requirements

Experienced company officers recognize the fact that the amount of extinguishing agent available for controlling a fire will determine the success of the operation. Water must be available and applied to a fire in sufficient quantity to completely extinguish it. Early application, through private fire-suppression systems, will help control a fire and reduce the amount of water damage that can occur if application is delayed. Therefore, the company officer must be able to determine the quantity of water required to control a fire in a specific structure through the application of mathematical formulas.

The National Fire Academy uses the term *fire flow* to describe the amount of water needed to extinguish a fire in an occupancy. Fire flow is not just the amount of water but also the available pressure (either from the water supply system or from a fire pump), available personnel needed to deploy, handle, and advance hose lines, and the number and type of apparatus needed to pump, transport, or support the application of the water. Fire flow is always stated in gallons per minute (gpm) **(L/min)** and should be available for a specified time period.

Fire flow calculations apply to the use of handlines in structures that do not have private fire suppression systems. Structures that have private fire suppression systems will require a specific fire flow for the system. If the system is operating properly, the number and size of handlines and fire flow required for them may be less.

A number of formulas are available to the company officer when trying to calculate the fire flow required for a location or occupancy. In each case, a safety factor should be added to the estimate to allow for any changes in the fire development at the location. The company officer should also understand that each formula has its weaknesses and is only an estimate of the quantity of water required.

The formulas were originally developed in the 1940s when fuel loads were smaller and the use of synthetic materials was less common. Therefore, the formulas are based on area of the structure and not the contents. Results are on the conservative side since they do not take into consideration the high flammability of new products.

Cubic Foot Formula

The cubic foot or Iowa State formula is used to estimate the required fire flow for the initial attack on the fire. This formula is based on the ability of water to absorb heat and turn to steam. This estimate is made during the preincident survey. The largest single area in the building is measured and its cubic foot capacity is determined. The number of cubic feet is then divided by 100 to obtain the total number of gallons of water needed for extinguishment.

For example, a space 50 feet (15.24 m) by 20 feet (6.10 m) by 10 (3.05 m) feet high would contain 10,000 cubic feet (283.54 cubic meters). Dividing this figure by 100 would result in an estimated 100 gpm (379 l/min) fire flow. Experiments indicate that the greatest efficiency results from the water being applied to the hottest part of the fire for only 30 seconds. This would mean that the calculation should be divided by half, resulting in a 50 gpm (0.70 l/min) requirement.

National Fire Academy Quick Calculation Formula

The next formula is known as the *National Fire Academy Quick Calculation Formula*. While the cubic foot (cubic meters) formula can be used in preincident planning, the NFA formula is intended for use by the first arriving company officer at a fire incident. It is intended to provide the fire flow for initial attack situations.

This basic formula is based on the square footage (square meters) of the structure. The result is divided by 3 and the resulting figure is the gpm (l/min) required to control a one story structure that is fully involved in fire. For multistory structures, the square footage (square meters) is multiplied by the number of floors of the structure. The resulting figure is divided by 3 and that number is multiplied by the percent expressed as a decimal of the total building that is involved in fire. One additional adjustment must be made to provide the required fire flow. An additional 25 percent must be added for each exposure to the building.

INCIDENT OBJECTIVES	1. INCIDENT NAME	2. DATE PREPARED	3. TIME PREPARED

4. OPERATIONAL PERIOD (DATE/TIME)

5. GENERAL CONTROL OBJECTIVES FOR THE INCIDENT (INCLUDE ALTERNATIVES)

6. WEATHER FORECAST FOR OPERATIONAL PERIOD

7. GENERAL SAFETY MESSAGE

8. ATTACHMENTS (✔ IF ATTACHED)

☐ ORGANIZATION LIST (ICS 203)　　☐ MEDICAL PLAN (ICS 206)　　☐ _____
☐ ASSIGNMENT LIST (ICS 204)　　☐ INCIDENT MAP　　☐ _____
☐ COMMUNICATIONS PLAN (ICS 205)　　☐ TRAFFIC PLAN　　☐ _____

9. PREPARED BY (PLANNING SECTION CHIEF)	10. APPROVED BY (INCIDENT COMMANDER)

202 ICS (1/99)　　　　　　　　　　　　　　　　　　　　　　　　　　　　NFES 1326

ORGANIZATION ASSIGNMENT LIST

1. INCIDENT NAME	**2. DATE** PREPARED	**3. TIME** PREPARED

POSITION	NAME

4. OPERATIONAL PERIOD (DATE/TIME)

5. INCIDENT COMMANDER AND STAFF

POSITION	
INCIDENT COMMANDER	
DEPUTY	
SAFTEY OFFICER	
INFORMATION OFFICER	
LIAISON OFFICER	

6. AGENCY REPRESENTATIVES

AGENCY	NAME

7. PLANNING SECTION

CHIEF	
DEPUTY	
RESOURCES UNIT	
SITUATION UNIT	
DOCUMENTATION UNIT	
DEMOBILIZATION UNIT	
TECHNICAL SPECIALISTS	

8. LOGISTICS SECTION

CHIEF	
DEPUTY	

a. SUPPORT BRANCH

DIRECTOR	
SUPPLY UNIT	
FACILITIES UNIT	
GROUND SUPPORT UNIT	

b. SERVICE BRANCH

DIRECTOR	
COMMUNICATIONS UNIT	
MEDICAL UNIT	
FOOD UNIT	

9. OPERATIONS SECTION

CHIEF	
DEPUTY	

a. BRANCH I- DIVISION/GROUPS

BRANCH DIRECTOR	
DEPUTY	
DIVISION/GROUP	
DIVISION/GROUP	
DIVISION/GROUP	
DIVISION/GROUP	
DIVISION/GROUP	

b. BRANCH II- DIVISION/GROUPS

BRANCH DIRECTOR	
DEPUTY	
DIVISION/GROUP	
DIVISION/GROUP	
DIVISION/GROUP	
DIVISION/GROUP	
DIVISION/GROUP	

c. BRANCH III- DIVISION/GROUPS

BRANCH DIRECTOR	
DEPUTY	
DIVISION/GROUP	
DIVISION/GROUP	
DIVISION/GROUP	
DIVISION/GROUP	
DIVISION/GROUP	

d. AIR OPERATIONS BRANCH

AIR OPERATIONS BR. DIR.	
AIR TACTICAL GROUP SUP.	
AIR SUPPORT GROUP SUP.	
HELICOPTER COORDINATOR	
AIR TANKER/FIXED WING CRD.	

10. FINANCE/ADMINISTRATION SECTION

CHIEF	
DEPUTY	
TIME UNIT	
PROCUREMENT UNIT	
COMPENSATION/CLAIMS UNIT	
COST UNIT	

PREPARED BY(RESOURCES UNIT)

203 ICS (1/99)

NFES 1327

1. BRANCH	2. DIVISION/GROUP	ASSIGNMENT LIST

3. INCIDENT NAME	4. OPERATIONAL PERIOD
	DATE _____ TIME _____

5. OPERATIONAL PERSONNEL

OPERATIONS CHIEF _____   DIVISION/GROUP SUPERVISOR _____

BRANCH DIRECTOR _____   AIR TACTICAL GROUP SUPERVISOR _____

6. RESOURCES ASSIGNED THIS PERIOD

STRIKE TEAM/TASK FORCE/ RESOURCE DESIGNATOR	EMT	LEADER	NUMBER PERSONS	TRANS. NEEDED	PICKUP PT./TIME	DROP OFF PT./TIME

7. CONTROL OPERATIONS

8. SPECIAL INSTRUCTIONS

9. DIVISION/GROUP COMMUNICATIONS SUMMARY

FUNCTION		FREQ.	SYSTEM	CHAN.	FUNCTION		FREQ.	SYSTEM	CHAN.
COMMAND	LOCAL				SUPPORT	LOCAL			
	REPEAT					REPEAT			
DIV./GROUP TACTICAL					GROUND TO AIR				

PREPARED BY (RESOURCE UNIT LEADER)	APPROVED BY (PLANNING SECT. CH.)	DATE	TIME

204 ICS (1/99)   NFES 1328

INCIDENT RADIO COMMUNICATIONS PLAN

1. INCIDENT NAME	2. DATE/TIME PREPARED	3. OPERATIONAL PERIOD DATE/TIME

4. BASE RADIO CHANNEL UTILIZATION

SYSTEM/CACHE	CHANNEL	FUNCTION	FREQUENCY/TONE	ASSIGNMENT	REMARKS

5. PREPARED BY (COMMUNICATIONS UNIT)

205 ICS (9/66)

NFES 1330

MEDICAL PLAN

	1. INCIDENT NAME	2. DATE PREPARED	3. TIME PREPARED	4. OPERATIONAL PERIOD

5. INCIDENT MEDICAL AID STATIONS

MEDICAL AID STATIONS	LOCATION	PARAMEDICS	
		YES	NO

6. TRANSPORTATION

A. AMBULANCE SERVICES

NAME	ADDRESS	PHONE	PARAMEDICS	
			YES	NO

B. INCIDENT AMBULANCES

NAME	LOCATION	PARAMEDICS	
		YES	NO

7. HOSPITALS

NAME	ADDRESS	TRAVEL TIME		PHONE	HELIPAD		BURN CENTER	
		AIR	GRND		YES	NO	YES	NO

8. MEDICAL EMERGENCY PROCEDURES

206 ICS 8/78	9. PREPARED BY (MEDICAL UNIT LEADER)	10. REVIEWED BY (SAFETY OFFICER)

NFES 1331

OPERATIONAL PLANNING WORKSHEET

1. INCIDENT NAME	2. DATE PREPARED		3. OPERATIONAL PERIOD (DATE/TIME)
	TIME PREPARED		

4. DIVISION OR OTHER LOCATION	5. WORK ASSIGNMENTS	6. RESOURCES BY TYPE (SHOW STRIKE TEAM AS ST)																							7. REPORTING LOCATION	8. REQUESTED ARRIVAL TIME
		RESOURCE TYPE																								
		REQ																								
		HAVE																								
		NEED																								
		REQ																								
		HAVE																								
		NEED																								
		REQ																								
		HAVE																								
		NEED																								
		REQ																								
		HAVE																								
		NEED																								
		REQ																								
		HAVE																								
		NEED																								
		REQ																								
		HAVE																								
		NEED																								
		REQ																								
		HAVE																								
		NEED																								

9. TOTAL RESOURCES REQUIRED	SINGLE RESOURCES																							
	STRIKE TEAMS																							
TOTAL RESOURCES ON HAND																								
TOTAL RESOURCES NEEDED																								

10. PREPARED BY (NAME AND POSITION)

215 ICS 9-86

NFES 1338

Appendix C • NIMS-ICS Forms **473**

ICS Form 201

INCIDENT BRIEFING	1. Incident Name	2. Date Prepared	3. Time Prepared

4. Map Sketch

ICS 201 Page 1 of 4	5. Prepared by (Name and Position)

6. Summary of Current Actions

ICS 201 | Page 2

7. Current Organization

ICS 201	Page 3

8. Resources Summary				
Resources Ordered	Resource Identification	ETA	On Scene	Location/Assignment

ICS 201	Page 4

Appendix D
Formula for Calculating Frequency and Severity of Risk

The following formulas may be used to calculate the frequency or incident rate and the severity of incidents.

The Occupational Safety and Health Administration (OSHA) calculates the frequency (incident rate) as follows:

$$N/EH \times 200,000 = IR$$

Where:

N = number of injuries and/or illnesses

EH = total hours worked by all employees during the calendar year

200,000 = base for 100 full-time equivalent employees
(provides standardization between agencies and companies)

IR = incident rate

OSHA calculates the severity as follows:

$$LWD/EH \times 200,000 = S$$

Where:

LWD = loss work days

EH = total hours worked by all employees during the calendar year

200,000 = base for 100 full-time equivalent employees

S = severity rate

Another method is to assign values to the frequency and severity in the following formula:

$$R = S \times IR$$

Where:

R = risk

S = severity

IR = incident rate

Assessment of Severity

8. Extreme — Multiple deaths or widespread destruction may result from hazard.
7. Very High — Potential death or injury or severe financial loss may result.
6. High — Permanent disabling injury may result.
5. Serious — Loss time injury greater than 28 days or considerable financial loss.
4. Moderate — Loss time injury of 4 to 28 days or moderate financial loss.
3. Minor — Loss time injury up to 3 days.
2. Slight — Minor injury resulting in no loss of time or slight financial loss.
1. Minimal — No loss of time injury or financial loss to organization.

Assessment of Incident Rate

7. Frequent   Occurs weekly.
6. Very Likely   Occurs once every few months.
5. Likely   Occurs about once a year.
4. Occasional   Occurs annually in the United States.
3. Rare   Occurs every 10 to 30 years.
2. Exceptional   Occurs every 10 to 30 years in the United States.
1. Unlikely   May occur once in 10,000 years within the global fire service.

Suggested Readings

By Authors

Anderson, Gregory M., and Robert L. Lorber, Ph.D. Safety 24/7: Building an Incident-Free Culture. Plano: Back Porch Creative, 2006.

Badaracco, Joseph L. Defining Moments: When Managers Must Choose Between Right and Right. Boston: Harvard Business School Press, 1997.

Beebe, Steven A., and Susan J. Beebe. Public Speaking: An Audience-Centered Approach. Needham Heights: Pearson, Allyn & Bacon, 2002.

Bennett, Lawrence T. Fire and EMS Law for Officers: Employment Best Practices. Oklahoma State University: Fire Protection Publications, 2005.

— Fire and EMS Law for Officers: Safety (Including Lights and Sirens). Oklahoma State University: Fire Protection Publications, 2005.

Brill, Laura. Business Writing Quick & Easy, 2nd Edition. New York: AMACOM, 1989.

Bruce, Andy. Project Management. New York: Dorling Kindersley, 2000.

Brunacini, Alan. Essentials of Fire Department Customer Service. Oklahoma State University: Fire Protection Publications, 1996.

— Fire Command. Oklahoma State University: Fire Protection Publications, 2002.

Bryson, John M. Strategic Planning for Public and Nonprofit Organizations: A Guide to Strengthening and Sustaining Organizational Achievement. San Francisco: Jossey-Bass, John A. Wiley & Sons, 1995.

Cantonwine, Sheila. Safety Training That Delivers — How to Design and Present Better Technical Training. Des Plaines: American Society of Safety Engineers, 1999.

Carter, Harry, Ph.D. Fire Fighting Strategy and Tactics. Oklahoma State University: Fire Protection Publications, 1998.

Chetkovich, Carol. Real Heat: Gender and Race in the Urban Fire Service. New Brunswick: Rutgers University Press, 1997.

Cole, Robert, Robert Crandall, and Jerold Bills. Firefighter's Complete Juvenile Firesetter Handbook. Pittsford: Fireproof Children Company, May 1999.

Collins, Jim. Good to Great. New York: HarperCollins, 2001.

Compton, Dennis, and John Granito, editors. Managing Fire and Rescue Services. Washington: International City/County Managers Association, 2002.

Compton, Dennis. Mental Aspects of Performance for Firefighters, 2nd Edition. Oklahoma State University: Fire Protection Publications, 2004.

— When in Doubt, Lead! Oklahoma State University: Fire Protection Publications, 1999.

— When in Doubt, Lead! Part 2. Oklahoma State University: Fire Protection Publications, 2000.

— When in Doubt, Lead! Part 3. Oklahoma State University: Fire Protection Publications, 2002.

Covey, Stephen R. The Seven Habits of Highly Effective People. New York: Simon and Schuster, 1990.

Covey, Stephen R. Principle-Centered Leadership. New York: Simon and Schuster, 1992.

— The 8th Habit: From Effectiveness to Greatness. New York: Simon and Schuster, 2004.

Dehaan, John D. Kirk's Fire Investigation, 5th Edition. Upper Saddle River: Prentice-Hall, 2002.

DePree, Max. Leadership is an Art. New York: Dell Publishing, 1989.

Devito, Joseph A. The Interpersonal Communication Book, 10th Edition. Needham Heights: Pearson, Allyn & Bacon, 2003.

Edwards, Steven T. Fire Service Personnel Management, 2nd Edition. Upper Saddle River: Prentice-Hall, 2004.

Fanning, Fred. Basic Safety Administration: A Handbook for the New Safety Specialist. Des Plaines: American Society of Safety Engineers, 2003.

Gaston, James M., Ph.D., CAE, and Dr. Riley Harvill. Fire Officer Coaching. Oklahoma State University: Fire Protection Publications, 2005.

Gaynor, Gerard H. What Every New Manager Needs to Know. New York: AMACOM, 2003.

Grimwood, Paul, Ed Hartin, John McDonough, and Shan Raffel. 3D Fire Fighting: Training, Techniques, and Tactics. Oklahoma State University: Fire Protection Publications, 2005.

Hersey, Paul, Kenneth H. Blanchard, and Dewey E. Johnson. Management of Organizational Behavior: Leading Human Resources, 8th Edition. Upper Saddle River: Prentice Hall, 2001.

Janing, Judy, and Gordon M. Sachs. Achieving Excellence in the Fire Service. Upper Saddle River: Prentice-Hall, 2002.

Kipp, Jonathan D., and Murrey E. Loflin. Emergency Incident Risk Management: A Safety and Health Perspective. New York: John Wiley and Sons, 1996.

Klaene, Ben, and Russell Sanders. Structural Fire Fighting. Batterymarch Park: National Fire Protection Association, 2002.

Klein, Gary. Sources of Power: How People Make Decisions. Cambridge: MIT Press, 1998.

Krieger, Gary R., and John F. Montgomery, editors. Accident Prevention Manual for Business and Industry, 12th Edition. Itasca, IL: National Safety Council, 2001.

Lacey, Brett, and Paul Valentine. Fire Prevention Applications. Oklahoma State University: Fire Protection Publications, 2005.

Linsky, Martin, and Ronald A. Heifetz. Leadership on the Line: Staying Alive Through the Dangers of Leading. Boston: Harvard Business School Press, 2002.

Lussier, Robert N., Ph.D. Management Fundamentals: Concepts, Applications, Skill Development, 2nd Edition. Mason: Thomson South-Western Publishers, 2003.

Macoby, Michael. The Gamesman. New York: Bantam Doubleday Dell Publishing Group, 1977.

Maira, Arun, and Peter Scott-Morgan. The Accelerating Organization: Embracing the Human Face of Change. New York: McGraw-Hill, 1997.

Markel, Mike. Technical Communication, 6th Edition. New York: St. Martin's Press, 2001.

Marks, Michael E. Emergency Responder's Guide to Terrorism: A Comprehensive Real-World Guide to Recognizing and Understanding Terrorist Weapons of Mass Destruction. Chester: Red Hat Publishing, 2003.

Northouse, Peter Guy. Leadership: Theory and Practice. Thousand Oaks: Sage Publications, 1997.

Osborne, David, and Ted Gaebler. Reinventing Government. Reading: Addison-Wesley Publishing Company, Inc., 1992.

Pearsall, Thomas E. The Elements of Technical Writing. Boston: Allyn and Bacon, 2001.

Phelps, Burton, and Robert Murgallis. Command and Control 2: ICS, Strategy Development and Tactical Selections. Oklahoma State University: Fire Protection Publications, 2004.

— Command and Control: ICS, Strategy Development and Tactical Selections. Oklahoma State University: Fire Protection Publications, 2001.

Robey, Cora L. New Handbook of Basic Writing Skills. Ft. Worth, TX: Harcourt College Publishers, 2001.

Smith, James P. Strategic and Tactical Considerations on the Fireground. Upper Saddle River: Prentice-Hall, 2002.

Snook, Jack W., Jeffery D. Johnson, and Mary Jo Wagner. Cooperative Service Through Consolidations, Mergers and Contracts — Making the Pieces Fit. West Linn: Emergency Services Consulting Group, 1997.

Snook, Jack W., Jeffery D. Johnson, Daniel C. Olsen, and John Buckman. Recruiting, Training, and Maintaining Volunteer Firefighters, 3rd. Edition. West Linn: Emergency Services Consulting Group, 1998.

Wallace, Mark. Fire Department Strategic Planning: Creating Future Excellence. Saddlebrook: Fire Engineering Books & Videos, PennWell Publishing Co., 1998.

Weiss, Joseph W., and Robert K. Wysocki. 5-Phase Project Management: A Practical Planning and Implementation Guide. Boulder: Perseus Books Group, 1992.

Wieder, Mike. The Sourcebook for Fire Company Training Evolutions, 2nd Edition. Oklahoma State University: Fire Protection Publications, 2000.

Wood, Julia T. Everyday Encounters: An Introduction to Interpersonal Communication. Florence: Wadsworth Publishing, 2001.

Wysocki, Robert K., Robert Beck, Jr., and David B. Crane. Effective Project Management, 2nd Edition. New York: John A. Wiley and Sons, Inc., 2000.

Others

Fire Data Analysis Handbook. Federal Emergency Management Agency, U.S. Fire Administration, U.S. Government Printing Office 1995 (620-956/82068 Out of print. See FEMA web site for public access version in PDF file).

Fire Department Safety Officer. Oklahoma State University: International Fire Service Training Association, 2001.

Fire and Emergency Services Instructor, 8th Edition. Oklahoma State University: International Fire Service Training Association, 2012.

Fire Inspection and Code Enforcement, 8th Edition. Oklahoma State University: International Fire Service Training Association, 2014.

Fire Investigator, 2nd Edition. Oklahoma State University: International Fire Service Training Association, 2010.

Fire and Life Safety Educator, 3rd Edition. Oklahoma State University: International Fire Service Training Association, 2011.

Fire Risk Analysis: A Systems Approach. Emmitsburg: National Fire Academy, 1984.

Harvard Business Review on Decision Making. Boston: Harvard Business School Press, 2001.

Incident Management System Model Procedures Guide for Emergency Medical Incidents. National Fire Service Incident Management System Consortium and Oklahoma State University: Fire Protection Publications, 2002.

Incident Management System Model Procedures Guide for Hazardous Materials Incidents. National Fire Service Incident Management System Consortium and Oklahoma State University: Fire Protection Publications, 2000.

Incident Management System Model Procedures Guide for High-Rise Firefighting. National Fire Service Incident Management System Consortium and Oklahoma State University: Fire Protection Publications, 2003.

Incident Management System Model Procedures Guide for Structural Collapse and US&R Operations. National Fire Service Incident Management System Consortium and Oklahoma State University: Fire Protection Publications, 1998.

Incident Management System Model Procedures Guide for Structural Firefighting. National Fire Service Incident Management System Consortium and Oklahoma State University: Fire Protection Publications, 2000.

Incident Management System Model Procedures Guide for Wildland Firefighting. National Fire Service Incident Management System Consortium and Oklahoma State University: Fire Protection Publications, 2000.

Many Faces, One Purpose: A Manager's Handbook on Women in Firefighting. Federal Emergency Management Association/U.S. Fire Administration, date unknown.

Retention & Recruitment in the Volunteer Fire Service — Problems and Solutions. NVFC & USFA, Final Report 1998.

Glossary

0 - 9

360-degree Feedback Evaluation — an **evaluation method** that incorporates feedback from multiple sources such as the worker, his/her peers, superiors, subordinates, and customers.

A

Ambient Conditions — Common, prevailing, and uncontrolled atmospheric weather conditions. The term may refer to the conditions inside or outside of the structure.

Area Contingency Plan (ACP) — A procedure to be put into effect should an emergency occur within a given region or area.

Aspect — The direction - north, south, east, or west - in which the slope faces.

Authority — Relates to the empowered duties of an official to perform certain tasks. In the case of a fire inspector, the level of an inspector's authority is commensurate with the enforcement obligations of the governing body.

Autoignition Temperature — Minimum temperature to which a fuel (other than a liquid) in the air must be heated in order to start self-sustained combustion; no external ignition source is required.

Automatic Aid — Written agreement between two or more agencies to automatically dispatch predetermined resources to any fire or other emergency reported in the geographic area covered by the agreement. These areas are generally located near jurisdictional boundaries or in jurisdictional "islands."

B

Backdraft — Instantaneous explosion or rapid burning of superheated gases that occurs when oxygen is introduced into an oxygen-depleted confined space. The stalled combustion resumes with explosive force; may occur because of inadequate or improper ventilation procedures.

Bowstring Truss — Lightweight truss design noted by the bow shape, or curve, of the top chord.

C

Capital Budget — Budget intended to fund large, one-time expenditures, such as those for fire stations, fire apparatus, or major pieces of equipment.

Career Fire Department — Fire department composed of full-time, paid personnel.

Career Firefighter — Person whose primary employment is as a firefighter within a fire department. *Also spelled* Career Fire Fighter.

Chain of Command — Order of rank and authority in the fire and emergency services.

Chain of Custody — Process used to record the history of a piece of evidence; all documents should include the name or initials of the person collecting the evidence, each person or entity subsequently having custody of it, dates the items were collected or transferred, agency and case number, victim's and/or suspect's name, and a brief description of the item.

Clear Text — Use of plain English in radio communications transmissions. No ten codes or agency specific codes are used when using clear text.

Compartment — A room or space within a building or structure that is enclosed on all sides, at the top and bottom. The term *compartment fire* is defined as a fire that occurs within such a space.

Competent Ignition Source — An initial energy source that can produce enough heat and energy, over a long enough period of time to raise the temperature of a fuel to its ignition temperature.

Conduction — Physical flow or transfer of heat energy from one body to another, through direct contact or an intervening medium, from the point where the heat is produced to another location, or from a region of high temperature to a region of low temperature. *See* Convection, Heat, Heat Transfer, Law of Heat Flow, and Radiation.

Convection — Transfer of heat by the movement of heated fluids or gases, usually in an upward direction.

County — Political subdivision of a state, province, or territory for administrative purposes and public safety. *Also known as* Parish.

D

Discipline — To maintain order through training and/or the threat or imposition of sanctions; setting and enforcing the limits or boundaries for expected performance.

Diversity — The inclusion of people of different races or cultures in a group or organization.

Draft Curtains — Noncombustible barriers or dividers hung from the ceiling in large open areas that are designed to minimize the mushrooming effect of heat and smoke and impede the flow of heat.

E

Egress — Escape or evacuation.

Employee Assistance Program (EAP) — Program to help employees and their families with work or personal problems.

F

Federal — National level of governments such as the U.S. and Canada.

Fire District — Designated geographic area where fire protection is provided, usually through a supporting tax, or an area where fire prevention codes are enforced.

Flashover — Stage of a fire at which all surfaces and objects within a space have been heated to their ignition temperature, and flame breaks out almost at once over the surface of all objects in the space.

Formative Evaluation — Ongoing, repeated assessment conducted over time to evaluate an employee's performance against an organization's standards.

Freedom of Information Act (FOIA) request — A petition to a federal, state, or local agency for access to records concerning a specific topic, individual, or organization.

Fuel Load — Amount of fuel present, expressed quantitatively in terms of weight of fuel per unit area. This may be available fuel (consumable fuel) or total fuel and is usually dry weight. *Also known as* Fuel Loading.

Functional Supervision — Organizational principle that allows workers to report to more than one supervisor without violating the unity of command principle; workers report to their primary supervisor for most of their activities but report to a second supervisor for activities that relate to an assigned function only, and both supervisors coordinate closely.

G

Grievance — A complaint against management by one or more personnel concerning an actual, alleged, or perceived injustice.

Groupthink — A pattern of thinking that includes self deception, peer pressure, and conformity to group ethics and values.

H

Hazard — Condition, substance, or device that can directly cause injury or loss; the source of a risk.

Heat — Form of energy associated with the motion of atoms or molecules and capable of being transmitted through solid and fluid media by conduction, through fluid media by convection, and through empty space by radiation.

Heating, Ventilating, and Air Conditioning (HVAC) System — Mechanical system used to provide environmental control within a structure and the equipment necessary to make it function; usually a single, integrated unit with a complex system of ducts throughout the building. *Also known as* Air-Handling System.

I

Ignition Source — Mechanism or initial energy source employed to initiate combustion, such as a spark that provides a means for the initiation of self-sustained combustion.

Incident Action Plan (IAP) — Written or unwritten plan for the disposition of an incident; contains the strategic goals, tactical objectives, and support requirements for a given operational period during an incident. All incidents require an action plan. On relatively small incidents, the IAP is usually not in writing; on larger, more complex incidents, a written IAP is created for each operational period and disseminated to all assigned units. Written IAPs may have a number of forms as attachments.

J

Job Shadowing — A program in which an individual can learn a particular skill set by following an active practitioner in the field.

L

Leader — A person who leads or directs a unit.

Lesson Plan — Teaching outline or plan for teaching that is a step-by-step guide for presenting a lesson or presentation. It contains information and instructions on what will be taught and the teaching procedures to be followed. It covers lessons that may vary in length from a few minutes to several hours.

M

Manager — Individual who accomplishes organizational objectives through effective and efficient handling of material and human resources.

Material First Ignited — Fuel that is first set on fire by the heat of ignition. To be meaningful, both a type of material and a form of material should be identified.

Mentoring — Instructional method in which an individual, as trusted and friendly advisor or guide, sets tasks, coaches activities, and supervises progress of individuals in new learning experiences or job positions.

Mnemonic Device — Any learning technique that assists in memory retention. Mnemonic devices may be used on various forms of information such as lists, short poems, acronyms, memorable phrases, and images.

Multiple Alarm — An additional alarm, such as second or third, that is a call for additional assistance or response.

Municipal — Functional division of the lowest level of local government.

Mutual Aid — Reciprocal assistance from one fire and emergency services agency to another during an emergency, based upon a prearranged agreement; generally made upon the request of the receiving agency.

O

Occupancy Classification — Classifications given to structures by the model building code used in that jurisdiction based on the intended use for the structure. Describes the use to which owners or tenants put buildings or portions of buildings; regulated by the various building and fire codes.

Operating Budget — Budget intended to fund the day-to-day operations of the department or agency; usually includes the costs of salaries and benefits, utility bills, fuel, and preventive maintenance.

Operational Period — Period of time scheduled for execution of a specified set of operational goals and objectives as identified in the incident action plan (IAP). An operational period may be 12 hours, 24 hours, or any other arbitrary amount of time. A new IAP is created for each operational period.

Outside Aid — Assistance from agencies, industries, or fire departments that are not part of the agency having jurisdiction over the incident.

P

Paid-on-Call Personnel — Person who responds to fires and emergencies and is paid for the responses they make on a response-to-response basis.

Peer Assistance — A process that involves having unit personnel assist each other in learning teamwork or perfecting new skills.

Piloted Ignition — Moment when a mixture of fuel and oxygen encounters an external heat (ignition) source with sufficient heat energy to start the combustion reaction.

Plot Plan — Architectural drawing showing the overall project layout of building areas, driveways, fences, fire hydrants, and landscape features for a given plot of land; view is from directly above.

Post-incident Analysis — General overview and critique of the incident by members of all responding agencies (including dispatchers) that should take place within two weeks of the actual incident.

Practical Training Evolution — Operation of fire service training or suppression covering one or several aspects of fire fighting.

Program (or Project) Evaluation and Review Technique (PERT) Chart — a statistical tool used in project management that is designed to analyze and represent the tasks involved in completing a given project.

Public Record — Any writing containing information relating to the conduct of government or the performance of any governmental or proprietary function prepared, used, or retained by any state or local agency regardless of form or characteristics.

Purlin — Horizontal member between trusses that support the roof.

Pyrolysis — Thermal or chemical decomposition of fuel (matter) because of heat, generally resulting in the lowered ignition temperature of the material; the pre-ignition combustion phase of burning during which heat energy is absorbed by the fuel, in turn giving off flammable tars, pitches, and gases. Pyrolysis of wood releases combustible gases and leaves a charred surface. *Also known as* Pyrolysis Process or Sublimation.

Pyromania — Psychological disorder in which the sufferer has an uncontrollable impulse to set fires, either to relieve tension or produce a feeling of euphoria.

R

Radiation —Transmission or transfer of heat energy from one body to another body at a lower temperature through intervening space by electromagnetic waves, such as infrared thermal waves, radio waves, or X-rays. *Also known as* Radiated Heat.

Rehabilitation — Allowing firefighters or rescuers to rest, rehydrate, and recover during an incident; also refers to a station at an incident where personnel can rest, rehydrate, and recover.

Risk — (1) Likelihood of suffering harm from a hazard; exposure to a hazard. The potential for failure or loss. (2) Estimated effect that a hazard would have on people, services, facilities, and structures in a community; likelihood of a hazard event resulting in an adverse condition that causes injury or damage. Often expressed as *high, moderate,* or *low* or in terms of potential monetary losses associated with the intensity of the hazard.

Risk Management — Analyzing exposure to hazards, implementing appropriate risk management techniques, and monitoring their results.

Risk Management Plan — Written plan that analyzes the exposure to hazards, implements appropriate risk management techniques, and establishes criteria for their effectiveness.

S

Sidestepping — The process of going around a link in the chain of command to deal with an issue.

Skip Level Notification — Notifying one's supervisor that one wishes to take an issue to the supervisor's supervisor.

Standard Operating Guideline (SOG) — *See* Standard Operating Procedure (SOP).

Standard Operating Procedure (SOP) — Rule for how personnel should perform routine functions or emergency operations. Procedures are typically written in a handbook, so that all firefighters can become familiar with them. *Also known as* Operating Instruction (OI), Predetermined Procedures, or Standard Operating Guideline (SOG).

State/provincial — Territory occupied by one of the constituent administrative districts of a nation whose rights are defined by a constitution.

Summative Evaluation — An assessment of an employee's performance against an organization's standards that are conducted at the end of a given period of time such as a probationary period, annually as part of a performance review, or for performance improvement or disciplinary purposes.

Supervisor — A person who is responsible for directing the performance of other people or employees.

T

Tribal — Term that describes the governmental structure of Native American and Aboriginal Peoples of North America (also known as First Nations, Aboriginals, Inuit, and Metis).

Index

Index

Conflict management, 90–94
  aggressive, 91
  assertive, 91
  benefits of conflict resolution process, 94
  conflict resolution steps, 91, 94
  methods of resolving conflict
    accommodating, 91, 92
    avoiding, 91, 92
    collaborating, 91, 93
    forcing, 91, 93
    negotiating, 91, 93
  passive (nonaggressive), 91
  resolution methods, 92–93
Consistency, leadership trait, 57
Consumer Product Safety Commission (CPSC), 356
Contemporary residential construction, 319–320
Contents, hazard of, 234, 314
Contingency plans, 77
Continuity within a group, 375
Controlling, management function, 75
Convection of heat, 307
Conversion, measurement, 9–11
Corrective action discipline, 96, 388
Corrective maintenance, 156
Counseling employees, 72, 377, 379–380
County government, 42
CPSC (Consumer Product Safety Commission), 356
Creativity, leadership trait, 57
Crew resource management (CRM), 293
Crew resources, 297
Crime concealment as motive for incendiary fires, 421–422
Criticism, acceptance of, 21
CRM (crew resource management), 293
Cross-training, 39
Crowd control, 306
Cubic foot formula, 466
Curtain boards, 278–279
Customer base, 145–146
Customer service, 144–147
  community relations, 214
  customer base, 145–146
  external customers, 145, 146
  information interpretation, 147
  information-gathering methods, 146
    informal interviews, 146
    meetings, 146
    surveys, 146
  internal customers, 145
  needs, wants, and desires, 145
  objectives, 144
  service-delivery monitoring, 147

D

Decentralized authority, 34–35
Decision, in size-up, 303
Decision point, 171
Decision-making authority
  centralized, 34
  decentralized, 34–35
  defined, 34
Decision-making skills, 76
Decisiveness, leadership trait, 56
Defensive operational mode, 334
Delegation of authority, 35, 38
Delegation of tasks, 68
Delivery of emergency services, Company Officer I, 291–341

fire attack considerations, 307–320
  fire behavior in compartments, 308–309
  fire behavior research affecting fire fighting tactics, 316–320
  fire development factors, 312–316
  fire spread, 307–308
  rapid fire development, 309–312
firefighter survivability, 292–294
  crew resource management, 293
  occupant survivability profiling, 292
  rules of engagement, 293–294
incident scene management, 295–306
  incident size-up, 300–303
  Initial Action Plan, 299
  NIMS-ICS, 295–300
  organizational levels, 296–297
  personnel accountability, 300
  resources, 297
  scene control, 303–306
  span of control, 299–300
  unified command structure, 297–298
incident scene operations, 320–335
  additional resource allocation, 334
  apparatus placement and positioning, 335
  command options, 331–334
  incident priorities approach, 321–322
  incident termination, 335
  Layman's RECEO-VS model, 322–327
  operational implementation, 331
  Operational Planning "P," 327
  size-up application, 328–331
postincident activities, 335–340
  analysis, 338–339
  critique, 339
  evidence preservation, 336, 337
  recommended changes, 340
  scene security, 335–336
Delivery of emergency services, Company Officer II, 429–441
  factors of command, 437
  information gathering, 429
  multi-unit operations, 430–436
    basic organization, 434
    command organization, 433
    communications, 436
    Company Officer II as Incident Commander, 430–431
    demobilizing resources, 432
    divisions/groups, 434–435
    incident command system, 430–433
    personnel accountability system, 431–432
    resource management, 431
    span of control, 435
    strategic level, 433
    tactical level, 433
    task level, 434
    transferring command, 432–433
  operational plans, 436–437
  postincident analysis, 438–440
  postincident critique, 440–441
Deluge sprinkler systems, 249
Demobilizing resources, 432
Democratic leadership approach, 68
Demographics of communities, 212–213
Demonstrations, 198–199
Denial change process stage, 361
Department of Defense (DoD), 43
Department of Health and Human Services, 356
Department of Homeland Security, 355–356
Department of Housing and Urban Development (HUD), 356

Incident Priorities approach, 321
in preincident surveys, 275–277
as reason for inspections, 230
rescue, 322–324
Lighting for exits, 232
Lightweight construction, 268
Line functions, 4
Line personnel, 33–34
Line-of-duty death (LODD), 156, 173
Listening skills, 111–112
attending, 111
for community relations, 215
evaluating, 112
remembering, 112
responding, 112
understanding, 112
Local aid agreements, 357
Local alarm systems, 243
Locations for practical training evolutions, 202–203
LODD (line-of-duty death), 156, 173
Logistics of practical training evolutions, 204
Loss of control or power, resistance issue, 362
Low hazard contents, 234
Loyalty of new company officers, 20–21
Lying, reasons for, 61

M

MABAS (Mutual Aid Box Alarm System), 49
Maintenance
corrective, 156
preventive, 155–156
records maintenance, 155–156
Management
behavior management. *See* Behavior management
defined, 64, 74
functions, 75
human resources. *See* Human resources management, Fire
  Officer I; Human resources management, Fire Officer II
labor/management relations, 97–98
planning function, 76–77
resources, 74
skills, 75–76
task management, 77
Management plans, 76–77
Manager, defined, 24
Manual organization, 6
Markings. *See* Hazardous materials markings
Markings for exits, 231–232
Mastery level of capability, 391
Material first ignited, 419
MDC (mobile data computer), 131
MDT (mobile data terminal), 131, 283
Means of egress
door hardware, 232
door swing, 232
egress, defined, 224
exit drills, 242
inspections of, 224–226, 231–232
lighting, 232
markings, 231–232
obstructions, 231
stairwells, 232
Measurement conversion, 9–11
Medical exposure, 183
Medical Plan (ICS 206), 436, 472
Medical records, 158
Meetings for customer information-gathering, 146
Memos, 121–123

cautions about contents, 122–123
comparison to letters, 123
general formats, 121
as public records, 121
value, 122
Mentoring employees, 73, 378, 381
Message element of interpersonal communication, 107, 108
Methamphetamine labs, 302
Metric conversions, 9–11
Military personnel for DoD protection, 43
Mitigation of the incident, 321
Mnemonic device, 112
Mobile data computer (MDC), 131
Mobile data terminal (MDT), 131, 283
Mobile radios, 129
Model building codes, 219
Monitors, 278
Moral philosophy, 59. *See also* Ethics
Moral principles, violation of, 61
Motives for incendiary fires, 421–423
Multiple alarm emergency scene operations, 430–436
basic organization, 434
command organization, 433
communications, 436
defined, 430
divisions/groups, 434–435
Incident Command System, 430–433
  Company Officer II as Incident Commander, 430–431
  demobilizing resources, 432
  personnel accountability system, 431–432
  resource management, 431
  transferring command, 432–433
span of control, 435
strategic level, 433
tactical level, 433
task level, 434
Multistory building preincident surveys, 273
Municipal fire and emergency services organizations, 40–42
Mutual aid agreement, 47, 48
Mutual Aid Box Alarm System (MABAS), 49
Mutual aid plans, 48–49

N

Narrative reports, 126–127
description, 126
justification, 126
progress, 126
recommendation, 126
National Board on Fire Service Professional Qualifications (Pro
  Board), 157
National Building and Fire Codes of Canada (NBFCC), 234,
  235–238
National Fallen Firefighters Foundation, 450
National Fire Academy (NFA). *See also* U.S. Fire Administration/
  National Fire Academy (USFA/NFA)
fire protection involvement, 355
purpose of, 43
Quick Calculation Formula, 467
National Fire Fighter Near-Miss Reporting System, 450
National Fire Incident Reporting System (NFIRS), 220
National Fire Protection Association® (NFPA®). *See also specific
  NFPA® standard*
Dictionary of Terms, 7
fire and life safety codes, 234, 235–238
injury and fatality information sources, 172
model building codes, 219
safety information and statistics, 450
National Firefighter Near-Miss Reporting System, 175

NFPA® 1584, *Standard on the Rehabilitation Process for Members During Emergency Operations and Training Exercises*, 175, 183–184, 432
NFPA® 1600, *Standard on Disaster/Emergency Management and Business Continuity Programs*, 449
NFPA® 1620, *Standard for Pre-Incident Planning*, 264
NFPA® 1852, *Standard on Selection, Care, and Maintenance of Open-Circuit Self-Contained Breathing Apparatus (SCBA)*, 175
NFPA® 2001, *Standard on Clean Agent Fire Extinguishing Systems*, 251
NFPA® 5000, hazard of contents, 234
NIMS-ICS. *See* National Incident Management System-Incident Command System (NIMS-ICS)
NIOSH (National Institute for Occupational Safety and Health), 172, 356, 450
"No Man's Land," 42
Nonaggressive (passive) management style, 91
Nonemergency casualties, 170, 173
Nonprofit fire and emergency service organizations, 45
Nonverbal communications, 109–111
    body language, 110
    eye contact, 110
    facial expression, 110
    gestures, 110
    personal appearance, 110, 111
    poise, 111
    posture, 110
    proximity, 111
    touch, 111
    vocal characteristics, 111
    vocal interferences, 111
    vocal tone and volume, 110
Norming, in team building, 69
Norming leadership style, 377
NRC (Nuclear Regulatory Commission), 356
NRP (National Response Plan), 359
Nuclear Regulatory Commission (NRC), 356
Numerical ratings, 276
NVFC (National Volunteer Fire Council) Rules of Engagement for Firefighter Health, 175

O

Objectives
    establishing and communicating, 66–68
    professional development, 390
    tactical objectives, 331
Obstructions in exits, 231
Occupancy
    classifications, 233, 235–238
    preparing for inspections, 227–228
    records for inspections, 227
Occupant services, 306
Occupant survivability profiling, 292
Occupational Safety and Health Administration (OSHA)
    2-in/2-out rule, 322–323
    Hazard Communication Standard, 239
    involvement in fire protection, 356
    safety information and statistics, 450
    29 CFR 1910.134, *Respiratory Protection*, 175, 323
    29 CFR 1910.1200, *Hazard Communication Standard*, 239
Offensive operational mode, 334
On-scene occupant services, 306
Operating budget, 151, 152, 400
Operation Plan, 296
Operational implementation, 331
Operational modes, 333–334

Operational period, 296
Operational Planning "P" model, 83, 327
Operational Planning Worksheet (ICS 215), 473
Operational plans, 436–437
Operational risk management process, 170, 171
Operational/administrative plans, 77
Oral communications, 112–117
    with the crew, 113
    speeches and presentations, 114–117
    training sessions, 113–114
Oral reprimand, 387
Orders, 150–151
Ordinances, 219
Ordinary hazard contents, 234
Organization, company officer responsibility to, 23
Organization Assignment List (ICS 203), 436, 469
Organizational levels, 296–297
    branch, 297
    command, 296
    command staff, 296
    division, 297
    general staff, 296
    group, 297
    section, 296–297
    unit, 297
Organizational policies, 83–90
    absenteeism, 89
    duty assignments, 84–87
        expectations of new personnel, 85
        first duty assignments, 84
        probationary periods, 84–85
        work environments, 85–87
    employee assistance program, 88–89
    leave and duty exchange, 88
    performance evaluations, 87–88
    promotions, 87
    retention, 87
    substance abuse, 89, 90
Organizational risk management, 170, 171
Organizational staffing, 45–46
    career (full-time) organizations, 45
    combination departments, 46
    paid-on-call organizations, 45, 46
    volunteer, 46
Organizational structure, 31–50
    decision-making authority, 34–35
        centralized, 34
        decentralized, 34–35
        delegation of authority, 35
    division of labor, 39
    flow chart, 33
    line and staff personnel, 33–34
    operational-structure model, 32
    private, 44–45
        industrial fire brigades, 44–45
        nonprofit fire and emergency services organizations, 45
        for-profit fire and emergency services organizations, 45
    public, 40–44
        county, 42
        federal, 43–44
        fire district, 42
        municipal, 40–42
        state/provincial, 43
        tribal, 44
    purpose of, 32
    resource allocation, 47–49
        aid agreements, 47–49
        local government funding distribution, 47

Index by Nancy Kopper

NOTES

NOTES